HC I

Practical Mechanic ... imile reprints
from long-lost copie ... ng Flea as well
as the 1937 Luton L ... LA.4a Minor.

by Arthur W. J. G. Ord-Hume, designer of the post-war LA.4a Minor

1

© 2009 Arthur W. J. G. Ord-Hume
First Published in the United Kingdom, 2009
Stenlake Publishing Limited
54-58 Mill Square, Catrine, KA5 6RD
www.stenlake.co.uk

ISBN 9781-84033-449-4

Acknowledgements

edition of the aircraft construction articles from *Practical Mechanics* spanning 1935 to 1960, I express my gratitude and appreciation to the former printing and publishing enterprise that was established by Sir George Newnes (1851-1910), and acknowledge the dedication of its outstanding editor, Frederick George Camm. It was Camm who conceived the whole series of magazines that embraced the concept of 'Practical' and it was he who demystified the amateur construction of aircraft in Britain. Without *Practical Mechanics*, several generations of home mechanics would have been starved of inspiration. The copyright in the articles concerning the Flying Flea cannot be traced now but has almost certainly expired. That for the 1937 articles on the Luton Minor was retained by my former business partner, Cecil Hugh Latimer-Needham. The 1959 series, prepared under the auspices of Phoenix Aircraft Ltd (of which I was co-founder and chief designer), was retained in copyright by myself. In presenting this facsimile edition, my thanks go to the now-forgotten editorial staff who laboured some seventy years ago in Southampton Street. As a founder member of the Ultra Light Aircraft Association, later the Popular Flying Association (now rather blandly called the Light Aircraft Association), I know that I am not alone in recognising the important part which *Practical Mechanics* played in seeding the revival of the home-built aeroplane in Britain. But, of course, the man who started it all was the Frenchman, Henri Mignet with his Pou-du-Ciel, forever known in the English-speaking world as The Flying Flea. The modern version of his creation still flies today while the origins of the Luton Minor go back to Latimer-Needham who, in explaining to me why there was so little welding in the first Minor, said that his little company, Luton Aircraft Ltd, could not afford the gas for welding! It was true amateur design and construction! Thanks to Times Newspapers Ltd. for permission to reproduce their 1958 news story and gratitude also to those who supplied some of the extra photographs. All rights to the post-war Luton LA.4a Minor, its design, revisions and all engineering drawings, are retained by me. My thanks to the constructors who have provided the extra pictures.

Contents

Additional Material

The First Home-Built Aeroplanes

How *Practical Mechanics* made History

Amateur aircraft construction is seen today as one of the modern achievements of home-engineering. This is a fine thought yet it overlooks the simple truth that all our great aviation pioneers were nothing else but gifted amateurs who had the good fortune to make good in a big way. Frederick Handley Page was an amateur as was Geoffrey de Havilland, the Short brothers, A V Roe and the rest of the founders of flying in Britain whom we dignify with the handle of 'pioneer'.

Getting down to building your own aeroplane is commonplace now, yet after the excitement of the true pioneering years, aviation quickly gained the status of an arcane science that effectively excluded the common man from the equation. By the early 1930s, the idea of somebody actually constructing an aeroplane in his backyard or on his kitchen table was as probable as the likelihood of success in attempting to poke half a pound of warm butter through a keyhole using a hot knitting needle.

Today's image of the 'do-it-yourself' enthusiast may only be as old as the acronym 'DIY' (standing for 'do-it-yourself' and with its roots in the 1970s) but the age of the amateur craftsman goes back very much further. Contrary to common belief, the concept of the ordinary 'man-in-the-street' enthusiastically tackling projects in science and engineering in his spare time goes back a very long time. In fact it all stemmed from the Mechanics' Institutes almost two centuries ago.

King William IV was still on the throne when the first of these Mechanics' Institutes was formed in London as the result of a public meeting held at the Crown & Anchor Tavern in the Strand. Around 2,000 people turned up on November 11th 1823 and the organisation they formed took the whole country by storm.

A Thirst for Knowledge

Their creation filled a growing thirst for knowledge amongst those working people who had achieved adulthood without the opportunity to realise their intellectual potential. In the same way that, three decades later, the great museums would provide educational inspiration to the less well-educated, Mechanics' Institutes were later to pave the way for the flourishing of other openly educational undertakings from the Working Men's College, soon (happily) followed by the Working Women's College and thence on to the Polytechnic Institute in London's Regent Street set up in 1838, revitalised in 1861 by Quintin Hogg (1845-1903) and today fashionably elevated to the title of University of Westminster.

But to return to the less-enlightened 1820s, like the spread of wildfire, Mechanics' Institutes were to emerge across the nation until within a mere three years there were one hundred. And just four years after the youthful Queen Victoria came to the throne, the year 1842 saw three times that number. By 1850 their number was an astonishing 650! These institutions formed up all over the nation as the acceptable alternative to beer houses meaning pubs and those stalwart social centres that appeared around the time of The Great Exhibition (1851) – the Working Men's Clubs. While they shared something of the social binding of the working man's club (which had been founded to bring alcohol and entertainment to those who worked unsociable hours), they tended to practise abstinence as members demonstrated a preference for reading over darts and drink in an environment that today might be patronisingly termed 'adult learning'.

They began as places where ordinary working-class men could consult learned books and developed with lectures on scientific subjects including physics and chemistry before going on to more practical activities as the years progressed. Members could attend courses to learn subjects as diverse as Latin and shorthand.

Curiously, the first magazine for those who wanted practical rather than theosophical reading started on Saturday August 30th 1823. At 3*d* a week, this was the robustly titled *Mechanics Magazine, Museum, Register, Journal, & Gazette*. At 16 pages an issue it was a good read and one of the articles in that ancient edition was called 'Flying in the Air'. The unnamed editor wrote: 'Though the science of aerostation [the old word for aviating] is of very modern date [meaning hot-air balloons], yet there is every reason to believe it was not unknown to the ancients…' and so on. The next page gives a cure for the common cold which is almost as unintelligible as the recipe for detecting lime-bleached linen that follows.

By the 1880s the ever-expanding band of people questing for knowledge formed a significant and loyal part of the populace and that meant that, with the growth of printing and newspapers, it was time for them to have their own weekly newspaper filled with useful tasks to keep the hands and minds of the male of the species occupied during his spare time.

In the pious belief that good clean activities such as fretwork and forming brackets out of wrought iron kept men on the straight and narrow and assisted them in resisting moral downfall through cheap women and drink (it was *always* cheap women and drink: only the upper classes gambled and could afford mistresses), magazines such as the densely-printed *Work* covered an astonishingly wide area of activities from building a pipe organ and repairing harmoniums, pianos and furniture to plumbing and bricklaying. It described procedures for colour-etching decorative glass and making concrete paths. With the harnessing of electricity came lengthy illustrated articles on storing the energy using accumulators such as the Leclanché cell invented in 1866.

This brought the exciting possibilities of installing electric light and doorbells within the realms of the amateur engineer.

Birth of the Home Handyman

By the outbreak of the First World War this type of home-activity was already well-established. Books such as the curiously-titled but amazingly valuable *Workshop Receipts for Manufacturers, Mechanics and Scientific Amateurs* by Robert Haldane, commonly called 'Spon's Workshop Receipts' instructed amateurs in the art of electro-plating objects at home, the preparation of a variety of domestic and manufacturing tasks using what are today frighteningly potent chemicals, how to make paint, light-sensitive emulsions for coating photographic glass plates, and so on. Changing gas-mantles, tap-washers, making Wollaston's cement and the like were now within the grasp of the man who rode the upper deck of the Clapham omnibus! The extent of subjects covered was enormous from optics and telescopes to lathes and blacksmithing.

We were now a nation of men accustomed to using our hands and our wives and girlfriends were already getting used to what would soon become known as the 'he's in his shed' syndrome.

Whereas today's young man (they are, by the way, *always* young men since there was never so much as a thought that women might wish to turn their hands to such matters) will be hard-pressed to learn the practical use of his hands by observing his father putting up shelves, painting a fence or building a chair, our previous generations learned from their parents by observation and helping. They saw spare-time toil as the creative use of the interval between the bread-winning hours and those spent with family before retirement to sleep. By the end of the First War, not surprisingly the revival of the Mechanics' Institutes philosophy took some while to establish. When the 'great depression' of 1929 began, high unemployment meant more people out of work and with less money to spend on the practical things in life. While women darned the socks and patched jackets along with bringing up the children and cooking, necessity suggested a basic urge to avoid having to pay somebody else to do tasks around home and garden. Men were instructed how to make furniture and fitments for the home that were durable, practical and fashionable. At the same time there was an unending quest for more knowledge of science, the arts, manufacture and design. The time was ripe for a whole new approach.

It was into this arena as a continuation of the furtherance of man's knowledge that a certain *Practical Mechanics* magazine was born.

A magazine called *Practical Mechanics*

The two Camm brothers were born at Windsor. Sydney (1893-1966) is remembered as Hawker Aircraft's renowned designer of the Hurricane fighter. The younger Frederick James Camm (1895-1959), on the other hand, is recalled as the father of the 'Practical' series of books and magazines published by George Newnes & Company of Southampton Street off the Strand. A pioneer in amateur radio, his *Practical Wireless* magazine was a leader in its field as was its sister *Practical Television*. With the aid of these you could build (as I did in my youth) a working valve-operated radio or even a 405-line TV receiver.

As brother Sydney valiantly sought the backing of T O M Sopwith against the Air Ministry hierarchy so as to build the monoplane Hurricane at a time when biplanes were seen as the future in the air, 'FJ' was planning a new title with his publishers. It was to be called *Practical Mechanics* and would take up where previous titles had left off. Above all, it would have up-to-the-moment news of projects throughout the world of science and invention and would be filled with practical articles.

The first issue of the bright bookstall magazine appeared in October 1933 with the strapline 'The Magazine without a rival' and an artistic colour cover displaying the key object from the contents. That Volume I Number I described how to control mechanism by electric ray, how to build a Tele-Discovisor to transmit images, an article on movie-making for the beginner, astronomy for amateur, making a Polariscope, an engine-driven model aircraft powered by compressed air, optics for the camera-user, several pages on wireless experiments – and so on. It was a formidable bundle of top-class information at 6*d* a month.

The philosophy was best expressed by the description appended by sister company The Waverley Book Company to its four-volume work *The Amateur Mechanic*, published at the same time. 'YOU can do 1001 Jobs and Save and Make Money… Make, Mend or Repair Everything…' This was an era when personal economy, not yet spoken of as such, was being challenged by costly tradesmen inspiring the man who could be useful with his hands to be eager to find new ways to improve himself. Saving money – the real goal – was never actually said, but everybody knew that pennies in the pocket could be spared.

Camm, always known to his staff and contributors as 'FJ', was a true pantheist when it came to science and the engineer. He believed that the amateur with his toolbox, paraffin blowlamp and copper-wedge soldering iron was capable of making anything that the factory workshop could make. Perhaps in a simplified form, but even so…

Topics covered in *Practical Mechanics* indicate that FJ was fazed by nothing so long as he could find a contributor to write that material which he either couldn't or didn't have time to pen himself. And he secured the services of the best writers and experts.

Over the years, *Practical Mechanics* addressed such diverse subjects as how to make a model steam turbine, simple Christmas magic tricks, how to split the atom, making a telescope, an aluminium boat, a water-powered generator, telephones, cycle frames, submarine escape, electric clock, camera, making a singing robot, woodwork lathe, accumulator chargers, a wireless aerial system, a bicycle trailer, pottery kiln, aquarium, steam launch, weaver's hand loom, steam engine, Christmas lights, chiming doorbell, military range-finder, paint spray-gun, diving bell, microscope, radio controlled systems, bookbinding, boomerangs, boats, baskets – and so on.

Nothing was too difficult or beyond the comprehension of FJ's readers and it was probably this single fact that made the magazine so popular. Whether or not people made or even *could* make what they read about, there was nevertheless a certain excitement in being able to read how something was done! In the 1950s, for example, articles described how to make an atomic bomb!

And readership ranged from the pre-teen schoolboy through to the mature and educated adult. A comparison with the better-class magazines read by lads would not be out of place and I personally used to reckon that *Practical Mechanics* continued on from where *Meccano Magazine* (which was always science and technology-based) left off.

The two Camm brothers had, in their youth, actually built their own car so, not surprisingly, the *Practical Mechanics* build-it-yourself motor car was an early topic. 'Build it for £20!' shouted the colourful front cover with its typical naive painting of fresh-faced smartly-dressed young men, often, like FJ, a pipe-smoker, assembling the wooden chassis.

Build Your Own Aeroplane!

And so, when in 1935 the French pioneer of amateur aircraft Henri Mignet emulated Louis Blériot's flight of barely 25 years earlier and flew his curious little home-made aeroplane from Calais to England, F J Camm immediately saw the opportunity to follow the £20 car with the £25 aeroplane. The Air League of the British Empire under Air Commodore Chamier added its weight to Mignet's venture and published a translation of his book calling it *The Flying Flea*. So extraordinary was the enthusiasm for the Flying Flea that the edition of 6,000 copies was sold out in under a month and a reprint had hastily to be arranged.

This was just the news that Camm needed, choosing his timing precisely and in *Practical Mechanics* for October 1935 published the first article in a four-part series called 'How to Build the Flying Flea'.

These monthly articles achieved legendary status in the history of both Camm's magazine and the British home-built aircraft movement. True, American-produced popular engineering magazines that catered for a similar market had published instructions for building your own aircraft, famously the Heath Parasol, but this was the first time a British magazine had ventured so far into that exciting unknown. The Air Ministry's acceptance of the Flying Flea for the then-new Permit to Fly system elevated the whole business to a high-status production for *Practical Mechanics*, for the Air League and for the air-minded enthusiastic reader.

Flying Fleas were now being constructed all over Europe and their amateur builders were openly encouraged to experiment.

Sponsored by a British national newspaper, the machine quickly appeared all over Britain as amateurs eagerly adopted Mignet's kitchen-table working policy. Soon finished ones started to appear and take to the skies. A few flew extremely well. Others, fitted with a variety of highly unsuitable engines borrowed (or stolen) from motor-cars, either didn't get as far as flying or merely stumbled about out of control to fall into ditches or, occasionally, to leap harmlessly into the relative safety of a hedgerow.

But behind this all was not well and, largely through Henri Mignet's then-imperfect knowledge of aerodynamics (he was entirely self-trained) Flying Fleas that flew began to fall out of the sky.

This uncovered the fatal flaw in the Flying Flea. Mignet's examples had succeeded because the performance of the aircraft was extremely marginal. Imagine a graph shaped like an inverted letter 'V'. By sheer good fortune, Mignet had built and operated his machine safely on the very apex of the performance graph. Whereas 'normal' aircraft usually have a gently-sloping curve of their performance characteristics which might allow some small variations from the design without too much risk of loss of performance, let alone increase in the risk of danger, Mignet's design balanced precariously on a performance pinnacle from which the minutest variation in construction would result in almost certain disaster.

There were some fatal accidents, three in Britain. Disconcertingly all involved highly-skilled pilots. One was the Air League's own Royal Air Force-trained test-pilot. In France, Mignet's best friend and demonstration pilot was also killed.

Authorisation to fly the Flying Flea was withdrawn and, understandably, the majority of Fleas found themselves grounded, converted into rabbit-hutches, used for Guy Fawkes bonfire celebrations, broken up, discarded... Even so, 120 Fleas had been registered and an estimated 350 more were in various stages of construction across the land.

It was a sad day for Camm and his magazine and, having been in business barely three years, there was a burden of responsibility shared only with Air Commodore Chamier and The Air League. The pre-War HM-14 Flying Flea was finished and the authorities were primed to be wary of the home-made aeroplane in any shape or form.

But the Flying Flea had actually achieved something which could not be forgotten or wiped off the slate. This was the fact that the man-in-the-street could build and fly his own aeroplane. The ordinary man had had a taste of aircraft-building and flying – and it was not something that would quietly go away.

Wanted: A Safe D-I-Y Lightplane

There was now a desperate need for a new homebuilt aeroplane design that would fill the void created by the experience of the Flying Flea. That need was met by a young ex-RAF technical officer, Cecil Hugh Latimer-Needham. It was he who, in 1926-27, had designed and built the Halton HAC.I Mayfly and the HAC.II Minus.

A pioneer in the sailplane and gliding movement in this country – he obtained the very first British gliding licence in Britain in 1930 – Latimer-Needham was born in 1900. During the First War he served in France with the Royal Flying Corps and later flew in Germany with the Army of Occupation in 1918 and 1919. As an RAF Technical Officer, he founded the Halton Aero Club in 1924 and in 1930 designed a perfectly adequate sailplane called the Albatross. Now, in 1936, he had formed a tiny 'one man and a boy' company called Luton Aircraft Ltd at Barton-in-the-Clay, Bedfordshire. Amongst its first activities was the supply of parts and materials for Flying Flea builders so he was not only aware of the demise of the Flea: it had a negative effect on his new business.

It was in a tiny shed-cum-hangar at Barton that he designed and built the first light aircraft to bear the Luton name. This was a curious tandem-winged aircraft clearly inspired by the Flying Flea and intended to eradicate the French design's flaws. Unfortunately it was a flying failure.

Using parts from the failed flyer he created a new and more conventional-looking aircraft having a proper tailplane but still with a Flea-type undercarriage. Called the LA.2 Minor it was a successful flyer. In fact it flew so well that Latimer-Needham decided to sell plans for building it.

Aware that *Practical Mechanics* was still smarting over the episode of the Flying Flea articles, he told Camm about it as a result of which in May of 1937 the magazine ran a 1¼ page story on the Anzani-powered V-braced G-AEPD, implying that here was a real, safe and easy-to-fly conventional-looking aeroplane.

This article drew a considerable number of reader enquiries as a result of which Camm's enthusiasm for aeroplanes, apparently undaunted by the Flea episode, was reawakened. To Latimer-Needham's surprise, FJ immediately commissioned a set of 'how to build the Luton Minor' articles from the Luton Aircraft Company and he wanted the first instalment within the week!

Now this was an embarrassment for CHL-N because, while he was overjoyed at the opportunity to promote his ultra-light aeroplane, he hadn't yet produced any proper drawings for the Minor. The prototype had been built 'on the fly' using eyeball engineering, albeit skilled eyeballs. Drawings, though, didn't quite exist. And there were precious few photographs!

There was also the matter of the undercarriage. This was so low that, as with the Flying Flea, taxiing in long grass was both difficult and wearing on the propeller as the grass blades tended to chip the varnish on the tips at high revolutions per minute. Furthermore the prototype Minor also had V-shaped lift-struts to the wings and these were a problem because the fuselage was not stiff enough at the

centre-section. This called for a long bracing wire to run from the wing-spar strut fixing to the engine-mounting – a clumsy, not really practical solution.

With *Practical Mechanics* magazine shouting down his ear, CHL-N began feeding material through to the offices in Southampton Street, just round the corner from the elegant art deco Strand Palace Hotel. This rather *ad hoc* method of producing the articles on the LA.4 Luton Minor explains why some of the illustrations, taken from the prototype aircraft, bear only passing resemblance to the actual aircraft.

The first article appeared in the issue for October 1937 with the aircraft featuring in a colourful artistic rendition on the front cover. The instalments were published every month until the last in the issue for March 1938. One year later, the edition for March 1939 included a two-page feature on a Minor built from the magazine articles.

Great Opportunity Curtailed by War

As well as publishing the magazine, George Newnes Limited had embarked on a series of hard-back books called 'Aeroplane Maintenance and Operation'. These were under the overall editorial control of E Molloy and were, so the title-pages of each book in the series told us, 'compiled by a panel of experts'. Possibly uniquely for such a small and insignificant company, Luton Aircraft was invited to include its little clutch of prototype aircraft in the book marked 'Airframes (*Part 2*)' and so here was yet more useful publicity for the Luton Minor to which almost nine pages were devoted. But it was already the summer of 1939 and the final fragile days of peace were fast ebbing.

All private flying was prohibited from the end of that August as a prelude to the outbreak of War on September 3rd. Amateur flying of all dimensions was now in abeyance until January 1st 1946. Throughout the bleak years of turmoil that followed the start of the conflict, Camm soldiered on with a much-depleted staff as the military call-up removed all but key men (and, later, women too) from most civilian jobs. Undeterred, despite stringent paper rationing which limited its print-run and the need to use both lower-quality paper and diluted utility ink, *Practical Mechanics* continued unabated. It instructed its readers on building model steam locomotives, amidst more urgent tasks like home repairs and furniture-making.

The War was a catalyst in so many ways as things were altered forever. During that time, aircraft and aviation underwent massive changes and the atmosphere in the immediate post-war years was virtually hostile to amateur construction. Home-made aircraft were effectively prohibited but eventually it was agreed that if an aircraft had been built and flown before the War, then it might be allowed to fly again. These arid times are described in a series of articles in *Popular Flying* and in the book *On Home-Made Wings* (see Bibliography).

In 1949, I had the opportunity to acquire a Luton LA.4 Minor that had been built to *Practical Mechanics*' plans in 1938 and damaged in a early summer 1939 crash leading to exposure to the elements for three wet months in a field of growing corn before the farmer who owned the land would allow it to be removed post-harvest. My acquisition was a damaged airframe that had been stored through the War in the hot, arid corrugated-iron roof of a garage in Leicestershire. It wasn't much of an airframe and it no longer had an engine but the 'golden key' was that it came with two vital pieces of paper – a pre-war registration document for G-AFIR and, more importantly, proof that it had existed in the form of the original Authorisation to Fly dated 1939.

There were numerous aspects of the 1939 design that were not particularly good among these being the poorly-engineered undercarriage, the lack of a fixed fin, the use of slender plank wing-spars and, above all, the one-piece wing. This 25-foot span wing was difficult to store, made transporting the aircraft by road tricky and, above all, needed the services of at least four people to fit onto the fuselage.

Perhaps most important was that the 1937 design was very lightly built and would not really take a bigger engine than the 32 hp Bristol Cherub, even then a long-forgotten motor. I wanted to be able to fit an engine up to and including the 55 hp Lycoming and, later, the heavy but robustly powerful converted Volkswagen aircraft engine.

The outcome was that I made so many modifications and improvements that by the time the new G-AFIR flew it was a very different aircraft from the LA.4. And after I had damaged the rebuilt machine in a landing after engine-failure, I rebuilt it with yet more alterations and improvements. I became expert at jacking up the registration letters and fitting a new airframe as the machine began to emulate the tale of the 100-year-old broom that had had six new handles and five new heads…

I managed to locate C H Latimer-Needham, then living in retirement just outside Bognor Regis in Sussex, and suggested that it would be nice to breathe new life back into the old 1930s design. At first he was unsure, quoting the old adage about 'pouring good money after bad'. He had lost all the aircraft prototypes and drawings in the War, burned in the old factory at Tatling End, Gerrards Cross.

I persevered, showed him the 'new' version I had built and revealed that I had design approval for the new aeroplane. The upshot was that together we founded a two-man business. Relating to the fate of the old Luton Aircraft Company, we called it Phoenix Aircraft Ltd and I produced a completely new set of engineering drawings for the revamped Luton Minor. I called it the Luton LA.4a Minor.

The New Luton Minor Arrives

Although the Popular Flying Association was quick to approve this, the first post-war 'new' British design for a home-built aeroplane, Phoenix Aircraft Ltd was at a turning point for we had no money to advertise and no way of promoting the design. If only we had had the ability to do something like Luton Aircraft Ltd had done before the War and get a magazine like *Practical Mechanics* interested…

It was a long shot but I had known F J Camm (who had, unfortunately, just died as recounted further on) and the people who ran George Newnes Ltd, his publishers. In a 'lightning striking the same place several times' move, I recalled another old adage about 'nothing ventured; nothing gained' and so, in one of those wild gestures of blind faith, I decided to push my luck. I arrived at the office of the newly-appointed managing editor of *Practical Mechanics* in 1959 with the crazy idea of getting the magazine interested in publishing plans for its third amateur aircraft in 25 years and its second go at the Luton Minor.

To my surprise, he thought it a good idea!

There were some interesting discussions that followed. Paramount was that whereas the Flying Flea had been covered in just four monthly issues and the first Luton Minor in six, the new design being more complicated would be spread over a whole year – twelve issues in all. This was great news for it meant that we would have the equivalent of a year's 'free' advertising and thus maximum exposure.

For a penniless small company run by two directors, one virtually retired and the other fresh-faced and bushy-tailed (me) it was the chance of a lifetime! Unlike the first set of articles in 1938, however, I had already completed all the drawings and had written the instruction manual. All the magazine had to do was to turn the text into *Practical Mechanics'* house style and cut it into monthly chunks. I delivered all the finished artwork which they re-lettered to match their format. There was still a shortage of actual photographs, though, and the few we had were used several times over.

Those articles cemented the reputation of the Luton LA.4a Minor as the first all-British design for a homebuilt aeroplane to be approved in the post-war era. Phoenix Aircraft Ltd sold many sets of plans and the Minor embarked on a new era of popularity – an era which still endures in this age of plastic super-fast assemble-it-yourself kit-planes. Yes, there is still a small demand for an aeroplane that can be built at very low cost and from scratch without huge financial outlay.

But the story is not quite finished for we ought to know the fate of the original magazine and its founder. Poor old F J Camm was a real workaholic who literally always worked. On the morning of February 18th 1959 a cleaner found him still sitting at his desk, an unfinished article before him. He had truly died on the job. The journal's 25th anniversary edition (which heralded the LA.4a Minor) had been produced just a few months earlier: it was that for October 1958.

Practical Mechanics fades away…

Practical Mechanics magazine quickly re-grouped around a managing editor and carried on as before. But things were different and times were changing. The issue published after the last of the Luton LA.4a Minor articles, the one dated September 1960, was the final edition in the original large-sized format that had been sustained since its inception. The magazine now became a small, pocket-sized publication. It was not a popular move in the face of an already-declining circulation. Writing was on the wall and the edition for August 1963 was the final one. It was number 353 of Volume XXX.

Camm's great creation made one final foray into amateur aviation. Its issue for April 1963 – by now one of the small A5 magazines – ran a familiar strip on its cover that read 'Build Your Own Aeroplane'. Inside was a five-and-a-half page descriptive article on the new post-war version of the LA.6 Luton Major which was then available as a set of drawings. Hampered by the extreme shortage of a suitable engine (it was designed for the pre-war 62 hp Walter Mikron inverted inline four-cylinder motor) only a few were built. But *Practical Mechanics* played no further part in that aircraft's history.

... and times change...

The Luton LA.6 Major two-seater ultra-light was a delight to build and fly but to the consternation of its designer somebody authorised the machine to be flown at an all-up weight considerably in excess of the design weight. This increase, approved without my authority, reduced safety margins to a dangerous level and action had to be taken to remedy this clerical oversight with overweight aircraft (fitted with heavy engines) grounded.

Nevertheless, the original 1,200 lb maximum all-up weight Major remains easy to build and fly and, of course, today there are many fine and very light engines available to power both it and the ever-popular Luton Minor single-seater.

As the author of the final series of Minor articles, I published a facsimile edition in 1963 for the benefit of Luton Minor builders. Called *Build your Own Luton Minor Ultra-Light Aircraft* and subtitled *Very Personal Flying*, this was a single-sided litho edition and ran to an edition of just 100 copies. Soon after this, a boardroom dispute centring on Cecil Latimer-Needham's decision to spend our restricted capital on developing a radical design by a young former RAF test-pilot resulted in my resigning from Phoenix Aircraft Ltd but, crucially, retaining all rights to the Luton LA.4a Minor and the new 1,200 lb all-up two-seat LA.6 Major.

Phoenix Aircraft ultimately spent a lot of money on a project which was a failure, acquired agencies for other aircraft, became financially overstretched, ran out of steam – and finally disappeared.

With Phoenix Aircraft gone, Latimer-Needham retired for the second time and went to Canada where he died in May 1975.

...but its enterprise lingers on!

Over the years, countless magazines have come and gone but some have retained much respect into the modern era. We can list *Punch* and *Picture Post* and so on, but one which many *practical* men miss is that beginning with another 'P' – *Practical Mechanics*. For a long time a number of enthusiasts have commented that it would be nice to see a facsimile of the Luton Minor articles while others, who are devotees for the old original Mignet HM.14 Flying Flea,

have longed to see those again. Of course, the original articles are long-since out of print and fetch 'rare item' prices on the second-hand market.

The purpose of this little book, then, is to fulfil those desires. But there is a crucially important caveat! The *original* HM.14 Flying Flea is presented here for reference and enjoyment only and you should **not** attempt to construct one. Post-war examples of the Flying Flea such as the HM.290 and onwards are different and provenly safe designs. If you want to build a Flying Flea-type aircraft, **only** build from a modern approved design and proper set of engineering plans.

As for the Luton LA.4 Minor, similar advice pertains. The pre-war design (from 1937) falls short of current design demands and is unsuitable for today's strict engineering and airworthiness requirements.

The post-war (1950s) Luton LA.4a Minor remains a fully-approved and sound design but since these articles were first published almost half a century ago there have been many detail modifications in a continuous programme of systematic development. If you want to build this aircraft, then you must use a current set of engineering drawings. The articles may, however, give you useful advice on processes and procedures.

It is imperative that anybody attempting to construct their own aircraft today should register their project with the Popular Flying Association (now called the Light Aircraft Association) *before* they make a start. This way the job goes along easily and you get into the air with safety.

Windows on the Past

These articles are presented here to be read and enjoyed merely as a little window on the past. A brief word about how we have reproduced them here. Wherever possible, the reproduction is an exact copy of the original *Practical Mechanics* pages complete with 'running head' and page-number. In one instance (the opening of the 1958 series) a double-page spread has been re-jigged to a suitable pair of single sides. The original page size of 280mm x 218mm overall has been slightly reduced. Occasionally, part of a page was used for some other purpose such as a different article. In these instances, I have filled that space with a photograph or related material, all clearly indicated so you can tell it was not part of the original.

The pre-war articles were nicely printed on good quality thick straw paper: by the 1950s the magazine was being printed on inferior quality thin newsprint displaying neither sharp impression nor truly 'black on white' and with considerable 'show-through'. These are much poorer to reproduce. This degradation of presentation was a characteristic of many contemporary publications and remained a legacy of the war years' austerity.

Practical Mechanics introduced their three D-I-Y aircraft articles with colour covers, also reproduced here. What is not commonly known that in the case of the Flea articles, there were two of these artistic covers. This rare second one is to be found here as well as the original.

With these Flying Flea articles there was a number of accompanying adverts placed by suppliers of parts and materials. These formed part of the original presentation. Because these, too, tell a story, I have included them. Just remember not to attempt to contact these advertisers – they're all probably long-dead by now! And remember

Phoenix Aircraft Ltd no longer exists either. And even the PFA has changed its name!

So step back in time and read from almost three-quarters of a century ago how people got fired with enthusiasm for making an aeroplane at home. I cannot over-emphasize that these articles are here only for your enjoyment: if you really do want to build a modern approved version of these designs, or any other design, come to that, there's a list of addresses following the Bibliography.

Bibliography:

Ellis, Ken, and Jones, Geoffrey P: *Henri Mignet and his Flying Fleas*, Haynes Publishing, Yeovil, Somerset, 1990

Mignet, Henri: *HM.290 Sport-de-l'Air*. Special edition of *L'Aeronef, Journal de L'Air* for June 1946 (includes set of construction drawings and instructions). *Edit*: Odilon Dubois, Bruxelles, Belgium, 1946.

Mignet, Henri: *Le Sport de l'Air*. Intro. by Georges Houard, editor of 'Ailes'. Taffin-Lefort, Paris, France, 1934 (and later editions).

Mignet, Henry: *The Flying Flea (Le Pou-du-Ciel): How to Build and Fly It*. Trans from the French. Intro by Air Commodore John Adrian Chamier, Air League of the British Empire, London, 1936 (several impressions).

Ord-Hume, Arthur W J G: 'The History of the Popular Flying Association' [story of the home-built aircraft movement in Britain], *Popular Flying*, Pt.1 January 2006, pp.31-34; Pt.2 February, pp.31-36; Pt.3 April, pp.41-46; Pt.4 June, pp.27-31; Pt.5 pp.45-49; Pt.6 December, pp.35-40. Popular Flying Association, Turweston Aerodrome, Northamptonshire. 'The Seventy-year Itch' [story of the Flying Flea in Britain], *Popular Flying*, January 2007, pp.23-30. Popular Flying Association, Turweston Aerodrome, Northamptonshire. *On Home-Made Wings*. GMS Enterprises, Peterborough, 1997. *Flight on Frail Wings*. GMS Enterprises, Peterborough, 1998. *British Light Aeroplanes; Their Evolution, Development and Perfection 1920-1940*. GMS Enterprises, Peterborough, 2000.

Contacts:

These are correct at the time of publication in 2009.

Flying Flea plans for HM-293, 360 and 380: Paul Pontois, 1890 Rang des chutes, Sainte Ursule, Quebec, JOK3MO, Canada.

Pou Renew, Newsletter of the English language Flying Flea group. HMS, PO Box 101194, Chicago, Illinois, 60610, United States of America.

Le Pou du Ciel, French language newsletter. Michel Jacquet, Amicale Pouducieliste, 30 rue Bourdon de St Amans, 47240 Bob-Encontre, France.

Luton LA.4a Minor plans: Arthur W J G Ord-Hume, 24 Shepherds Lane, Guildford, Surrey, GU2 9SL.

Popular Flying Association (Light Aircraft Association), Turweston Aerodrome, Nr. Brackley, Northamptonshire, NN13 5YD. Tel: 01280 846786

How to Build the "FLYING FLEA"

The "Flying Flea," which has been successfully flown and demonstrated all over England by its designer, M. Mignet, is probably the first practicable attempt to provide the man in the street with an easy and cheap means of learning to fly and of building his own aeroplane. The "Flying Flea" may be built and flown by any home mechanic, and its total cost for engine and materials of about £75 brings it within the means of most. It is a safe machine for beginners for it has a low landing speed, a low cruising speed, and the construction does not call for a greater degree of skill nor of tool equipment than is possessed by most amateurs. Its span is only 13 ft. ! This first article deals with the construction of the fuselage. We shall be pleased to answer any questions which intending builders care to put to us.—Editor.

Full list of materials appears on page 7.

THE fuselage is constructed like a packing case. But since the plywood cannot be nailed on to itself, one has to interpose a lath of spruce in the angles as a means of receiving the nails, and these laths are glued over a large area on each surface. In this way, the sides of the plywood are united to each other, not by nails, which is not a solid form of construction, but by plenty of glue, which makes an efficient welded construction of wood.

These laths allow metalwork to be fixed to the angles of the box in places where plywood would only present a local and feeble resistance. These angles are nodes, or strong points, which are more or less irreducible in number and are firm bases for attachments. The laths at the rear end of the box prolong its solidity to the rear, and form a very strong triangulated pyramidal construction. At the risk of being a bit heavy, the fuselage is constructed in plywood 2 mm. thick.

The Glue

Make the glue ready for work in advance ; for four hours in warm weather and for a whole day in winter, powdered glue and water are mixed in equal volumes, not heaped up, but measured exactly. Stir the glue with a wooden spatula. The mixture settles down into a smooth, viscous paste, about the consistency of thick oil. You do not need a brush.

Before you start to use it, test your

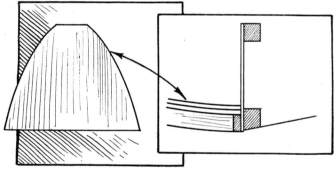

Fig. 3.—How the tongue is formed.

wood. It must be sound and must not have any green colour, reminding you of worm-eaten stuff. Each lath and strip of wood, carefully chosen, is pinched in the vice at one end, and twisted lightly in the direction of its length. It ought not to break or crack. Examine it closely. The grain should be straight or very slightly slanting. Throw away any piece which has knots and/or splits in it.

The Body Sides

Draw out the first side on a piece of plywood 3 mm. thick, following the dimensions given in Fig. 1. The run of the grain is shown by arrows. All the dimensions are given in millimetres ; mark out the angles with a protractor.

Cut out two sides exactly similar, with a fine saw.

One lath 2 metres 40 cm. long is nailed and glued in the position shown in Fig. 2.

Fig. 1.—Details of the sides of the body.

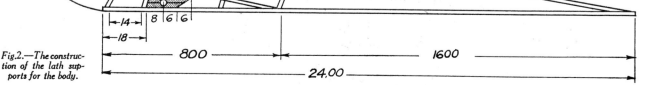

Fig. 2.—The construction of the lath supports for the body.

It extends beyond the body towards the rear for 1·6 metres. In order to glue it, proceed as follows :

Spread the glue on 800 mm. of the lath in such a way that after a minute the face of the wood is covered uniformly without any blank spaces. One nail at each end will keep it steady, and then nail it in zigzag fashion approximately every 20 mm. (see Fig. 2). After nailing it, the glue will ooze out along the edge. You can smooth it off when it is dry.

Proceed in the same manner with the other laths, which, as you see, leave 30 mm. spare along edge No. 1. Fix the other laths in the positions shown, and then the stops. The rear lath, before it is put in place, should be pierced with two holes at a

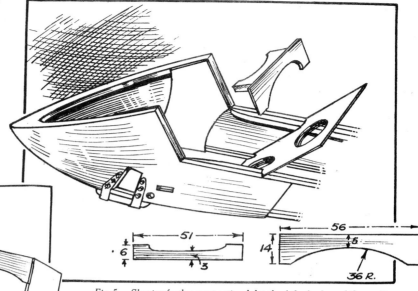

Fig. 5.—Showing further constructional details of the fuselage of the machine.

Fig. 4.—Fitting the parts to form the nose of the machine.

distance of 40 mm. These will receive, later on, the anchorages in the screwed rod of the harness. Take care that there is no empty space at the end of each lath.

Make the fillings (Fig. 2) with the ends of laths. With the point of a knife cut out the plywood sides opposite this empty space, where the pulley which takes the rudder cables is to be fitted. Cut out also the quadrilateral through which the axle will pass.

Cover all this assemblage with the panel (Fig. 7) in 3 mm. plywood. Prepare the other side exactly the same as the first, but in the reverse order.

It must be understood that where wood touches wood there is gluing and nailing.

From a piece of mild steel 1 mm. thick cut with shears two strips which, when folded, will clasp simply by gluing under the feet a skid (Fig. 12) in hard wood, such as oak, walnut or beech. The holes in these straps will be drilled beforehand on one side only. The other side will be drilled for receiving the bolts, after it is in place and solidly fixed by a binding or by a hand vice on the longeron. These bolts, in screwed rod, will fix as well the short strips which are inside the fuselage.

The skid and the straps are designed to reinforce the longeron when the axle strikes it after jolts. A block in hard wood is glued and screwed on the skid at an equal distance from the straps, to prevent the elastic shock absorber of the axle from slipping.

Glue the blocks one made of for bolting the —this last hard wood— metalwork

Fig. 6.—Showing the " Flying Flea " ready for flight.

Fig. 7.—The side panel.

for the wing bracing wires. The lath which serves as the reinforcement gets progressively thinner towards its end.

Joining the Sides

The two sides now have to be joined by the back of the pilot's seat, made of 3 mm. plywood as is shown in Fig. 13. The holes, reinforced with circles of plywood, give access to the luggage compartment. The holes and the plywood circles can be cut quite easily with a carpenter's compass, of which one arm has been ground to a knife edge. Any ironmonger's shop will provide one of these tools.

On the panel you should only place the bar and nail the sides in front of the laths. Then put on the crosspiece, making its edge bevelled and level with the underside of the longerons.

The short strips in front will then be joined by the panel (Fig. 8), cut out in such a way that the crossbar fits on to the block, and its crossbar on to the lower end of the short strips; thus, the crossbar and the ends of the short strips all come level with longerons. The height of the panel will be decided on the spot. Do not forget to reinforce the hole with a circle of plywood. File away anything which might obstruct the straps.

The short strips in the rear are also joined at their lower ends by a slat and double gussets. In the same way, the short strips are united by the panel with the crossbars. The slats are all on the same level, and serve to support the plank

which forms the seat, of which the underneath view is shown in Fig. 10. This panel is fixed by 12 screws with round heads. It is double; that is to say, two thicknesses of 6 mm. are glued together under weights. There is no point in nailing it together.

Two strips connect the crossbars near the edges to the central hole in which the joy-stick works. At each end of these reinforcing strips use a wood screw with a washer.

The Front Point

The lyre-shaped piece of wood will be cut out from a plank of 20 mm. of hard wood, as shown in the sketch Fig. 9.

Because of its sloping position to the fuselage it will be necessary to bevel off its outside faces in order to diminish the upper face. The arms of this piece of wood will be separated a distance of 550 mm. by adjusting the flat faces, and they will be joined underneath by a triangle of plywood which is glued to them; and again in the middle by the plank of hard wood of 40 mm., thinned down at the ends to 20 mm., well-fitted and held from underneath by the gussets, which are 6 mm. thick. All are fixed simply by gluing. This plank, later on reinforced by bolted metalwork, will support the motor.

Bevelling, adjusting, and fitting should be commenced with a plane and finished off with a large half-round file—a metal file bought and kept for this purpose. This file will be used only on wood. It is better than a wood rasp, and after the glue is dry the file eats into the wood just as well as a rasp, even if it hits up against some nails. The rasp or the plane would very soon

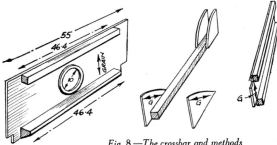

Fig. 8.—The crossbar and methods of fitting.

together and nailing it in such a way that the two sides, when drawn together, go a little bit beyond the desired shape. Nail the plywood carefully all along the edge of the arms with one nail every 10 mm. Cut off the edges which go beyond the end of one lyre, and plane off the amount which extends above it. (This has been allowed for in Fig. 2 by using 30 mm. instead of 20 mm.) You now have a smooth joint which allows the whole to be covered by a triangular sheet of plywood.

From a plank of hard wood 20 mm. thick cut out a piece and nail it on to the panel, which is 6 mm. thick; this will join the two arms of the lyre and the laths.

Planking

Turn the skeleton upside down. Cut out the tongue at 20 mm. and fit it to the edge. Copy this fourteen times in plywood of 3 mm. thickness. Seven thicknesses glued together, one on top of the other along the edge, will make a longeron curved in two directions to which you can nail, one after the other, the two bits of 3-mm. plywood (Fig. 3). Put one on top of the other, and glue, which will make the planking of the cockpit.

The planking is supported at the rear with the batten adjusted in front of the panel. With a file, smooth off all the lower faces of the curved strips so that a piece of 3-ply 3 mm., curved in a triangular form, can be well glued every-

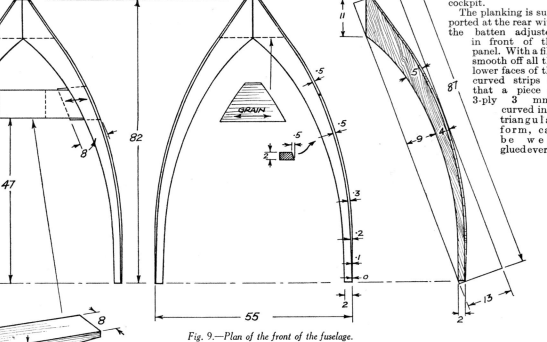

Fig. 9.—Plan of the front of the fuselage.

be damaged if it struck projecting nails.

Enclose the two arms of the lyre between the bits of plywood (Fig. 9), gluing them

where from the point right up to the batten. This will make a part of the base of the fuselage.

Now cover the lyre right up to the panel with plywood of 3 mm.

Rear Joints

Damp the longerons with a piece of rag soaked in water over one metre's length for ten minutes, starting from the rear point. Join them together in a point with a wood screw of 4 × 40, with a countersunk head, taking care to interpose at 440 mm. from the back a piece of 20 mm. × 20 mm. × 410 mm. Place into position the planking of the

Fig. 10.—Underneath view of seat platform.

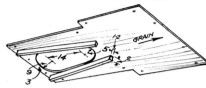

tool chest, and also two stops of hard wood fixed by two screws of 4 mm. × 40 mm. with round heads, spaced at 40 mm., supported on the inside with plates of 3-ply of 3 mm. with the grain running vertical.

Cut out the two metal pieces in mild steel of 1 mm., which will be bent. One will do to fix to the rear points, by means of screws with round heads 4 mm. × 15 mm., and the other to the stern post made of hard wood 15 mm. × 40 mm. × 450 mm.

Place on the back piece the laths (Fig. 11), then the longerons, which are fixed on in front by two gussets, and joined together in the rear by a screw, with the crossbar of 410 mm. as for the lower point. The second piece of metalwork will join them on to the stern post.

During this work take care that the stern post is not out of line with the fuselage. Plane it and file it until it is exactly vertical with the fuselage. The upper crossbar is fixed on to the longerons by two gussets at 350 mm. from the bar.

In addition, this crossbar carries a piece of hard wood, screwed and glued. The whole is pierced with a hole of 7 mm. Carry on in a like manner with the crosspiece, which carries a piece pierced with two holes of 6 mm., spaced 40 mm. apart. Place in and glue into position the bulkhead furnished with laths. Bevel off with a file the plywood on the sides, following the shading so that you can apply over it, without getting the extra thickness, the plywood sides of the rear of the body, which will be at this spot similarly bevelled.

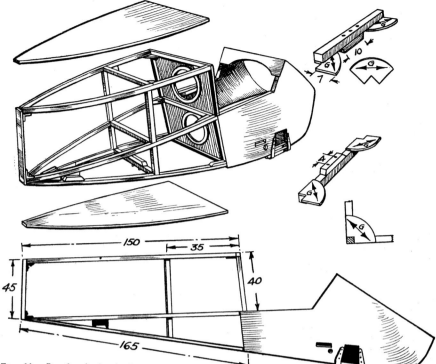

Fig. 11.—Details of the fuselage, showing the simple construction from 3-ply and laths.

having glued it everywhere. When you are gluing on the second panel, see that the stern post is still kept quite straight. After it is dry, finish off all the rough edges nicely with a plane or file. The construction then appears as in Fig. 11.

You can close up the box by the lid, which is pierced with a 7 mm. hole. Take the screws out of the rear blocks and mark their places exactly on the sides. Now place the bottom of the box into place and pierce with holes right up to the seat.

The piece of 3-mm. plywood which will form the base between the crossbars can be made ready, and will be placed in position later. The fuse-

longerons is joined by a metal strap, 2-mm. material, by three screwed rods (Fig. 14) of 5-mm. metal.

The pivot post of the rudder is of mild steel tubing. It turns freely with a play of 1 mm. in the metal strap which is closed by a little tube, 24-mm. material, fastened by a bolt. This tube is obtained by rolling in the vice a piece of material of 2 mm. around a rod of 6 mm.

The other end of the rudder post is inserted into a T, which carries the small axle for the wheels (Fig. 16). This T turns (with a play of 1 mm.) in an eye made from a piece of mild steel wire of 10 mm. diameter, heated to red heat and bent into an eye, or welded with the bar.

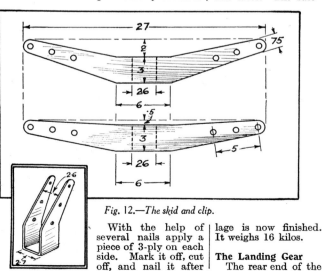

Fig. 12.—The skid and clip.

With the help of several nails apply a piece of 3-ply on each side. Mark it off, cut off, and nail it after | lage is now finished. It weighs 16 kilos.

The Landing Gear

The rear end of the

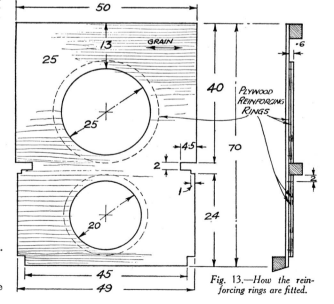

Fig. 13.—How the reinforcing rings are fitted.

The arms of this triangle are bent inwards, and the two ends, carefully aligned to one another, make the axle which works in the metal straps. These latter straps are placed against the holes of the bolts and marked off, taking great care that the rudder post is carefully aligned on the stern post. It is separated from the latter at the lower end by 40 mm. to 50 mm. and at the upper end by 10 mm. to 15 mm.

An opening cut in the sides gives access to the nuts of the bolts which fix a 2-mm. plate of steel on to the piece of hard wood. Little pieces of aluminium sheeting ·6 mm. in thickness, and some wood screws, close these openings.

The T holds the eye between metal and rubber washers, which are held from moving by the two bolts which join the T to the rudder post.

The rudder post is fastened to the rudder by the aid of four strips of 2-mm. metal which are bolted to it. At the spot where the bolts will pierce the rudder post, one will have strengthened it with a filling of hard wood, greased with wax or paraffin. The washers of metal and of rubber absorb the shock of the straps on the collar.

The metal strips are also fixed on to a tube of 24 mm. length by a bolt.

A rudder shock absorber of 12-mm. section, 500 mm. long, joins the rudder post to the base of the stern post, passes under a metal fitting, and is fixed by a plate and two big wood screws. The two ends of this

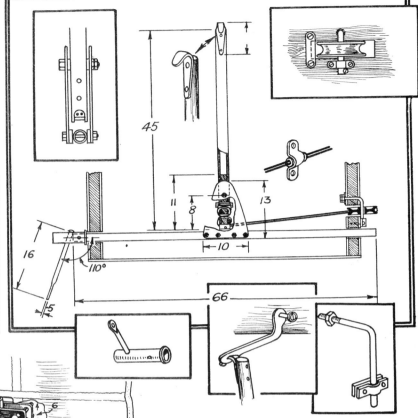

Fig.15.—Constructional details of the stick control.

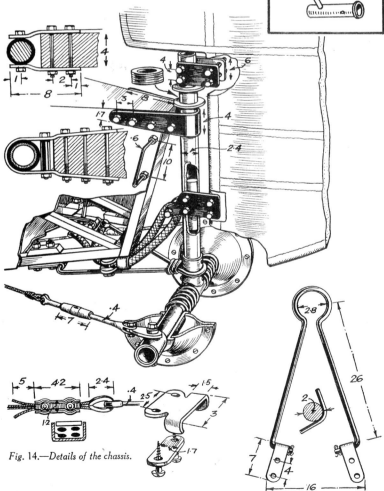

Fig. 14.—Details of the chassis.

shock absorber are pushed inside the fuselage through a 30-mm. hole cut in the bottom at a distance of 100 mm. from the stern post.

It is lightly stretched in such a manner that the weight of 30 kilos. placed on the fuselage begins to make the metal straps move.

Wheels

The rudder post of 24 mm. diameter, is pushed into the T of 24 mm. × 27 mm. section. Make this a good fit by smoothing up with a file and emery cloth the end of the tube; the fit should be a close one. The two bolts will keep the one from turning in the other.

The tube in 21 mm. × 24 mm. material is welded square on the tube.

Two rivets of 4 mm. fix the axle in the tube. These rivets will be flush with the tube.

The wheels are made out of two discs in 1·5 mm. material, which are embossed by a hammer, and joined along their circumference by twelve rivets of 4 mm., taking care that they are properly centred on the tube.

You can do this quite easily by hammering a sheet 200 mm. × 200 mm. on a piece of wood which has been hollowed out, using a round-faced hammer. After you have hammered out the material, you can then describe a circle.

The tube, with its ends slightly flared by hammering with little blows on the top of an anvil, goes through the middle of the wheel, and then one flares the other end in the same way. It would be a very good thing to weld all this together.

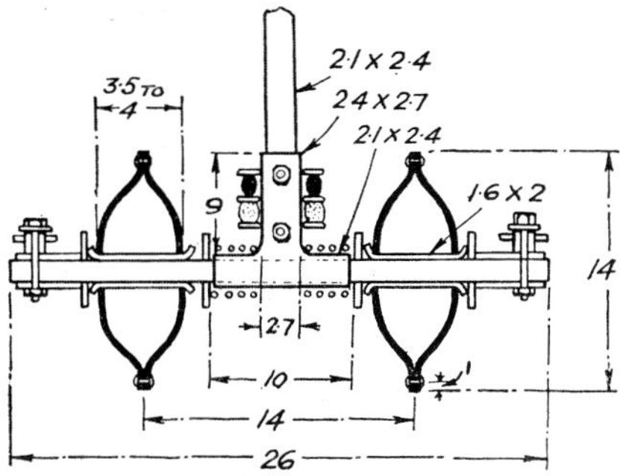

Fig. 16.—The rudder post and fixing.

A spring of eight turns in steel wire of 3 mm. is threaded on to the tube and capped by a washer next to the wheel. A sleeve is fixed level with the end of the axle by a 6-mm. bolt. This bolt goes through the little tube, which is 6 mm. high and 10 mm. in diameter, under the washer. This tube serves as an axis for the metal strap, to which one will attach the turnbuckle of the rudder cable.

All this mechanism may seem to you most complicated. It is clearly much more so than a simple wood skid fixed by two bolts, but how often would you break that ?

With wheels like these you will not worry about cross-wind take offs, and will take off correctly every time. You can avoid obstacles on the ground, and you can steer yourselves amongst the spectators who seem firmly rooted to it. That is the fruit of my experience, believe me. Sacrifice two days to realise this arrangement, which altogether weighs 2·5 kilos.

The hand grip in steel rod of 6 mm. bolted to the left-hand side of the stern post will enable you to lift the tail about without sticking your fingers into the covering of the rear wing or rudder.

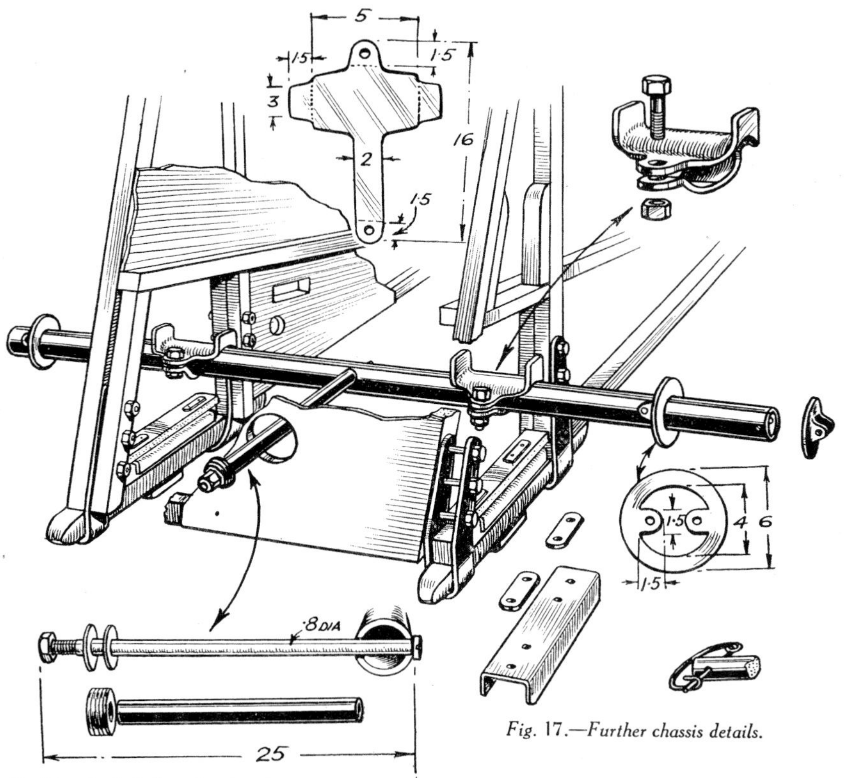

Fig. 17.—Further chassis details.

LIST OF MATERIALS

Materials should be o first-grade quality, but need not be special aviation materials, nor A.I.D. inspected. For example, steel tubing, bolts and nuts, and sheet steel for fittings are of good quality commercial mild steel, and not special high-tensile aviation specifications.

Plywood.

Birch or other good plywood of " superior " or " aviation " quality.
6 sheets 6 ft. × 3 ft. 3 mm. thick.
4 ,, 6 ,, × 3 ,, 1·5 mm. thick.

Laths.

Good quality spruce, straight grained, free from knots or shakes, capable of being twisted and bent, breaks with long fibres. You require:

6 lengths of 5 metres	15 mm. × 60 mm.
(or 10 lengths of 3 metres 20cm.)	15 ,, × 60 ,,
10 lengths of 4 metres	20 ,, × 20 ,,
50 lengths of 3 metres	6 ,, × 12 ,,

These can be obtained, sawed and planed to size.

Linen Fabric.

Only aviation materials are suitable. The linen fabric as used for full-sized aeroplanes is rather heavy, and strong covering material as used for gliders is approved. This is usually a strong nainsook material at about 10*s*. per piece of 12 yds. Cheaper stuff than this is likely to be low in strength.

You require 36 yds. fabric 38 in. wide; 100 yds. notched strip about 2 in. wide, obtainable from:
Messrs. Stevenson & Son.
Messrs. Woods, Sons & Co. (Nainsook No. 200 or higher).
Messrs. Abbott-Baynes Sailplanes.
Messrs. Aircraft Materials, Ltd.
Messrs. B.A.C. (1935), Ltd.
The Dunstable Sailplane Co.

Dope.

Clear glider dope is the cheapest; it should be suitable for use in an unheated shop. You need about 4 gallons.

Messrs. Cellon Ltd. (or any of the last four names given under " Fabric " above).

Wheels and Tyres.

These present for the moment some difficulty. M. Mignet insists on large sections—for example, 450 × 100 medium pressure.

Normal aeroplane wheels and tyres are very expensive.

Metalwork.

(*a*) Tubing drawn (not welded or jointed) of mild steel suitable for welding.

M. Mignet's Specification.	*British Equivalent.*
4 metres in 13 × 16 mm.	5/8 in. 16 gauge.
2 ,, ,, 16 × 20 ,,	3/4 ,, 14 ,,
2 ,, ,, 17 × 20 ,,	3/4 ,, 16 ,,
2 ,, ,, 21 × 24 ,,	15/16 ,, 16 ,,
0·5 ,, ,, 24 × 27 ,,	1 ,, 16 ,,
1·2 ,, ,, 31 × 35 ,,	1 3/8 ,, 14 ,,
1·2 ,, ,, 36 × 40 ,,	1 9/16 ,, 14 ,,
0·2 ,, ,, 40 × 44 ,,	1 3/4 ,, 14 ,,
Also tow bar if you wish.	
1·8 metres in 31 × 35 mm.	1 3/8 in. 14 gauge.

If the exact sizes are unobtainable take the next larger, e.g. for substitute 7/8-inch.

Mild Steel Sheet.

You require:
2 mm. or 14 gauge (about 3 sq. ft.).
1·5 ,, ,, 16 ,, small quantities as required.
1·0 ,, ,, 19 ,, ,, ,, ,,
0·6 ,, ,, 24 ,, ,, ,, ,,

Drawn Rods, Screwed Rods, Bolts and Nuts.

You will need a total of about 2 metres of mild steel drawn rod in
4 mm., 6 mm., 8 mm., and 10 mm. sizes.
or 3/16 in. 1/4 in., 5/16 in., 3/8 in. (or preferably 7/16 in.), also about 3 metres of mild steel screwed rod in
4 mm., 5 mm., and 10 mm. sizes with nuts
or 3/16 in., 1/4 in. 3/8 in. (or preferably 7/16 in.)
also 50 bolts of 5 × 40 mm. or 2 B.A. × 1·6 in.
30 bolts of 6 × 40 mm. or 1/4 B.S.F. × 1·6 in.,
with their nuts and a large quantity of spare hexagon nuts particularly in 4 mm., size (for the screwed rod) and 5 mm. for the bolts—a lot of nuts get lost. You will want about 200 of each of the above popular sizes and 20 lock-nuts for the 10-mm. screwed rod.

In case of doubt take nearest size above the millimetre measurements.

Aircraft Steel Cable.

Extra flexible.
10 metres in 4·5 mm. for wing bracing, with 20- or 25-cwt. thimbles and 20 attachments for ends.
15 metres in 2·4 mm. for wing controls, with 15- or 10-cwt. thimbles and 15 attachments for ends.
10 metres of 5 cwt. for rudder controls, with 5 thimbles and 5 attachments for ends.

Glue.

Use casein glue, which is used cold and has marvellous adhesive and weathering qualities.

Shock Absorber Cord.

You require about 12 metres of 12-mm. diameter (1/2-inch) which should start to " give " at about 35 lb. pull.

Miscellaneous.

In addition you require an amount of piano wire, screws, nails, copper tacks for fabric covering, etc., which can always be bought locally as required. Use thin steel brads about 20 gauge for 3-mm. ply, and thinner still for the 1·5 mm.

Engines.

Carden 4-cylinder, water-cooled (converted Ford).
Douglas 750 c.c. horizontal air-cooled, 4-stroke twin.
Scott 2-stroke, air-cooled, inverted twin.

Airscrews.

The Airscrew Company can supply, if particulars are given regarding engine, h.p., rev., gear (if any), speed, and weight of aeroplane.

Cost.

Carefu l buying should give the constructor a list of materials for about £25, excluding engine and proprietary articles.

How to Build the "FLYING FLEA"

This Month we Deal with the Construction of the Wings of the "Flying Flea"

TO cut a metal fitting out of a mild steel sheet of 2 mm. thickness might frighten some amateurs.

Look at the illustration first of all, and cut a pattern in cardboard with the holes cut in it. Place this pattern on the steel sheet and mark it with a thick pencil or chalk. Fix the steel in a vice having jaws at least 4 in. long, and chisel it off with the edge of a cold chisel. Hold your chisel almost horizontally.

If you are obliged to hold the piece which has to be cut, beyond the jaws, give the chisel a slight slant in order not to tear the metal. You will soon acquire the knack of holding the chisel at the correct angle for free cutting.

Bending

One ought never to bend a piece of steel at a right angle, even for the smallest fitting, owing to the hammering necessary which cracks the metal.

Always interpose between the piece you have to bend and the jaws of the vice a piece of steel of the same thickness which has already been correctly bent.

Pierce the holes some distance from the edges. Where the drawings do not show the exact dimensions always leave between the hole and the edge of the material a distance of 8 mm. to 10 mm. all round the hole.

All bolts on an aeroplane ought to be made so that they cannot become loose. When it is a case of a piece which will often have to be taken down, fix the nut with a split pin or a safety pin. In very careful assemblages, use castellated nuts, or lock-nuts.

When one does not foresee the necessity of frequently taking the pieces apart, it is quite easy simply to burr the end of the bolt with several blows of the hammer on the end of the bolt which extend 2 mm. beyond the nut. Before taking it apart, a few strokes with a file will replace the thread and remove the burr.

Every screw, axle, and wire bracing must be securely fastened, because if you neglect to fix, voluntarily, a dozen screws, it may be that none will come loose; but if you forget one only, and one which may be important, you can be quite certain that that one will come away.

As you construct, or file, or screw, always think that one day the piece upon which you are working will hold you suspended in space several thousand metres above the ground.

The Main Landing Gear

The axle is a tube 1·2 metres long in 36 mm. × 40 mm., reinforced internally with another tube 800 mm. long in 31 mm. × 35 mm. This makes a thickness of 4 mm., and weighs 4 kilos. It is very heavy, but it is solid and will not bend. You will not be afraid of damage when you are running over bumps. A single tube would not be sufficiently strong.

The play of 1 mm. between the two tubes allows one to be pushed inside the other. If they were both the same size, you would not be able to get the inner one in place. A filling of hard wood is not suitable, because, although it is lighter, it only stops bending, but will not prevent breaking. Its elasticity allows the metal to fracture,

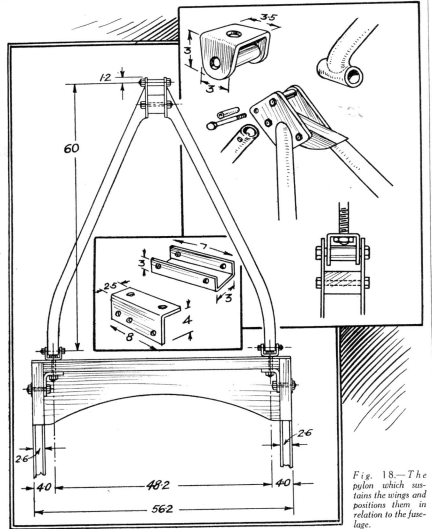

Fig. 18.—The pylon which sustains the wings and positions them in relation to the fuselage.

and one day the axle will break under a light shock.

A collar is fixed on to the tube by a 6-mm. bolt. It will prevent the tube from sliding in the rubber shock absorber, in the same way that the block holds the latter under the skid of the body.

Do not drill any hole in the axle at this spot.

A piece of 8-mm. rod goes through the axle at its middle point, and a tube made out of sheet metal of 1 mm. is rolled round. The rubber washers are then inserted between the two metal washers and the whole is held in place by a nut. This prevents the axle from turning, by supporting it on the front planking through the hole.

The axle bears down on the pad of rubber of a thickness of 12 mm. cut from the tread of an old motor-car tyre (Fig. 19). This pad is fixed on the ·6-mm. aluminium washer and held by two screws and a plate.

Elastic Suspension

The rubber shock absorber of 12 mm. diameter, which commences to stretch under a pull of 40 lbs., and which has a length of 1 metre 90 mm., is fixed at each end into a metal fastening in metal of 1 mm. with a bolt of 4 mm. One end of the shock absorber is fixed under the axle by a screw in 4 mm. × 20 mm. The shock absorber passes behind the stop, and afterwards six times round the axle, and under the skid, as shown in the drawing. One pulls on it until it is just slightly stretched. The other end receives a wire 2 mm. diameter, which will be securely attached to a screw placed conveniently under the seat planking. The screw prevents the last turn from slipping.

Before cutting the shock absorber, bind

turns of shock absorber. The machine could roll on one wheel without stretching the shock absorber, except over bumps.

The wheels are fixed on the ends of the axle by washers and collars (using a 5 mm. bolt horizontally) cut out in metal of 2 mm. thickness.

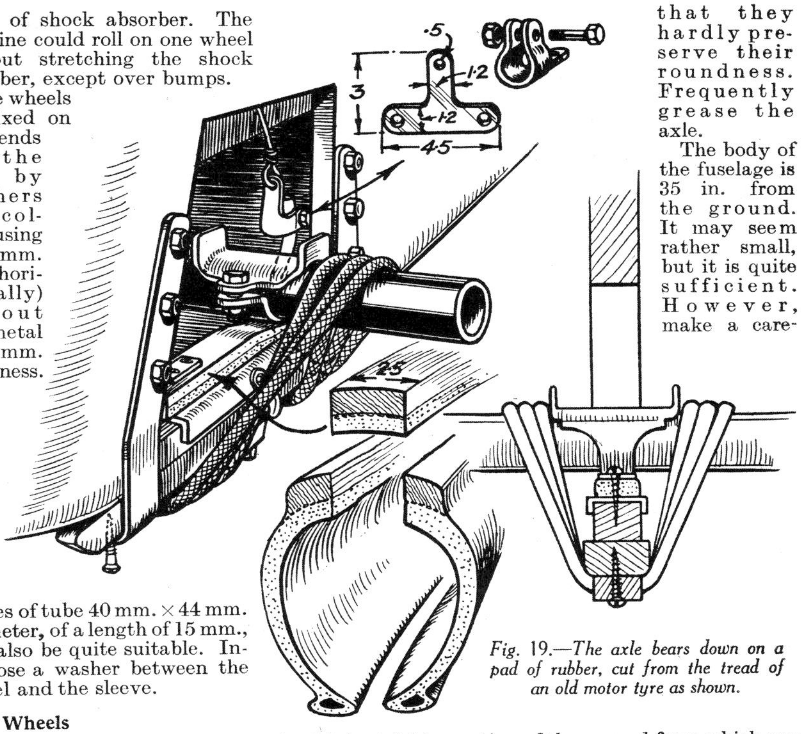

Pieces of tube 40 mm. × 44 mm. diameter, of a length of 15 mm., will also be quite suitable. Interpose a washer between the wheel and the sleeve.

The Wheels

The dimensions of the tyres should be 450 mm. × 100 mm., which, when lightly inflated, absorb most of the roughnesses of the ground. Only the bigger shocks will have to be taken by the shock absorber. One blows up these pneumatic tyres so

that they hardly preserve their roundness. Frequently grease the axle.

The body of the fuselage is 35 in. from the ground. It may seem rather small, but it is quite sufficient. However, make a careful inspection of the ground from which you are taking off, and flatten with blows from a spade any bumps which seem a bit too high.

The Control Stick

A tube traverses the fuselage from side to side underneath the rectangular hole.

The centre of the tube is held between two blocks and two cheek pieces by four bolts 5 mm. diameter. Between these strips, and the 6 mm. bolt and the washers of 1 mm., the control stick pivots. On the top of this stick is riveted a steel hook of 2 mm., which will prevent your hand from slipping off, and also will enable

Fig. 19.—The axle bears down on a pad of rubber, cut from the tread of an old motor tyre as shown.

it with rubber tape (two turns), and cut in the middle of the binding with a knife.

In its longitudinal view the suspension appears as shown in Fig. 19, which shows the axle, its collar, its pad of rubber, the strip of aluminium, the longeron of the fuselage, the skid which reinforces it, and the lower stop with the three turns of the shock absorber on either side; which make altogether, on each side of the body, twelve

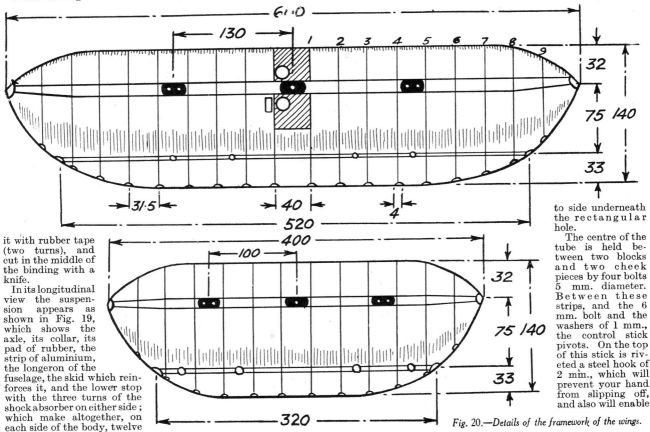

Fig. 20.—Details of the framework of the wings.

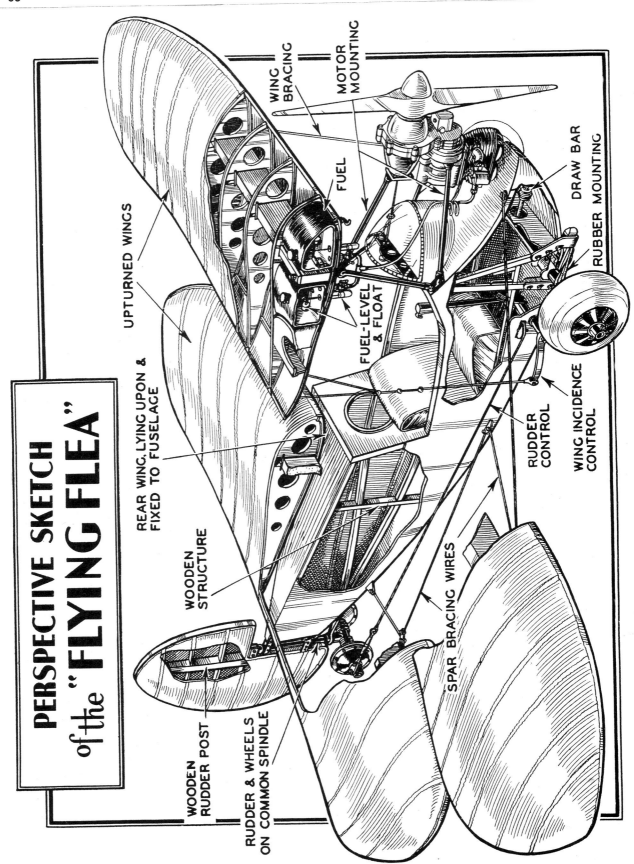

PERSPECTIVE SKETCH of the "FLYING FLEA"

WING BRACING

MOTOR MOUNTING

FUEL

DRAW BAR

RUBBER MOUNTING

UPTURNED WINGS

FUEL-LEVEL & FLOAT

REAR WING, LYING UPON & FIXED TO FUSELAGE

WOODEN STRUCTURE

RUDDER CONTROL

WING INCIDENCE CONTROL

WOODEN RUDDER POST

RUDDER & WHEELS ON COMMON SPINDLE

SPAR BRACING WIRES

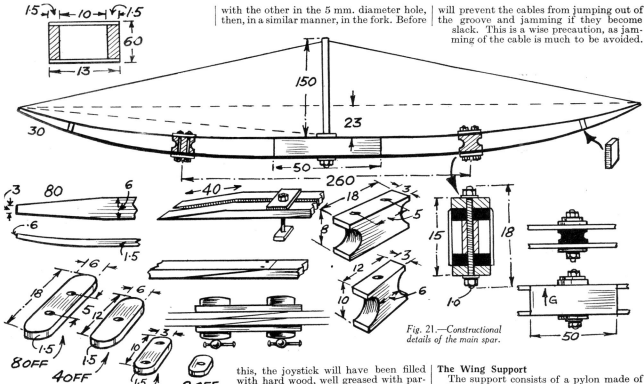

Fig. 21.—Constructional details of the main spar.

you to join the stick to the dashboard by rubber strips cut from an old pneumatic tyre. These strips will relieve the pilot of the continuous pull of the stick in a forward direction.

The tube extends beyond the sides of the fuselage for about 50 mm. Two flared sleeves prevent it from sliding laterally, and, if possible, without any play. Put washers between the fuselage and the sleeves.

These sleeves carry the levers made from 10-mm. bar heated to a red heat, flattened at one end and riveted at the other so that they will not come out of the sleeve. This sleeve is fixed to the tube by a bolt of 6 mm., taking care that the lever, when looking at it from the end of the tube, is at right angles to the joystick.

This latter disposition is for the control of the wing, to which the eyes of the levers, one on each side, will be fixed by a control cable.

Fitting the Rudder and Wing Control

The control of the rudder and wheels can be placed in position. Two cables 5 metres long of 2·4-mm. section steel and extra flexible, will be passed through the 6 mm. diameter hole in the joystick, and prevented from moving at the middle point by the 5 mm. diameter bolt. Each double turn will cross

with the other in the 5 mm. diameter hole, then, in a similar manner, in the fork. Before this, the joystick will have been filled with hard wood, well greased with paraffin wax, level with the base of the stick. The fork, partly of wood and partly of metal, should be filed round. The 4-mm. rivet prevents the cables from escaping from the fork. It is flush with the outside of the joystick. A drop of oil will prevent wear on the cables.

Each double cable, of a length of 2 metres 50 mm., passes over the pulley. (This is a cast pulley and has a very wide groove : the diameter at the bottom of the groove being 40 mm. at least, which revolves on the axis of a diameter appropriate to the hole through the centre of the pulley.) A nut on the interior of the fuselage at one end, a bearing at the other, and a screw 184 × 5 × 25 mm. fix this axis, which will be slightly inclined by means of a block under the bearing in order that it can be aligned with the bottom of the control stick.

Finally, the double leads join up with the turn-buckle where they are attached by the grip, adapted for cable of 4·5 mm. Bind each free end and join the ends to the cable. They will be about 50 mm. to 100 mm. beyond the grip.

The little piece of strip steel of 2 mm., fixed by two screws close up to the pulley,

will prevent the cables from jumping out of the groove and jamming if they become slack. This is a wise precaution, as jamming of the cable is much to be avoided.

The Wing Support

The support consists of a pylon made of tubes which sustain the wing and positions it in relation to the fuselage, after it has been fitted with its bracing wires.

It is made of two tubes in 17 mm. × 20 mm., welded to two cheek pieces of 2 mm. separated by a block of hard wood and joined by two bolts of 6 mm. (see Fig. 18). Where welding is not possible it can be bolted together. This is the head of the pylon.

The feet of the pylon, lightly bent (at red heat), are blocked with hard wood, and are pivoted at the U-piece in 2 mm. material, furnished with a 6-mm. bolt. This is joined to another piece of metalwork by two 6-mm. bolts which go right through the crosspiece, to which they give great rigidity. On the other hand, the metal piece is fixed by three 4-mm. bolts to the three laths of the landing gear.

It would be better if the feet of the cabane were finished off by a transverse tube welded on to them.

The head of the pylon is kept in position by a tube about 300 mm. long—the exact length will be decided at the moment when the wing is adjusted—and which is pivoted at either end on the 30-mm. tubes made of a 1·5-mm. strip rolled.

The axis tube of the foot is fixed between two strips of metal, which will be bolted to the motor when that is in place.

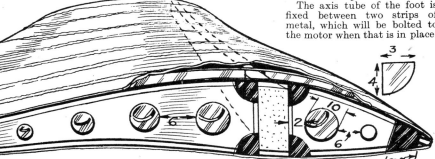

Fig. 22.—A sectional view of the wing, showing the rib construction.

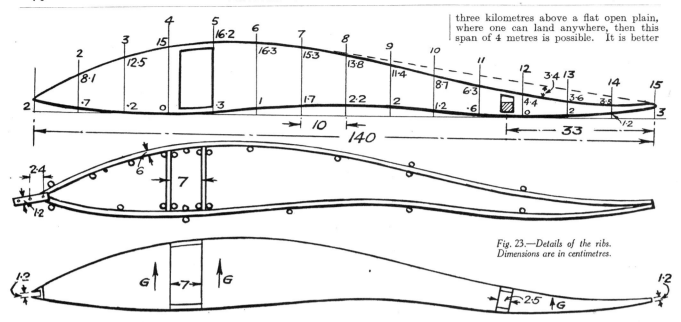

Fig. 23.—Details of the ribs.
Dimensions are in centimetres.

The Wing Pivot

The tube of the head of the pylon is the axis on which the wing will pivot. For that, a bolt made of screwed rod of 10-mm. material, 200 mm. long, goes through the wing, and holds to it the metal piece which is bent into a ∪ and welded on to a tube made of rolled strip of 2-mm. thickness. The pivoting is assured by these two tubes revolving one on the other, one being fixed on to the pylon, and the other fixed to the wing. In case it is impossible to weld, one can arrange a metal fitting without a tube, but doubled. The tube will be so arranged that the metal piece moves freely on it, but without lateral play. Perfect adjustment of these two tubes is useless; whether there is 1 mm. or 2 mm. of play is of little importance, provided that they are approximately round. A drop of oil is all that is necessary.

Choice of Span

The wing span should be adapted to the space in which it is to be constructed.

The ideal is a room or apartment of 3 metres × 4 metres. The machine itself is small, but this room should suffice for it. The wing is the largest part and has a span of 4 metres.

The plane was first tried with a 5½ metres span, but it was decided to try 4 metres as a test.

The first profile, with a flat lower side and the tail turned up, showed itself perfectly stable, but it did not lift well. The machine meandered across country, but it wanted the full power of the motor, and it scarcely climbed at all.

Lateral Stability

If one only wants to flutter, so to speak, to learn to fly on little journeys of two or three kilometres above a flat open plain, where one can land anywhere, then this span of 4 metres is possible. It is better than a machine which only rolls on the ground; better than a "penguin" because it really flies "in the air," and the principle incorporated in the "Flea" will permit faults of piloting which, in an ordinary aeroplane, would lead to catastrophe. Its lateral stability is immense.

Commence in that way if your room will not allow you to make a bigger wing. This wing of 4 metres for the standard model will be suitable for the rear wing of another "Flea," or perhaps will be the means of doing a kindness to a pal.

If you are light (10 stone) and are only thinking of short journeys, then a span of 5 metres will suit you very well, but on 6 metres you can weigh 12 stone, and you can carry with you enough petrol for three or four hours' flight.

Whether on 4-, 5-, or 6-metre span, the construction is identical. You only have to elongate, at your discretion, the ends of the wings (which means a few extra normal ribs to nail) and alter the attachment of the bracing wire. The central part remains unchanged.

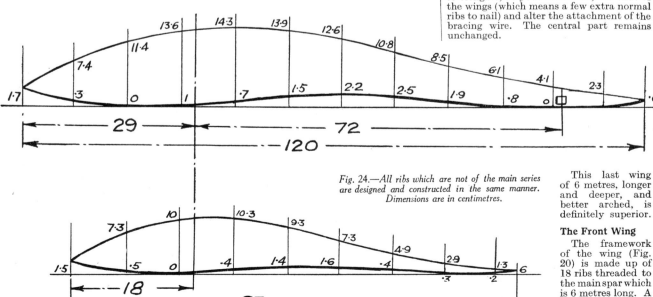

Fig. 24.—All ribs which are not of the main series are designed and constructed in the same manner. Dimensions are in centimetres.

This last wing of 6 metres, longer and deeper, and better arched, is definitely superior.

The Front Wing

The framework of the wing (Fig. 20) is made up of 18 ribs threaded to the main spar which is 6 metres long. A small rear spar of 5 metres 20 mm. is

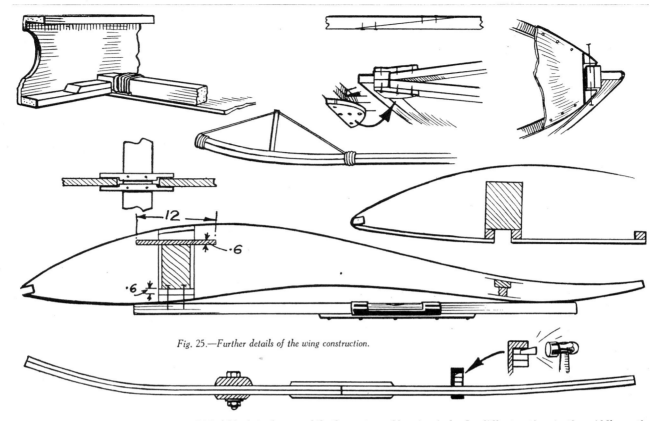

Fig. 25.—Further details of the wing construction.

inserted into the tails of the ribs, which are all of the same pattern.

The two ribs on the extreme ends are of a different pattern, because of the tapering of the wing in plan.

The leading edge and the trailing edge (in treble strips glued together), with the small spar, triangulate the framework, which does not need any other stiffener. And so, in the interior of the wing, except for the nailing of the plywood, there is not a single piece of metal. No fittings, no wires, no turn-buckles. The wing is supported on the pylon by its centre at a place where the block is shown, while the system of bracing cables, joined to the wing, keeps it steady but allows it to pivot about the axis.

The pivoting is controlled by the cable which joins the lever of the control column to the small spar, to which this cable is fixed at the spots marked by the four blocks. A spring, attached as shown, pulls down the wing in front.

The Main Spar

The spar is made of two flanges in 15-mm. × 60-mm. material, planed up to points and curved and maintained in correct form by two webs of 1·5-mm. plywood, of which the grain is vertical to the depth of the spar. The depth of the spar is 130 mm. (see Fig. 21).

It is perhaps difficult to find ordinary pine as long as 6 metres free from knots. This great length, on the other hand, is rather inconvenient for delivery. Let us start, then, with lengths of 3 metres 20 mm., which can be glued solidly together in the middle on the bevel.

Plane up at the same time the ends of the two 15-mm. × 60-mm. planks to a length of 400 mm., and they are then placed side by side and fixed together by a·bolt. Take care that the surface is quite flat and regular. After planing it pass a file or rasp over it in order to take off the polish.

Join the bevels together with glue and align carefully the two planks, which will be temporarily fixed by two small nails. Glue all over this and press it carefully between two blocks in two vices or two strong screw presses. Leave it for about 24 hours in which to dry.

Next, prepare for the two wings two blocks which can be of good pine or of beech. All the holes are of 11 mm. diameter. Get ready also five screwed 10-mm. rods 180 mm. long.

Assembling the Spar

After removing the two flanges out of their presses and smoothing their four faces correctly, drill a 11-mm. hole in the middle and two holes 500 mm. apart at 1 metre 300 mm. on both sides of the centre. Stated more exactly, these double holes will be 3 mm. closer to the centre in the upper flange.

Place the two planks on two trestles and glue them together. Make certain that

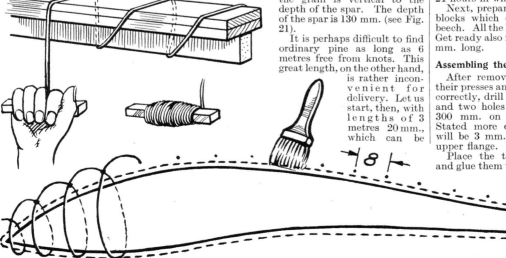

Fig. 26.—The method of covering the ribs.

these two planks are quite parallel end to end.

Now glue on each side two plates of plywood 1·5 mm., 130 mm. broad and 500 mm. in length.

With the aid of a cord or a wire 2 mm. diameter and the king-post made of a tube 1·5 metres long, pull up the points of the flanges in such a way that the thread, stretched between the points, passes at a height of 230 mm. above the central boxed portion.

A temporary block, 40 mm. in height, will separate the flanges at 300 mm. from the ends.

Take care to see that the arch of the flanges, as checked by the thread, is approximately equal to the right and to the left hand. Next, provide both faces of the spar from end to end with strips of 1·5-mm. plywood (nailing it with fine nails 8 mm. long in a zigzag at every 15 mm.). Place the plywood strips side by side without overlap.

Altogether this 6-metre-long spar requires 1 square metre of plywood. It weighs 15 lbs.

Construct in the same way the spar of the rear wing, but on a span of 4 metres, and with a curve of 180 mm. under the thread. This spar weighs 11 lbs.

To facilitate the folding of the wings for transportation along the road, place some blocks at the same distance apart as on the front wing.

Let everything dry for 12 hours before taking out the screw rods and the blocks.

You will be surprised at the stiffness of these beams. They give the impression—

and a perfectly correct impression—of really solid bits of stuff, to which one could trust one's life. You can make these two spars in one day.

The Ribs

Cover a board measuring 300 mm. × 1,500 mm. with white paper, and mark out on it the profile of the rib as follows :

Draw a straight line (Fig. 23) at 50 mm. from the lower edge. On this line draw 15 perpendiculars spaced 100 mm. apart, and mark them in accordance with the drawing given. For example, 2—0 marks the point of the leading edge, ·7 and 8·1 are the respective distances to the line of the lower side of the upper side of the wing, and so on right up to the tail of the rib, of which the trailing edge is 3 cm. above the line. This line is the chord of the wing.

Join all the points together, and this will give you the form of the profile of the wing.

Two laths in 6-mm. × 12-mm. material are held between nails 2 mm. long, of which you will have cut off the heads, and which mark out the lines required.

At 320 mm. from the leading edge mark off the line for the axis of the bolts of the spar. Place the 6-mm. × 12-mm. laths on either side of this line, leaving a free space of 70 mm. This is where you will thread the spar on to the ribs.

Join the two flanges by a web of plywood 1·5 mm. thickness. Keep the grain in the position shown by the arrows. Nail it every 25 mm. with nails of 8-mm. length. Dismount it and the rib is now retained in form.

Now nail the leading edge and the four gussets.

In this way construct 22 ribs.

With a cutting compass lighten the ribs. This should prove a simple matter, and should remove about 20 grammes from each web ; it is very little, but it will lighten the set of ribs by half a kilo, and that is certainly proper aviation practice.

The rib weighs 160 grammes. It requires ten minutes to nail it up.

The ribs which are not of the main series —the ribs 8 and 9—each one repeated four times over, will be designed and constructed in the same manner in accordance with the drawing (Fig. 24).

One can prepare the webs and laths in five hours. All 31 ribs can be nailed up in one afternoon, although you should allow several hours for rubbing up with sandpaper.

The batch of 18 ribs weighs 3 kilos.

One square metre of plywood of 1·5 mm. makes webs for eight ribs.

You will find it very easy to nail two nails in three seconds, but if you utilise a box of nails put on a slant. This slope will have the effect of making the nails roll until their heads are all pointing downhill. With a pair of pinchers you can then easily pick up each nail, and bring it under the hammer with the point about 1 mm. from the wood ; at your first blow the nail is stuck into the wood. Take away your pincers, and with one more blow the nail is driven home.

You will get along quite fast, and will avoid damaging your thumb and fingers.

Take the pot of glue well away from the box of nails.

How to Build the "FLYING FLEA"

The Profile of the "Flea"

THE pointed leading edge has been designed for those conditions in which it is actually better than any other profile—for proof of this look at the wings of the superracing machines of the Schneider Trophy—but it would present an inferior efficiency, for example, if one climbed at a high angle of incidence, providing that the motor allowed us to do so.

For simplification, lightness, and speed of work this pointed leading edge is unrivalled. It is also more solid, which is very much more important.

Assembly of the Wings

Place your spar on two trestles, with its points turned towards the ground. Thread the ribs on it in order, with their lower sides uppermost.

Further Constructional Details, Including the Mounting of the Engine

---

400 mm., and the remaining ribs are 315 mm. apart.

Turn the skeleton upside down, and place in position the twin joining blocks measuring 6 mm. × 12 mm. × 120 mm. Nail on to the main spar, and simply glue on to the web of the ribs in such a manner that all the lower surfaces of the ribs are parallel, which can be verified with a spirit level.

The small rear spar is in two pieces, right and left, each one threaded through its seven ribs all of a kind, and through the one of different pattern. Each half-spar is made out of two strips of 10 mm. × 20 mm. (or one strip of 20 mm. × 20 mm. split), 2 metres 700 mm. long, whose elasticity

allows it to join the turn-up of the ribs, following the curve of the main spar.

These two half-spars are joined between the two middle ribs by two 10 mm. × 20 mm. strips 400 mm. in length.

Glue them together before threading them into place, and make quite certain that the glue holds properly by nailing or binding them. If you are afraid of deformation of the trailing edge of the wing, before you bind up the little spar by means of a cord and a kingpost, bend up its points as you did in the case of the large spar.

The little spar of the rear wing is made out of one single piece 3 metres 200 mm. long, constructed in a similar manner.

The bottom strip of each rib is directly nailed with a single nail to the small spar. After this, block the upper surface of each rib with little bits of lath 6 mm. × 12 mm., as in Fig. 23 last month. Keep the ribs the same distance apart as they are on the main spar, to which they will be approximately at right-angles.

Between the ribs 2 and 3, and 4 and 5, fix the blocks with washers and 5-mm. bolts. At these points will be fixed the cables which govern the incidence of the wing.

The Leading Edge

With regard to the leading edge, a lath made of 6 mm. × 12 mm. material is fixed flat at the bottom of the nose of the ribs with two nails. This lath goes from end to

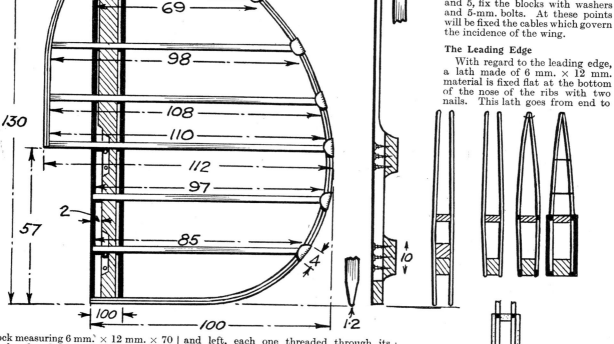

Fig. 27.—Showing the construction of the framework of the rudder.

A block measuring 6 mm. × 12 mm. × 70 mm. is placed under each rib, is nailed and glued on to the spar by two fine, long nails (Fig. 25, shown last month). Let them dry for two hours.

The two middle ribs are separated by

end of the spar. If it is necessary to make it of more than one piece, then join together by bevelling. Another lath, also placed flat, is fixed to the first one, and then the third one, which is stood on edge, is attached. This latter is simply glued, and is bound strongly into place with a thread, which makes one turn about every 30 mm.

Proceed in a similar manner for the trailing edge; in this case the first lath is fixed between the tail end of the ribs by two semi-circular gussets. As a safeguard against breaking the laths when bending them, it is well to moisten each with a rag soaked in water five minutes before starting work.

Two gussets join the two edges—the leading edge and the trailing edge—in the point at the end of the main spar. Two other gussets join the trailing edge to the small spar (see the plan of the wing, Fig. 20). After it is dry—one night—trim up the edges with a file.

The fuel tanks are placed in the front wing between the central ribs—one tank in front of the main spar, of 12 litres capacity; the other behind it, of 15 to 20 litres. This capacity gives altogether a total of about four hours of flight and a range of 400 kilometres.

These tanks are placed on strips of 3-mm. plywood, glued and screwed under the central ribs, the main spar, and the leading edge. They are afterwards wedged in their compartment and finally kept in place by the covering.

Without the tanks, the wing skeletons weigh 31 lb. and 20 lb. for the front and rear respectively, and require five hours' work to assemble.

Covering

The material for covering the wing is generally sold in a width of 1 metre. For the front wing six of these widths, 3 metres 10 cm. long, will be joined on a sewing machine along their edges. Cover the skeleton of the wing with this piece of material, of which the free edges will be at the trailing edge of the wing (Fig. 26).

Stretch it first along the whole of the bottom of the wing, nailing the turned-up edge at the trailing edge and proceed as follows:

1. Tack it between ribs No. 1.
2. Tack it then at rib 6, pulling it tight between 1 and 6.
3. Tack it on the back (tack every 40 mm.) between 1 and 6, making certain that it is quite straight as regards the run of the thread.

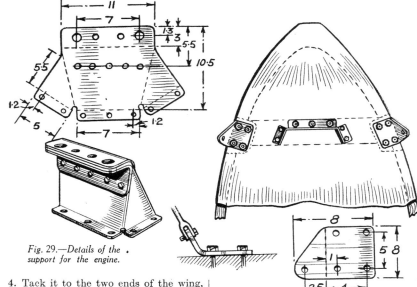

Fig. 29.—Details of the support for the engine.

4. Tack it to the two ends of the wing, pulling it very hard and fixing with four tacks.
5. Now tack between the ends of the wing and rib No. 6, pulling it tight in the direction of the span.
6. Now stretch the bottom face by pulling the cloth from the direction of the leading edge, and put in one tack at the nose of each rib.
7. Turn the wing over and tack it on its back, pulling firmly, and following the same order as on the bottom face. Note that the free edge is eventually tacked (after turning over) along the lower surface of the trailing edge.

Applying the Fabric

Now finish the rounded parts of the leading edge. Tacking is best carried out when holding the wing vertical, standing on its leading edge. An assistant holds it upright, and at the same time can hand you the box of tacks. Stand on a small stool about 200 mm. high, and get right opposite your work.

Do your work when the weather is warm and dry, or else in a room which is reasonably warm. Cut off the excess of the cloth, leaving after the final tacking a free margin of about 40 mm.

The skeleton is now enclosed in a sack like an ordinary mattress. Sew it through from side to side along each rib, with the aid of good hemp string and a mattress needle 22 cm. long. Knot the string every 80 mm. without cutting the thread between the knots, which will be on the top of the wing. Pull the string quite tight. This sewing, due to the dihedral of the wing, helps to stretch the cloth covering very firmly. The time for the covering is about four hours, and for the sewing two hours.

All round the rounded ends and along the trailing edge, the spare strip of 40-mm. material referred to before should be glued with cellulose varnish, moistening the cloth well with this above and below, and leaving it to dry completely (five or six hours).

Doping

Choose a warm, dry, sunny day. Operate outside in the shade in the afternoon. Fill a bowl with the doping varnish and, taking up a good brushful with a "cod's-tail" brush 60 mm. long, apply a layer, rubbing it well into the cloth, which becomes semi-transparent. Spread well any excess dope all round with strokes of the brush.

Do not economise with the dope; its purpose is not to make the wing look pretty but to stiffen the covering. Carry on progressively from front to rear, rib by rib. On going on to the next strip run over the blobs which formed on the earlier one, but do not take too much trouble about it.

Provided that the weather is warm you can start on the second layer two hours after the last stroke of the brush. Two layers are enough; an extra layer on the back is better; four layers are better still. All joints should be covered with a band of notched fabric. One applies the dope bit by bit to the surface and then to the band, which is rubbed down with a brush soaked in dope. When it is dry, watch it to see that the notches do not tend to spring up, and press them down with the fingers.

Before it dries, wash the brush in soap and water, when the dope will come off in little white pellicles.

The two wings are entirely constructed, assembled, covered, and varnished in eight days. They weigh each as follows:

The wing with the tanks for petrol and oil about 44 lb., and the tail wing about 26 lb.

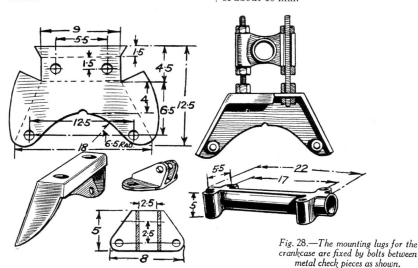

Fig. 28.—The mounting lugs for the crankcase are fixed by bolts between metal check pieces as shown.

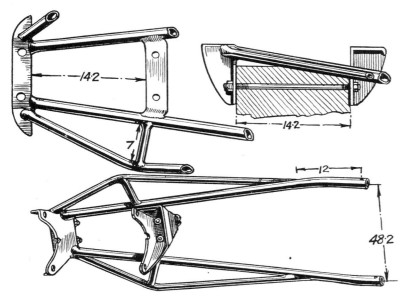

Fig. 30.—Further details of the engine mounting.

Rudder

The construction of the rudder follows the principle of the single spar (Fig. 27).

A lath in 20 mm. × 20 mm. material carries a reinforcement of hardwood, and is thinned down to 20 mm. × 12 mm. section. With the lath of 20 mm. × 12 mm. section it forms the flanges of the spar. Nail on the top of it at every 200 mm. strips 6 mm. × 12 mm., forming ribs cut off to the lengths indicated. The upper ribs go beyond the spar in order to make the leading edge and compensating surface ; the lower ones do not go in front of the spar Fill up the space between the ribs with strips of 6 mm. × 12 mm. section running along each flange on both sides, and cover with a strip of 3-mm. plywood, 100 mm. wide and 1 metre 300 mm. long, with the grain in the direction of the length. This plywood strip goes 12 mm. beyond the sharpened ends of the flanges. In the empty space so formed, place two strips chosen from material with good straight grain, curved after being damped for ten minutes, then bound and glued after having

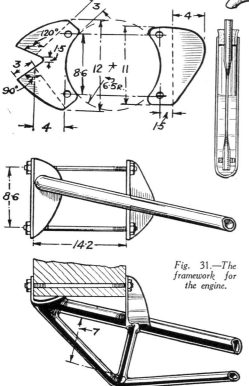

Fig. 31.—The framework for the engine.

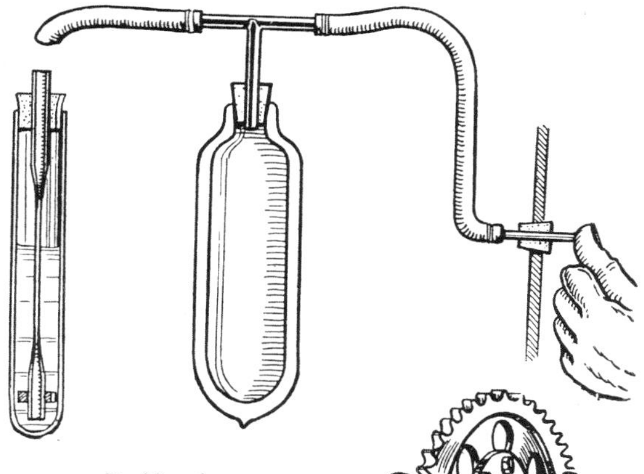

been nailed on to the ribs. As in the case of the trailing edge of the wings, gussets help to fix the edge to the tails of the ribs.

A web of 1·5-mm. plywood makes the rib rigid. The rudder is covered with fabric just like the wings, and four coats of dope are applied.

The time required for making the skeleton is four hours ; for covering, one hour. The weight is about 4½ lb.

Fig. 32.—A statoscope made from a thermos bottle, to enable the aviator to see if he is going up or down.

The air-frame is now finished, and it remains to adapt to it the motor-airscrew group.

Mounting

The inclined triangular platform of the body allows for the very easy installation of any kind of engine. The principle of mounting is as follows :

1. A lower piece supporting the weight of the engine.

2. A structure which triangulates the engine on the inclined platform.

3. This structure is also triangular in plan.

4. The crankcase of the engine will receive directly the support for the mounting of the airscrew shaft.

All this means that the engine will be placed head downwards or inverted, for ease and security in the mechanical installation, and for the improvement it gives to the pilot's vision.

The mountings are of a type which can be used as models for any other kind of engine whether two- or four-stroke, with or without reduction gearbox.

The Support for the Engine

Most engines have a detachable head, which is fixed to the cylinder by four bolts. The two rear bolts will be replaced by threaded rods (ask the makers for these) in order that they may hold the head on top of the metal fitting, made of 2-mm. material and reinforced with two angle pieces, the whole being solidly riveted together with 5-mm. rivets (Fig. 29). This metal fitting will be bolted along its lower side on the cross-bar of the platform of the fuselage.

Do not omit, at the same time, to put in position the metal fittings for the bracing which encloses the crossbar and the lyre-shaped piece of wood between them and the gussets by four 6-mm. bolts. After you put the engine in position, you would find it very difficult to drill the holes for these bolts.

The Engine Supports

It is assumed that you have bought an engine without reduction gear and that you wish to construct this gear yourself.

The reduction gear, of which a description follows, is suitable for an engine for elementary practice flying above an area where landing is easy. It may be that after a dozen hours of flight your mounting will have given no trouble. After all, all motor-cycles to-day

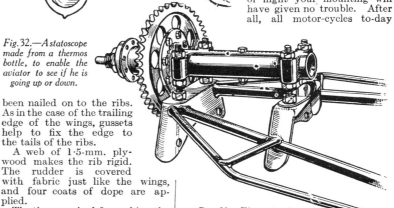

Fig. 33.—The axis of the airscrew made from the hub of a sidecar.

transmit power by chain, and the problem which you have to solve is exactly the same.

The engine mounting is work for a welder, and the professional will find it easy to make. In places where you cannot get welding done you must replace the tubes by angle iron of 30 mm., riveted to the fastenings which are modified to meet your requirements. The rivets may be made of drawn rod of 6 or 7 mm. diameter.

Engine Position

Place the fuselage level in line of flight, that is to say, with its back portion horizontal. The engine is placed upside down with its two bolts in the holes of the fitting. For the moment do not fasten any nuts. With a piece of cord fasten it to the foot of the pylon so that its crankshaft is horizontal. Make sure that the engine is straight with the axis of the fuselage and is not leaning either to right or left. The mounting lugs of the crankcase will be fixed by bolts (in 10-mm. screwed rod) between the cheek piece of 2-mm. metal (Fig. 28). Make certain that the top edges are quite parallel (Fig. 30).

Offer up to them from the side a tube made of 16 mm. × 20 mm. material, so that when it is soldered to the two cheek pieces it fits into the fitting at the foot of the supports of the *cabane*. It would be a good thing to bend, after heating to red heat, the end of the tube a little so that it comes straight into this fitting. Fit the end of the tube on to the front cheek piece, mark all the necessary points and take it to the welder.

The welder will fix the tube on to the second cheek piece. Protect the engine by rags soaked in water, which should be ready to place on the weld as soon as it is finished.

Take all the assembly and triangulate it by the cross piece and the arc, of which the end that comes close to the fitting will last be welded in a position at a distance of 100 mm. from this fitting.

The axis of the airscrew will be

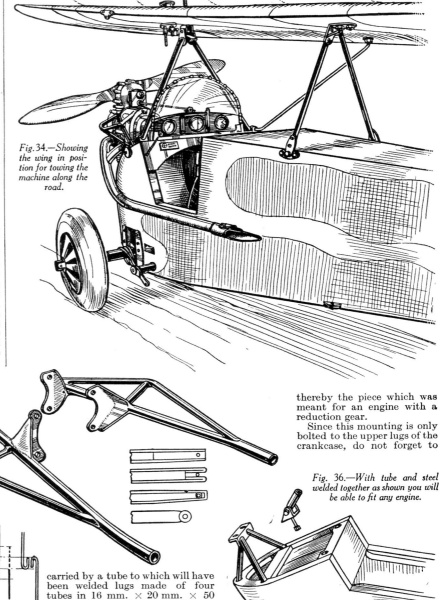

Fig. 34.—*Showing the wing in position for towing the machine along the road.*

Fig. 36.—*With tube and steel welded together as shown you will be able to fit any engine.*

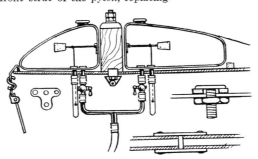

Fig. 35.—*Details of the petrol tanks.*

carried by a tube to which will have been welded lugs made of four tubes in 16 mm. × 20 mm. × 50 mm. material, which will slide on four 10-mm. screwed rods and of which one will regulate the position by the screws. A fitting will be fixed to the screwed rods of the rear platform to receive the foot of the front strut of the pylon, replacing

thereby the piece which was meant for an engine with a reduction gear.

Since this mounting is only bolted to the upper lugs of the crankcase, do not forget to clamp the lower lugs by two other 10-mm. bolts.

Axis of Airscrew

The axis of the airscrew is the hub of a front wheel of a motor-car, cycle-car, side-car, etc. The axle is fixed and bolted to a tube. The hub of the wheel, mounted on ball-bearings, carries at one end a toothed wheel driven by chain from the engine, and at the other end the airscrew.

A 3-mm. flat steel plate, riveted (twenty 4-mm. steel rivets) to the rear rim of the

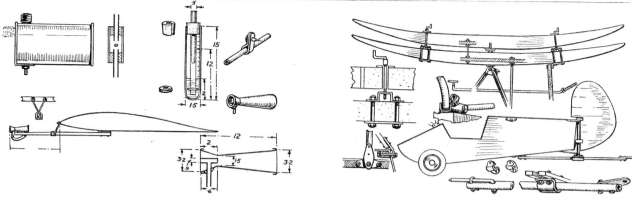

Fig. 37.—*The head of the speed indicator is soldered in place as shown.*

Fig. 38.—*Showing how the wing is removed for towing purposes.*

hub, is bolted (by eight short 8-mm. bolts) to the 44-toothed wheel; it must be carefully centred on the rim after cutting out the central portion. You can get toothed wheels with 36, 40, 44, or 48 teeth.

The airscrew is fixed to the other rim of the hub between two discs by ten 6-mm. bolts 80 mm. in length.

The chain wheel on the engine will have 16 teeth. The reduction will then be 1 to 2·5. If the engine is too heavily braked, use a wheel with 15 teeth; if it races, use one of 17 or 18 teeth.

The chain has a pitch of 15 mm. × 9 mm.; do not compromise on quality. Have simple, sound fastenings easily applied, and

a tool to detach them. The chain is carefully lined up and its tension adjusted by nuts. The axle is locked in its support, after which it is adjusted by ten 6-mm. bolts.

Make arrangements for oiling the chain in flight, using either a spraying tube from the crankcase, or a tube from the oil tank with screw adjuster which will feed a drop of oil every two seconds at the spot where the chain meets the wheel. Adjust the drip a little forward because of the wind.

The distance between the two chain wheels will be about 30 mm. to 40 mm., and you will want 80 cm. to 90 cm. of chain.

The time required is one day for the engine mount and one day for the fitting up of the reduction gear. The total weight without airscrew or chain is under 16 lb.

"THE FLYING FLEA"—AIR MINISTRY REQUIREMENTS

THE conditions relating to the flight of the "Flying Flea" type of aircraft, and of certain other experimental types when covered by a policy of Third-Party Insurance, permit of the flying of the aircraft without the possession of a Certificate of Airworthiness, but will not enable the other requirements of the Air Navigation regulations to be dispensed with. It will be necessary in connection with all flights of such aircraft that the pilot should be in possession of a pilot's licence valid for all types, or valid for the specific type concerned, unless the flights in question are being carried out under the conditions laid down in paragraph 112 of the Air Navigation Directions, 1932 (A.N.D. 11). The normal rules as to registration and markings will also apply.

The special permission (in lieu of a Certificate of Airworthiness) to fly the aircraft will embody the following conditions and limitations :

    (1) The aircraft shall not be flown outside Great Britain and Northern Ireland.
    (2) The aircraft shall not be flown over any populous area or concourse of people.
    (3) The aircraft shall not carry passengers, goods or mails for hire or reward. The aircraft shall not be used for the purpose of giving instruction in flying for which payment is made, or is deemed to be made under the provisions of the Air Navigation (Consolidation) Order, 1923, for the time being in force.
    (4) The aircraft shall not be used for acrobatic flying.
    (5) The aircraft shall not be flown unless it is in a state of adequate repair, and in sound working order.
    (6) The aircraft shall not be flown on any occasion unless there is in force in relation to its flying on that occasion a policy of insurance approved by the Air Ministry for the purpose of the present permit against legal liability which may be incurred in respect of third-party damage to persons and property on the ground.
    (7) The aircraft shall not be flown in any manner whereby the said policy of insurance would be invalidated.
    (8) This permission may be withdrawn at any time.

Before the permission for the flight of the aircraft is issued it will be necessary for the constructor to forward to the Air Ministry for prior approval, the policy of insurance mentioned under condition 6. It should be noted that one of the conditions which the Air Ministry will require is that the policy should not embody a condition or warranty requiring that a Certificate of Airworthiness must have been issued or must be in force in respect of the said aircraft. Should a general form of policy be obtained which includes a warranty as above, it will be necessary to obtain from the Insurance Company an endorsement to form part of the policy and embody the following paragraph :

    " It is understood and agreed that the aircraft has not been certified as airworthy under the Air Navigation (Consolidation) Order, 1923, and it is agreed that the indemnity given by this policy is not affected by the absence of a Certificate of Airworthiness (any warranty or condition in the policy notwithstanding)."

When forwarding the policy for Air Ministry examination a statement should be furnished that the total all-up weight of the aircraft, including pilot and other person or persons, will not exceed a specified figure. The amount of insurance covered by the policy must be at the rate of £100 for each 100 lb. all-up weight of the aircraft, but shall not be less than £5,000 in respect of *each of an indefinite series of accidents* without any over-riding total limit.

Copies of the Air Navigation (Consolidation) Order, 1923, and the Air Navigation Directions, 1932 (A.N.D. 11), and Amendments thereto giving particulars in regard to the flight of aircraft in Great Britain and Northern Ireland, may be obtained from the Sale Office of H.M. Stationery Office at Adastral House, Kingsway, W.C.2.

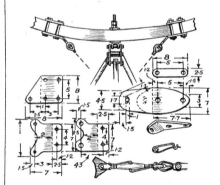

Fig. 39.—*The bracing cables.*

Engine with Reduction Gear

Assume that you have bought an engine complete with reduction gear. The work is then much simplified and there is no hitch to be feared. Two plates at the front and rear in 2-mm. steel (Fig. 31) are welded to the three tubes as in the first case. In this case each arm is free, and the plates are bolted to the four mounting wings on the crankcase (Fig. 36). Each arm complete weighs just over 2 lb. without its bolts.

The rear ends of the mounting are stuffed with hardwood, tube-welded inside or tube-welded outside. The last procedure is recommended.

There are five strong points on the top of the front of the fuselage (Fig. 36). With tube and steel welded together, you will be able to fit any engine on the principles given above. The only precaution is to see that the axis of the airscrew is parallel to the top of the fuselage, 100 mm. above it, and correctly lined up with the axis of the fuselage.

Above: One of the earliest Fleas built in Britain was that of Cyril Brooke of Huddersfield who used the Scott Flying Squirrel engine. This photo, taken in Brook's workshop, was subsequently very heavily (and extremely well) retouched and then used for the Scott Company's publicity material. The two-cylinder inverted inline Scott was a development of its successful and famous motor-cycle engine made specially for the Flea.

Left: G-ADPY was one of a small batch manufactured commercially by the E G Perman Company of London and fitted with the Scott.

Below: An improved Flea called the Abbott-Baynes Cantilever Pou was built in Farnham, Surrey. Here Stephen Appleby flies the prototype at Heston. The engine is the 30 hp water-cooled Carden-Ford. Appleby went on to set up Puttnam Aircraft Co Ltd, another attempt at the commercial production of Fleas.

How to Build the "FLYING FLEA"

This Month we Deal with its Engine Accessories, the Instrument Board, and Give Instructions for Flying

YOU must not use the decompressor of two-stroke engines to stop the engine until it is throttled back. If you use it at open throttle, you may burn the valve of the decompressor, which will cause a leakage of power.

To stop the throttled engine, always use the decompressor to avoid back-fires as the airscrew stops.

The length and diameter of the exhaust pipe, i.e. its volume, is important to ensure the emptying of the cylinders, their cooling, and full power. The pipe shown in Fig. 40 is given as a guide, but your engine maker will advise you on this point. You can fly just as well without exhaust pipes, but it will be found advisable to fit one.

The Fuel Filter

The use of a fuel filter is absolutely indispensable in the carburetter delivery line, and should be fixed to one of the arms of the motor support. However clean your spirit may be, you will always find a little dirt in the filter, and often water. You cannot prevent it, and you might have a stoppage at any time whilst in flight. There are plenty of good filters on the market; get a car model and not a motor-cycle filter, as the latter is too small.

The Petrol Tank

As with the prototype, the tank is placed in front of the spar. It holds 12 litres, i.e. two 5-litre cans of fuel and a good measure of oil (1½ hours' flying). Sheet brass, although a little more expensive than tinned sheet, should be used for the tank as this will last for a considerable time.

Cut a sheet of 4 mm. thick brass as shown in Fig 35 (shown last month) just wide enough to go between the central ribs of the wing and about 800 mm. long. At each end hammer the edge for a width of 5 mm. over a piece of metal of ·6 mm. to make a joint. Join together and insert a single rivet of copper at each end; then hammer flat.

After marking off with chalk the position of the bends, pass a plank, supported on the backs of two chairs, through the hollow drum thus formed, and bend it according to the template, and cut out in 3 mm. plywood.

This template, which follows the profile of the wing, except that it can project a bit on the curve of the upper surface, should be able to be forced gently into the bent drum.

While pressing on the plank, cut out with a carpenter's compass a disc of suitable diameter for a brass screw stopper (as from an oil can or other container). You had better try this job out first on a piece of

brass. Next cut out the lower hole about 50 mm. diameter.

Over this latter hole, rivet a 1-mm. brass plate drilled with two holes, ready to take two valve stems from a motor cycle tyre; see that the holes are drilled so that their washers are not up against the edges of the large opening. After riveting solder carefully.

The Fuel Gauge

Now rivet and solder the small piece of rolled metal which will carry the aluminium rod, and also the float of cork measuring 40 mm. by 40 mm. A piece of ·3 mm. steel wire unravelled from a spare piece of cable and straightened out, should be fixed to the aluminium rod vertically above the front hole. Passing through the valve body (you will have dispensed with the rest of the valve) the rod enters a 8 mm. glass tube (such as that which is in soda water syphon) closed at one end, and fixed at the other to the valve by a ring of treated rubber. At the end of the steel wire is a small black bead. This forms a gauge which will always tell you how much fuel you have left.

Jam your template of plywood into the tank, and, letting the edge rest on a metal block, flare out the edge with light taps of the hammer for a depth of 5 mm. When this has been done on both edges, place the tank flat on one edge on a piece of brass. Push down your template to the bottom to

ensure that the shape is maintained, and mark off along the flared edge, one side of the tank. When you cut this out with the shears, leave a spare edge of 5 mm. all round beyond the flare of the tank edge. Turn up the edge of the flat plate by hand with flat-nose pliers and bend it over the edge of the tank. Then turn it over again, hammering all along the joint. Hold up this work along the nose by a bar of metal shaped as shown in Fig. 35 (shown last month) held firmly in a vice and pressed up from the inside. After the first side has been done, put the float and its wire in place (but not the valves) and fit the second face. You will have to cut a 40-mm. hole in the first side through which to insert your metal bar for hammering over the second side.

Soldering

All along the turn-up, spread a little soldering paste or killed spirits, and solder with a hot iron. This is quite easy on an edge already jointed. Also solder the stopper seating and a disc of metal to close the opening in the first side. Rinse with hot water, and test for leaks with a litre of spirit. The finished tank should weigh 1 kilo. 500 mm. If you are anxious to make long flights, make another tank which will balance the first on the other side of the spar. It can hold 22 litres, so that you can have sufficient fuel for a 4 hours' flight.

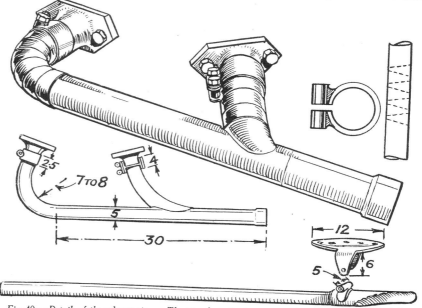

Fig. 40.—Details of the exhaust pipe. The pipe shown is given as a guide to the constructor, and the maker of the particular engine employed should be consulted

29

The Piping

The valves from the tyre tubes of which you will have cut off the head, will be furnished under their feet with a washer of fibre, passed with the aid of a piece of wire through the filling opening and screwed up tight by a nut. The valves and the wire receive a glass tube, and the others a petrol cock; these are joined by a tube of hardened rubber (insoluble in petrol), threaded on to each of them. A little alcohol varnish (insoluble in petrol) makes the fixing permanent. Remember that benzol may, in time, affect the rubber. If you are careful to bring the ends of all tubes flush together, you need not fear the obstruction of the pipes by the swelling of the rubber, and the arrangement will last for several months. The elasticity will prevent breakage. Soldered and screwed joints should not be used.

The two cocks are joined by a collector tube in brazed red copper (you can get T pieces ready-made in the shops). A hardened rubber piece joins the collector tube to the filter, before the carburetter. The length and flexibility of the tube permits the wing to pivot freely. Look over this hardened rubber tube often, and line it with a coiled spring (the guide tube of a Bowden assembly) to prevent its swelling. Drill a 2-mm. hole in each filter cap to let the air in as the fuel is used. The piping is so arranged that a single drop of fuel leaving the tank, will arrive under gravity, at the filter.

The Oil System

An oil can of 2 litres (tins as sold by oil vendors) can be fixed behind the spar next to the tank (see Fig. 37). Change its filter to the side. The weight is 300 grammes. Place a dropper under the oil tap (two corks in a large glass tube) to control the flow of oil (3 drops a second: five hours' supply). Use large pipes of 6 to 8 mm. interior diameter and beware of freezing in winter. Do not try to regulate the flow by the tap otherwise you may starve the pump. The weight of the tanks does not affect in any way the movement of the wing: it would not matter if they weighed 100 kilos. The control movements in flight are, in practice, of small amplitude and the inertia of the wing is of very small effect.

A shock absorber rubber of 12 mm. diameter and 250 mm. long, holds the wing in front and controls the incidence; it is hardly extended when the rear edge of the wing is raised to the full extent. It is fixed to a metal fitting of 1 mm. material fixed to the leading edge by three wood screws. At the lower end it is fixed to the foot of the front tube of the cabane.

The shock absorber prevents the wing from falling whilst the plane is at rest, but is not of any use in flight. Many people, on seeing the "Flea," will fix their attention on the central pivot of the wing, thinking that your life hangs on a 6 mm. bolt which fixes the unseen tubular axis. They forget that the wing is mainly supported by the bracing wires.

The Instrument Board

The dashboard instruments are delicate and fragile, but they are also heavy. It is desirable, therefore, to group them on the same support—the dashboard—and to give the whole assembly a certain independence from the machine. In this way, the vibrations of the engine are much reduced when they arrive at the instruments, and are only just enough to cancel out the inertia of their indicators without making the needles vibrate. The dashboard proper (Fig. 41) is a 6 mm. panel pierced with the necessary openings. In the middle is the revolution counter, on the right is the watch, on the left is the air-speed indicator and the barometer is placed next to it, as shown.

This panel is nailed to a piece of hard wood making an angle with the piece marked A (Fig. 41) which is of 1·5 mm. plywood cut in a semi-circle, and edged with a cane (cane for clearing sinks) on which is nailed the rounded vertical piece in 1·5 mm. material thus making a sort of box. An arc in thin 6 mm. aluminium or duralium tube, or a 10-mm. cane, reinforces a plate of celluloid of very transparent quality. The dashboard is secured to the boxwork by small screws, and to the arc by small collars of aluminium, held by an eyelet or a rivet. The whole assembly is placed on three pads of soft rubber (sponge rubber) leaving a gap of 10 to 15 mm. from the top of the cockpit. Three springs of 1 mm. steel, only lightly loaded, hold it more or less in position between the two rear legs of the cabane. The altimeter, the most sensitive instrument of the lot, will be simply an ordinary barometer. You can fix on the glass, a disc of paper showing the heights corresponding to the pressures marked on the

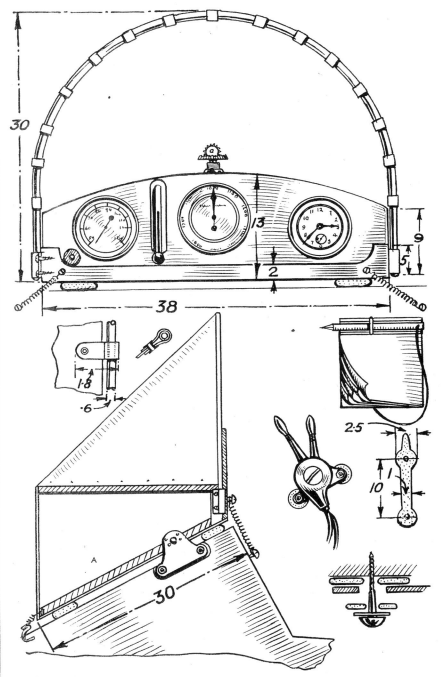

Fig. 41.—*Showing the instrument board and position of the various instruments.*

scale. A table of barometer readings is given below.

29·92 in.	= 760 mm. =	0 ft.
28·86 in.	= 733 mm. =	1,000 ft.
27·82 in.	= 706 mm. =	2,000 ft.
26·81 in.	= 681 mm. =	3,000 ft.
25·84 in.	= 656 mm. =	4,000 ft.
24·89 in.	= 632 mm. =	5,000 ft.

Using the Table

Before leaving the ground, set the barometer so that zero is opposite the barometer needle. Let us imagine that at this moment the pressure indicated by the needle is 76 on the original pressure scale. When in flight, at a given moment, the needle will have moved say to the mark 70, which means that you are flying at 2,000 ft. A good place for the barometer is to hang it by three springs from the arc above the dashboard. At your right hand on the panel, fix a few leaves of paper under a little aluminium strip with a rubber ring, through which you can pass a pencil fastened with a string. Before you take off you can write on it notes of use for your flight, things to think about when in the air, etc. During the flight, while flying with the left hand, you can make notes such as time of climb, etc.

The Compass

This is held in front of the pilot and ahead of the revolution counter at 40 mm. from the instrument board, by two arms made of 4 mm. rod of duralium or brass, bolted to the bar. A thin red line, the "lubber's" line, is painted on the glass right along the centre line of the machine.

The metal work, more or less magnetic, which comes near the compass may make the needle deflect in the following manner:

N.	N.E.	E.	S.E	S.	S.W.	W.	N.W.
9°	55°	104°	149°	194°	234°	287°	325°

Thus, when the "lubber's" line is pointed at 234° on the card you know that the machine is pointing towards the S.W.; if you want to retrace your steps, turn until the figure 55° comes under the "lubber's" line, and you know that you are then pointing N.E.

These corrections were made by placing the machine with the engine running on a compass platform marked out to the exact points of the compass. This can be done by anybody with strings and pickers, or can be obtained at any aerodrome.

The Mapholder

An aluminium box measuring 140 mm. by 190 mm. fixed to the left of the panel, carries two tubes of 10 mm. aluminium. Wind on them a strip of map of 180 mm. width, under a celluloid cover. Right across the celluloid is a black line perpendicular to the line of the roller, and this has a small 1 mm. brass wire fixed under a washer. The wire is between the map and the celluloid, whilst the washer is above it. The unrolling of the map and the movement of the needle, enables one to mark the point over which one is flying.

The Throttle Controls

The throttle controls, with two handles belonging to a motor-cycle, are fixed outside on the left side of the cockpit (Fig. 41) with a strip of steel fixed by two wood screws, or rubber will be useful perhaps, to hold the throttle levers so that they will not close themselves under vibration.

Speed Indicator

The head of the speed indicator is made of brass and soldered according to the dimensions given in Fig. 37 (shown last month) and will be fixed at the end of a tube under the wing, to the metal fitting which holds the bracing wire. A small V made out of 2 mm. material, screwed on to the leading edge and bound on to the rod, will hold it steady. A 3 mm. or 4 mm. aluminium or copper tube will run along the leading edge to which it will be fixed with small fastenings, and will join the pressure head to the manometer (indicator). This latter is made from a glass tube which is inserted into a few centimetres of water diluted with alcohol, half and half, and coloured with a drop of red ink. The whole assembly is carried in a test-tube, fitted with a cork as shown in Fig. 32 (shown last month).

On the outside of the tube, graduations spaced at 10 mm. apart, will be painted in black except above the level of the liquid. This manometer functions very well when one is flying smoothly without turning near the ground or up aloft in calm air, but being very sensitive it shows up all gusts of wind. It shows a speed of 10 as well as 120 kilometres an hour. When one is swerving, being pivoted or turning, the accelerations rather spoil its indications. It would be better, therefore, to have a genuine airspeed indicator which is made like a barometer, and is independent of acceleration, centrifugal force, etc.

THE SCOTT "FLYING SQUIRREL" ENGINE

A Light Aeroplane Engine which can be fitted into the "Flying Flea." It is Highly Economical, Unusually Light, and, coupled with Sturdiness in Design, makes for a High Degree of Reliability. The Construction of the "Flying Flea" was dealt with in Previous Issues.

The Scott "Flying Squirrel" light aeroplane engine which develops 28 h.p. and sells at the moderate price of £50.

AN engine that will be found eminently suitable for the "Flying Flea," in fact, for any type of ultra-light aeroplane, is the Scott "Flying Squirrel" shown on this page. This moderately priced and compact little engine is being manufactured by the Scott Motor Cycle Co., Shipley, Yorks, England. The secret of its simplicity lies in the fact that it has only five working parts, none of which are subjected to hammer blow action, and no valves, valve gear or tappets.

The Cylinders

These are made of light alloy, with encast chromidium liners. Special attention has been given to the fining and graduation of wall thickness in order that distortion may be avoided, and an even cooling effect obtained. The pistons are in die-cast alloy with a Scott patented arrangement of skirt, and gudgeon-pin fastening. This arrangement ensures that the area around the gudgeon-pin boss has a greater clearance than the rest of the piston. Three gas rings are fitted but no scrapers. Scraper grooves are provided, however, which effectively control the oil distribution.

The engine has a standard Amal car-buretter, and a two-spark magneto running at engine speed. The drive is taken from an extension of the propeller shaft.

Reduction Gear

Because of the high engine speed, the propeller shaft is geared down with reduction gear of the straight spur type having a ratio of two to one. A feature of the reduction gear is that the driving pinion is mounted between the two crankshaft sections, and not at the end. The reduction wheel, which is splined to the propeller shaft, is machined from solid forging, and the shaft and its gear are dynamically balanced. The lubricating oil consumption is given as 0·03 lb., and the fuel consumption is 0·56 lb. per brake-horsepower hour. Four trunnion stubs are provided for mounting the engine.

Proposed "Flying Flea" Clubs

WE have recently received from Messrs. E. G. Perman & Co., 24/26, Brownlow Mews, Gray's Inn Road, W.C.1, particulars of their proposed scheme to enable the public to pilot their own aircraft, and to fly cheaply and with safety. They propose that where sufficient encouragement is forthcoming from any one centre, to send one or more "Flying Fleas" to the aerodrome nearest the centre, or to any suitable field or aerodrome stipulated by the members of that centre. These machines will then become the property of that branch of the club, the members of which are entitled to fly the machine for payment of 2s. (the cost of the fuel and oil). All readers interested should communicate with the above firm, who will supply them with full details of this offer.

Showing a "Flying Flea" in flight fitted with a Scott "Flying Squirrel" engine.

SCOTT "FLYING SQUIRREL" DATA

Direction of Rotation of Airscrew.	Anti-clock viewed from Propeller.
Bore.	73 mm.
Stroke.	78 mm.
Swept volume.	652 c.c.s.
Compression ratio.	6·8 : 1.
Normal b.h.p.	16.
Normal r.p.m.	3,200.
Maximum b.h.p.	28 at 4,000 r.p.m.
Weight complete.	85 lb. + or − 5 lb.
Fuel consumption at normal r.p.m.	0·56 lb./b.h.p./ h.r.
Oil consumption.	0·03 lb./b.h.p./hr.
Oil pressure.	30 to 40 lb. per sq. in.
Oil in circulation.	0·5 gallons.
Length over spinner.	600 mm. (23½ in.) approx.
Height overall.	575 mm. (22½ in.) approx.
Greatest width.	250 mm. (10½ in.) approx.

The Luton " Minor," which brings flying within the reach of all.

FLYING FOR ALL

By Captain Needham, B.Sc., etc.

WHEN the "Flying Flea" first made its appearance in this country, with its revolutionary methods of construction and control, there were many who doubted whether it could ever be a success and who were not sure of the wisdom of adopting such an unorthodox design. However, the "Flea" movement spread with great rapidity and hundreds of these diminutive little machines were built in all parts of the country.

Then came disillusion : accident followed accident, some were fatal, many merely resulted in a few cuts and bruises, though in most cases the machines suffered considerable damage. Practically all flying "Fleas" were first suspended and later abandoned.

An Experimental Machine

In order to determine whether the tandem-wing arrangement, as employed with the "Flying Flea," possessed the many advantages claimed and largely borne out by theory, Luton Aircraft Ltd., built an experimental machine having two wings in tandem but with an orthodox tail unit and normal controls, and this was subjected to flight trials lasting over a period of some two months. None of the vices which characterise the "Flying Flea" showed

> *The Development of one of the Newest and most Successful Light Aeroplanes, the Luton " Minor "*

itself, but a certain amount of mutual interference took place between the wings at certain flight attitudes, noticeably in the climb, which reduced the aerodynamic efficiency to an undesirable extent.

The experiment had proved that if a light aeroplane was to be produced for the novice pilot and at a price that could be afforded by the many interested amateurs, it must be designed along orthodox lines, provided with effective but gentle-acting and well synchronised controls, essentially stable in flight and on the glide, and with simple take-off and landing qualities so that the aeroplane practically performs these manoeuvres of its own accord. Manufacturing costs must be reduced, not by eliminating one or more of the essential surfaces, but by simplicity of construction throughout and by the generous employment of building jigs.

The " Minor " Produced

To meet this specification the "Minor" was then produced and the illustrations show the long fuselage for giving flight stability, whilst the ample size of all control surfaces, with carefully selected gearing, is also noticeable. The first flight proved the correctness of the theories on which the design had been based and not a single modification, from an aerodynamic standpoint, has been found necessary for incorporation in the production model.

The "Minor" is a parasol monoplane, the wing being supported on steel pylons at the fuselage and one pair of steel tubular lift struts run from the fuselage base to the mid semi-span point on each plane.

The wing is of simple but sturdy construction, immensely strong, and is ply covered at the leading-edge and tips. The wing section was carefully selected for its high aerodynamic characteristics and docile behaviour at the lower speeds of flight. The plywood covering maintains the correct shape over the whole span and gives the wing great robustness that is so desirable for handling, storage and transport. No rigging adjustments of any kind are necessary with this machine, as once the MINOR is built there is nothing to get out of place.

The Luton " Minor " outside the hangar   *A close-up of the Engine.*

The Fuselage

The fuselage is of spruce construction, ply covered, with curved top decking and is of pleasing appearance. The pilot's cockpit is roomy and includes a locker for tools and luggage. Shock-absorbers are included in the under-carriage.

The wing is not made to fold, but is easily detached for housing, 5 minutes being required for this operation and about 15 minutes for assembly.

The " Minor " will cruise comfortably at 75 m.p.h., at which speed the flight range is 225 miles, but it also cruises with engine at half throttle, perhaps one of the best tests for aircraft of this category, at 60 m.p.h., giving a flight duration of 270 miles. Larger tanks can be fitted if required.

The Luton " Minor "

Specification.		Performance.	
Span	. 25 ft.	Top Speed . . .	. 80 m.p.h.
Length . . .	. 19½ ft.	Cruising Speed . .	. 70 m.p.h.
Wing Area . .	.125 sq.ft.	Landing Speed . .	. 30 m.p.h.
Weight, empty . .	. 380 lbs.	Take-off Run . .	. 80 yds.
Weight, loaded . .	. 600 lbs.	Landing Run . .	. 30 yds.

Fuel Consumption

Fuel consumption varies between 1 and 1½ gall. per hour at 60 to 75 m.p.h., or 60 miles to the gallon with negligible consumption of oil.

The " Minor " is available with a choice of six engines, of from 25 to 34 h.p., including such refinements as dual ignition and impulse starter, the price ranging from £180 to £200. For those enthusiasts who wish to build their own light aeroplanes, kits of materials and parts are available at £40 and £75 respectively, including in each case a set of Constructional blue-prints.

EDITED BY F. J. CAMM

SUBSCRIPTION RATES

Inland and Abroad, 7s. 6d. per annum

Canada - - 7s. per annum

Editorial and Advertisement Offices : "Practical Mechanics," George Newnes Ltd. Tower House, Southampton Street, Strand, W.C.2. 'Phone : Temple Bar 4363. Telegrams : Newnes, Rand, London. Registered at the G.P.O. for transmission by Canadian Magazine Post.

PRACTICAL MECHANICS

VOL. IV. OCTOBER, 1937 No. 49.

Building Your Own Aeroplane

WITHIN the brief space of 20 years aircraft has progressed from the stage where it was the expensive hobby of the moneyed few, and the interesting work of the scientific investigator, to that where it takes place as a standard method of travel, and the hobby of the multitude. You have probably noticed that in almost every industry there are the professionals and the amateurs. This is true of wireless, the gramophone, photography, stamp collecting, cycling, motoring, motor cycling, microscopy, boat building, and so on. Aircraft is no exception, for the science has advanced to the point where it is not only safe but cheap. All of the principles are well-known and have been widely disseminated ; the knowledge now is general. The skilful amateur able to work in wood and metal can build his own light aeroplane ; this hobby has been going strong in America for a number of years, although in this country and in Germany activity has been restricted to the construction and use of gliders and sailplanes. Mon. Mignet demonstrated with the Flying Flea that a simple aeroplane used

Fair Comment
By The Editor

as he intended it to be used was practicable and safe. Its unorthodox lines, however, operated somewhat against its popularity, and inspired others to produce a machine of more conventional lines which could be built and flown by amateurs. Accordingly in this month's issue I present instructions and drawings for building the Luton Minor Monoplane, which is a really practicable light aeroplane having a top speed of over 80 miles an hour, cruises at 70 miles an hour, and lands at only 30 miles an hour. The newspapers and the aeronautical press have all satisfactorily commented on it ; complete and ready for flying, it costs from £180, whilst the set of prepared materials cost £40, or including engine and airscrew £97. Many of my readers will, of course, be able to reduce these prices. It is a parasol monoplane, the wings being supported by steel pylons on the fuselage, and one pair of steel tubular lift struts.

Its flight range is 225 miles at 75 miles an hour, or 270 miles at 60 miles an hour. Fuel consumption varies between 1 and 1½ gallons per hour at these speeds, and constructors have a choice of 6 engines. The Luton Minor has been designed to comply with Air Ministry requirements for the acrobatic category of the Certificate of Air Worthiness and has a load factor greater than 7½. The great advantage is that sets of finished parts and partly finished parts are available for those constructors who have not the necessary equipment or experience to make them.

Further articles on the Luton Minor will appear in subsequent issues.

Readers will agree that we spare neither money nor effort in regularly presenting to them exclusive articles and information. This journal was alone in describing the construction of the Flying Flea. We have described how to make speed boats, motor cars, gliders, petrol driven models, and many other devices and pieces of apparatus upon which information has been lacking. I hope that my readers will appreciate the exclusiveness of the contents of PRACTICAL MECHANICS.

Building the "LUTON MINOR" Light Aeroplane

The First of a Series of Articles Describing the Construction of a Really Practical and Successful Light Aeroplane, Designed to Air Ministry Standards and Requirements for the Acrobatic Category of the Certificate of Airworthiness. It may be Built and Flown by Amateurs. Simplicity and Safety are its Keynotes. It is of the Parasol Type. It has been Granted a "Permit to Fly."

Construction Described by The Designer

THERE are many amateurs who would like to build their own light aeroplane, but who refrain from doing so, since they are unable to obtain approved drawings, or to get their own designs checked for strength and airworthiness, and no one wishes to spend time and money on the construction of a machine that may never fly. There are several keen builders to-day who are struggling to make a show from sketchy designs, but most do not progress far before they " come unstuck " on account of insufficient or incomplete data.

We are, therefore, offering our readers a design which has proved its flying ability, which has been designed and produced by a competent aircraft company along recognised lines in conformance with Air Ministry standards and which has been granted a " permit to fly " by the proper authorities. The design is the well-known Luton Minor, which has already been adopted by the National League of Airmen, after flight trials were carried out by the President of the League, Captain Norman Macmillan, M.C., A.F.C.

The " Minor " is a parasol monoplane, this arrangement having been chosen for its simplicity of construction, safe flying and structural qualities, good view in flight and the maximum aerodynamic efficiency which it offers.

It is recommended that, where possible, two or three constructors should work in collaboration, and when the aircraft is completed, if no aerodrome is available in the immediate vicinity, constructors may get together for the formation of local clubs and by finding a reasonably large, flat field they may found what may one day prove to be a network of aerodromes covering the whole country which should be of inestimable value in the development and defence of these lands.

Choice of Engines

The " Minor " may be powered with any engine of from 25 to 40 h.p. Thirty horse-power gives a top speed of 80 m.p.h., whilst a speed of 100 m.p.h. is obtainable with 40 h.p. The higher powered engine, however, provides a better take-off and gives a reserve of power that may on occasion be desirable. It should be noted that a high top speed has not been aimed at in the " Minor " design—it is a quality easily obtained by decreasing the wing area, but is accompanied by a rise in the landing speed, and it is a low value of this latter, together with a quick take-off, that were sought in the design.

The following table gives brief particulars of engines available, though there are other suitable units not included in this list.

The Luton Anzani is a re-designed version of the inverted " V " twin, the re-design having been based on extensive experience with this engine both in " Minors " and other aircraft. It is also the cheapest engine available. The " Sprite " is a well-made little engine, a horizontally opposed twin, but the power is rather low. Two-stroke enthusiasts may prefer the Scott, a two-cylinder in-line engine, though it cannot be regarded as having been thoroughly tried out on the Luton Minor as yet, whilst its power also falls short of 30 h.p.

The Carden engine offers the advantage of four cylinders, but against this must be set the complications of water cooling and the total weight of about 150 lb., or roughly half as much again as the other engines mentioned.

Provision is made in the " Minor " design for alternative petrol tank locations. The standard position is in the fuselage top, just behind the engine, but in the case of the Carden engine the petrol has to be placed inside the wing on account of the excessive engine weight at the nose. The wing tank becomes necessary also where

This photograph shows the attractive lines and sound design and construction of the Luton Minor.

POWER UNITS	
Anzani	34 h.p.
Sprite II	25 h.p.
Scott Flying Squirrel	28 h.p.
Carden-Ford	30 h.p.
	(water cooled)

ENGINE PRICES			
Luton Anzani, 34 h.p. improved model	£52	10	0
dual ignition and impulse starter	£62	10	0
Sprite II, 25 h.p., with impulse starter	£58	0	0
dual ignition and impulse starter	£65	0	0
Carden-Ford, 30 h.p., 4-cylinder, radiator, etc.	£55	0	0
with dual ignition	£63	10	0
Scott, 28 h.p., 2-stroke	£53	0	0

Rear View of the Luton Minor.

the carburettor is too high to allow a gravity feed from the fuselage tank, unless a petrol pump is fitted.

The "Minor" was designed from the outset to provide the easiest possible construction for amateur building. There are no complicated box or "I" section spars to make, and all machined metal parts have been avoided. The woodwork and bent up sheet metal fittings are of the simplest kind. The amount of welding has been kept down to a minimum, and no difficulty should be experienced in getting this done by a proficient welder.

The Main Plane

The wing is normally made in one component, of 25 ft. span, but for those who are unable to accommodate the full span in their workshops, an alternative design has been prepared whereby the wing is built in two halves and joined together for assembly. The wing building will be described for the single unit, and the necessary modifications for halving the wing will be explained later.

Ribs

The rib arrangement is shown in the sketches and consists of $\frac{1}{2}$ in. $\times \frac{3}{16}$ in. flanges, with verticals and diagonals of the same section, all of which are set with the larger dimension perpendicular to the plane of the figure, or parallel to the wing span. The ply nose web and the remaining web pieces are all cut from $\frac{1}{16}$ in. plywood, with a circular lightening hole cut in the nose web. Slots are cut in the leading-edge, $\frac{1}{2}$ in. deep $\times \frac{3}{8}$ in. for the later accommodation of the leading-edge member, which will be pinned and glued to the small vertical member $\frac{3}{8}$ in. $\times \frac{1}{2}$ in. near the front of each rib. The lower flange is cut short at the rear and the top flange is shaped to take the trailing-edge member.

Except for the end three ribs at each wing tip, all the ribs are similar, and it is recommended that a jig should be made up for these standard ribs.

Making the Rib Jig

First obtain a straight board of deal or other wood, about $\frac{5}{8}$ in. thick and 65 in. long $\times$ 12 in. deep, and on one face of this set out the shape of the rib in pencil, from the ordinates given in the table. Next mark out the positions of the front and rear spars and the aileron spar, leaving a 1-in. gap for the aileron hinges. The front spar

Illustrations by our own Artists and Draughtsmen

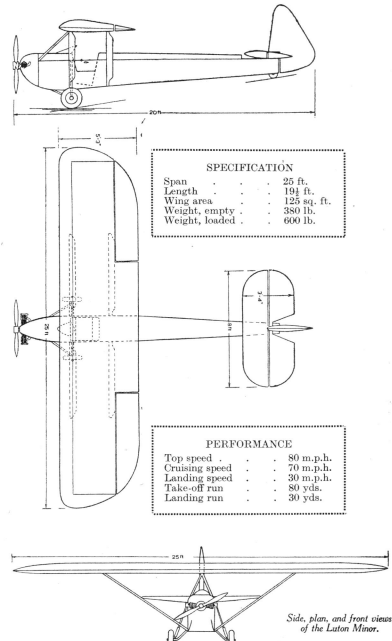

SPECIFICATION

Span	. . .	25 ft.
Length	. .	19½ ft.
Wing area	. .	125 sq. ft.
Weight, empty .	.	380 lb.
Weight, loaded .	.	600 lb.

PERFORMANCE

Top speed .	. .	80 m.p.h.
Cruising speed	.	70 m.p.h.
Landing speed	.	30 m.p.h.
Take-off run	.	80 yds.
Landing run	.	30 yds.

Side, plan, and front views of the Luton Minor.

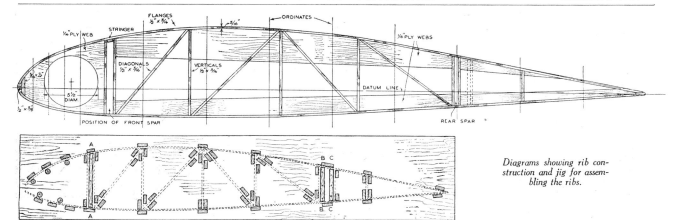

Diagrams showing rib construction and jig for assembling the ribs.

centre is 9·45 in. from the L.E. and the rear spar is 34·65 in. from the former. Cut lengths of wood to represent the spars on the jig, of width $\frac{5}{8}$ in., $\frac{1}{2}$ in., and $\frac{5}{16}$ in. (the spar width) and about $\frac{3}{4}$ in. deep. Screw these to the jig face in the spar positions AA, BB, and CC, so that they protrude $\frac{3}{4}$ in. from the face. Next cut a number of small blocks, roughly 1 in. ×

Building the Main Ribs

Material required : 500 ft. of $\frac{1}{2}$ in. × $\frac{3}{16}$ in. spruce, and 72 sq. ft. of $1\frac{1}{2}$ m.m. plywood. Place two lengths of prepared flange strip in the jig, first steaming the front portions if necessary to assist in obtaining the curvature. Cut verticals of the required lengths and slip into position ; also the diagonals. Spread glue (cold water casein

In making up the end ribs, the same procedure may be followed, but since two only of each pattern are required, the jig may be simplified by using headless nails in place of the wood blocks. The end, or tip rib, has a solid plywood web, and this may be marked out, cut to shape, and used in place of a jig, by simply attaching the spruce flanges in position.

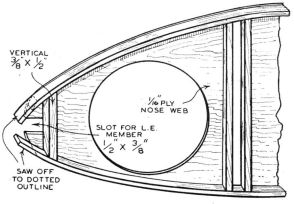

Leading edge of rib.

$\frac{1}{2}$ in. × $\frac{1}{4}$ in., which will be required to hold the rib members in position.

Tack these blocks in pairs at each end of all vertical and diagonal members, as shown in the sketch, so that the $\frac{3}{16}$-in. strip of spruce may be laid in position between the blocks. Further blocks are then tacked on externally to the rib outline for positioning the flanges. Inside the flange, position over the more cambered leading-edge portion; half-a-dozen eccentric buttons may be screwed on to assist in getting the flanges to the required curvature over this part.

cement) over the faces to which the ply-wood webs are to be attached. Place the webs in position and fix with brass gimp pins—$\frac{3}{8}$ in. × 20 gauge—or wire staples ; leave for a few hours to dry and then ease gently from the jig with the aid of a chisel, having first released the eccentric buttons. Make good any damage or loosening caused in extracting from jig. The nose and tail of the rib are left for cleaning and shaping when all is quite set, and also the outer edges of the ply webs are cleaned down with the aid of a spokeshave, and finally sandpapered.

Notice that web gap at the rear spar is larger for the ribs over the aileron portion of the wing, shown dotted. The ten main ribs over the central part of the wing have a $\frac{1}{2}$ in. spar gap, the remainder being $1\frac{3}{16}$ in.

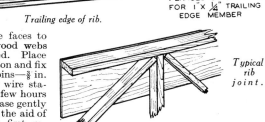

Trailing edge of rib.

Typical rib joint.

Wing Spars

The front spar consists of a 25 ft. length of spruce, $\frac{5}{8}$ in. thick and 6 in. deep. This should be prepared from aero quality Grade A spruce, should be straight grained and free from knots, resin pockets, shakes, etc. The most important portion of the

LUTON MINOR
PRICE LIST OF COMPLETED PARTS

Main plane, covered and doped .	£50	0 0
Fuselage, painted . . .	£36	0 0
Tail unit	£17	10 0
Undercarriage, with wheels and shock absorbers	£14	0 0
Controls	£2	10 0
Tanks	£3	10 0
Wing pylons and fittings . .	£1	0 0
Lift struts (streamline steel tube) and bracing	£6	10 0

PRICE LIST OF COMPONENT PARTS, READY FOR ASSEMBLY

Set main plane ribs . . .	£7	10 0
Main plane and aileron spars .	£6	4 0
Fuselage sides made up (cost extra to materials) . . .	£3	0 0
Fuselage made up, complete with decking (extra)	£24	0 0
Complete set fittings and controls made up	£20	0 0

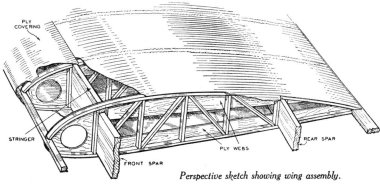

Perspective sketch showing wing assembly.

spar is that in the vicinity of the left strut attachment, say a 5 ft. length, running inboard from a point 4 ft. from each tip. The spar remains parallel over the central length of 17 ft., leaving the last 4 ft. at each end to be shaped in accordance with the sketch.

Mark in the datum line 2·55 in. from the base, mark all rib positions and set off the distances 3·45 in., 2·8 in., 2·17 in., 1·75 in., etc., above and below the datum line, as shown. Saw and plane the tapering ends accordingly.

Repeat for the rear spar, the section being 5⅝ in. × ½ in., again using carefully selected spruce and paying particular attention to the region adjacent to the left strut attachment.

Next comes the pair of aileron spars, made from 5/16 in. spruce, 4·83 in. deep, each spar being 7 ft. long. The procedure is as before, but in this case the top and bottom edges take the shape of the wing contour and are therefore bevelled as shown.

Wing Fittings

The sketches on pages 9 and 10 show the fittings required for the wing assembly, Nos. 1W to 8W. They are all simple fittings, bent up from sheet mild steel (Specification 2S3 28 ton steel) of 18, 16, and 14 S.W.G. Each fitting should be carefully marked out in the flat by means of a scriber, dividers, and straight edge, cut roughly to shape, taking care that the cuts do not touch the marked lines, and finally filed carefully to the correct shape. All centre lines and positions of holes should be marked, and in most cases the main centre line should be used as datum from which all other measurements are taken. Scribed lines should not be pressed deeply into the metal but should only lightly scratch the surface, or film. Scribe on the *inside* of all bends to prevent the start of cracks when bending takes place. This is best done by marking out on the side to which flanges are

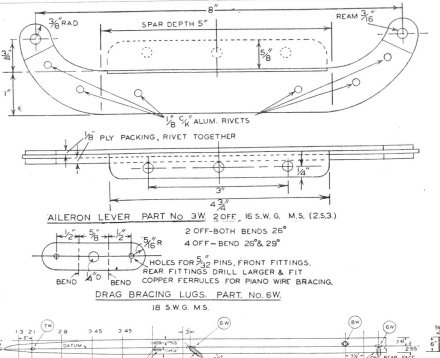

These diagrams illustrate the wing spars, aileron lever, and drag bracing lugs.

Photograph of the fuselage sides.

TABLE OF RIB ORDINATES

The ordinates for the main plane ribs are given below, the dimensions being the distances of the upper and lower surfaces from a horizontal datum line.

Distance from L.E.	Main Rib.		Rib 1.		Rib 2.		Rib 3.	
Inches.	Upper.	Lower.	Upper.	Lower.	Upper.	Lower.	Upper.	Lower.
3	3·15	2·21	2·85	1·73	2·25	1·67	2·05	1·32
6	4·2	2·65	4·0	2·2	3·38	1·9	2·85	1·47
9	5·42	2·85	4·7	2·41	4·18	1·98	3·23	1·58
12	6·3	2·97	5·2	2·5	4·35	2·06	3·68	1·58
18	7·15	2·97	5·52	2·52	4·97	2·06	3·6	1·41
24	7·15	2·84	5·5	2·52	4·35	1·90	2·87	1·23
30	6·05	2·6	5·12	2·13	3·43	1·67	1·93	0·88
36	5·3	2·27	4·32	1·84	3·07	1·37	0·95	0·49
42	4·23	1·90	3·3	1·45	2·16	0·97	—	—
48	3·1	1·39	2·2	1·05	1·1	0·66	—	—
54	1·83	0·95	1·01	0·55	—	—	—	—
60	0·5	0·44	—	—	—	—	—	—
Chord	63		60		51		42	
L.E. radius	1·2		0·96		0·72		0·48	

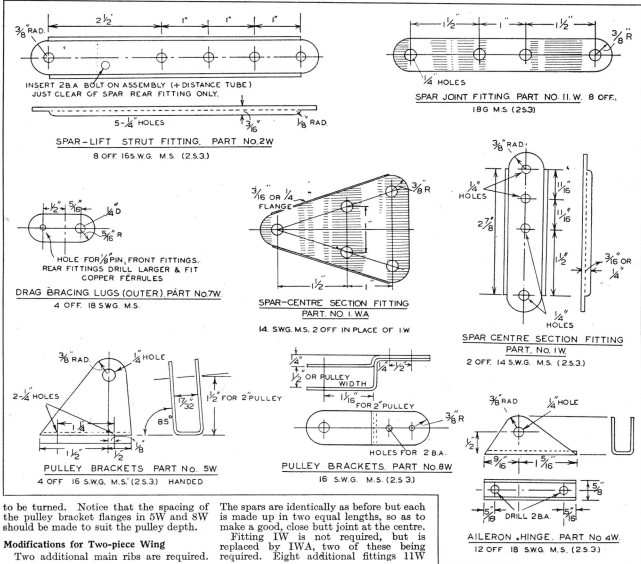

INSERT 2 B.A. BOLT ON ASSEMBLY (+DISTANCE TUBE) JUST CLEAR OF SPAR REAR FITTING ONLY.

5-¼" HOLES

SPAR–LIFT STRUT FITTING. PART NO. 2W
8 OFF. 16 S.W.G. M.S. (2.S.3.)

SPAR JOINT FITTING. PART NO. 11.W. 8 OFF.,
18 G M.S. (2S3)

HOLE FOR ⅛" PIN, FRONT FITTINGS.
REAR FITTINGS DRILL LARGER & FIT COPPER FERRULES

DRAG BRACING LUGS (OUTER). PART No. 7W.
4 OFF. 18 S.W.G. M.S.

SPAR–CENTRE SECTION FITTING
PART. NO. I. W.A.
14. S.W.G. M.S. 2 OFF IN PLACE OF I.W.

SPAR CENTRE SECTION FITTING
PART No. 1 W.
2 OFF. 14 S.W.G. M.S. (2.S.3.)

PULLEY BRACKETS PART No. 5W
4 OFF. 16 S.W.G. M.S. (2.S.3.)   HANDED

PULLEY BRACKETS. PART No. 8W
16 S.W.G. M.S. (2.S.3.)

HOLES FOR 2 B.A.

DRILL 2 B.A.

AILERON HINGE. PART No. 4W.
12 OFF. 18 S.W.G. M.S. (2.S.3.)

to be turned. Notice that the spacing of the pulley bracket flanges in 5W and 8W should be made to suit the pulley depth.

Modifications for Two-piece Wing

Two additional main ribs are required.

The spars are identically as before but each is made up in two equal lengths, so as to make a good, close butt joint at the centre. Fitting IW is not required, but is replaced by IWA, two of these being required. Eight additional fittings 11W

The pilot's cockpit.

are necessary for connecting the half spars together finally, and 4 fittings 7W are needed in place of the 2 fittings 6W (26°).

We are now ready to commence the assembly of the wing.

The " Minor " may be obtained, ready to fly, from the manufacturers, Messrs. Luton Aircraft Ltd., of Phœnix Works, Gerrards Cross, Bucks., the price varying from £180 upwards, according to the engine fitted. Messrs. Luton Aircraft also supply semi-manufactured sets of parts at £75 and complete sets of materials required for construction at £40, or the parts and materials may be obtained in component lots, i.e. wing, tail unit, fuselage, etc., for those who do not wish to put down the total cost initially. Messrs. Luton Aircraft have consented to reply to any queries, provided a stamped addressed envelope is enclosed, and to supply any materials, or small parts, and to carry out any welding that may be required. Furthermore they undertake to supply all types of engine and to allow a reduction to those who purchase both the sets of parts, or materials, together with the engine unit from them.

Those readers who desire to obtain a full

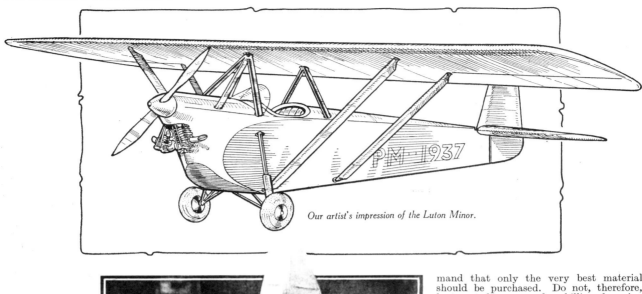

Our artist's impression of the Luton Minor.

The tail and rudder.

mand that only the very best material should be purchased. Do not, therefore, be tempted to save a few shillings by using green, unseasoned, knotty, or "shaky" timber. The grain must be straight and the various scantlings free from warps and twists.

It is also necessary to follow the drawings very accurately. Every detail will be illustrated and the construction fully described. We cannot, for obvious reasons, supply this information in advance of publication, although we shall be glad to answer any questions or problems which the text of these articles does not make clear. The best plan is to study the drawings and the accompanying text as carefully as possible before attempting construction, for in this way you will ensure that you do not scrap material and make expensive mistakes. Collect the complete material for each unit first, and carefully examine it.

set of blue prints, showing all parts drawn out to larger scale than is possible here, should write to Messrs. Luton Aircraft, Ltd., at Gerrards Cross. Five pounds is the cost of the complete set.

Additional Materials Required

Besides the spars, ribs and fittings, the following material is required :

Spruce :
  1 length, $23\frac{1}{2}$ ft. $\times \frac{1}{2}$ in. $\times \frac{3}{8}$ in. for leading edge.
  1 length, 17 ft. $\times$ 1 in. $\times \frac{1}{4}$ in. for trailing edge.
  1 length, $24\frac{1}{2}$ ft. $\times \frac{1}{2}$ in. $\times \frac{3}{8}$ in., for supporting ply nose above front spar.
  2 lengths, 24 ft. $\times \frac{1}{2}$ in. $\times \frac{3}{16}$ in., for ply packing strip at front spar.
  About 60 ft., $\frac{3}{16}$ in. $\times \frac{1}{4}$ in. packing strip, rear spar and aileron.
  1 length, 13 ft. $\times \frac{7}{8}$ in. $\times \frac{7}{8}$ in., for compression struts.
  7 lengths, $7\frac{1}{2}$ ft. $\times \frac{1}{2}$ in. $\times \frac{3}{16}$ in., for wing and aileron tip bends.
Ash : 1 length, 12 ft. $\times \frac{1}{2}$ in. $\times \frac{3}{16}$ in., for wing tip bends.
  ★ *in. Plywood :* 5 sheets, 4 ft. $\times$ 4 ft., or say 80 sq. ft. in all, for wing nosing and wing tip covering.
Piano Wire : 16 S.W.G., 52 ft., or say 1 lb.
Turnbuckles : 5 cwt., eight required.

It is most essential that the correct materials, as here specified, be used. Inferior wood will not do, for the factor of safety and Air Ministry requirements de-

The Luton Minor in Flight.

Building the "LUTON MINOR" Light Aeroplane
PART II

Fig. 1.—A rear view of the plane showing its attractive lines.

Assembling the Wing

OBTAIN two trestles, 2½ ft. to 3 ft. in height and 4 ft. or more long, and set these parallel about 12 ft. apart (or 6 ft. apart if the wing is being built in halves). Place the two main spars across the trestles, having first pencilled on them the positions of all ribs, i.e. 1 ft. spacings, and thread the ribs into position. The central 10 ribs have the small rear spar gap, but the outer ribs accommodate the aileron spars also. Thread the aileron spars into position also.

Cut the drag struts to the required length, 34½ in., there are 5 of these; one for the centre, and a pair 6¼ ft. to either side (see the general wing arrangement, Fig. 2). Cut 4 triangular biscuits of ⅛-in. ply for the end fixings of the central strut. These

Construction Described by The Designer

may be cut from 2 squares, 4 in. by 4 in. Attach, by glue and brads, one pair of these biscuits at each end of the strut, as shown in Fig. 3, and cut away small gaps, roughly ½ in. by ⅛ in. to accommodate the wire bracing fittings (Fig. 3).

The Drag Struts

The outer pairs of drag struts are faced on both ribs with ply sheets, 34·1 in. by 5 in. deep and so form hollow boxes, the ends having central cutaways ½ in. by ¹⁄₂₀ in. as before.

The positions of all wing spar fittings will have been marked on the spars before assembly and the bolt holes may have been drilled. On the front spar, rear face (see page 9 of October issue of PRACTICAL MECHANICS) starting from the centre, there are fittings 6W and 1W on the centre line; the pulley bracket 8W, 13½ in. outboard; the pair of lift strut attachment fittings 2W, one on either face of the spar, set as shown in the diagram. The top bolt through these fittings takes also the drag bracing fitting 6W, and the upper parts of the flanges of 2W

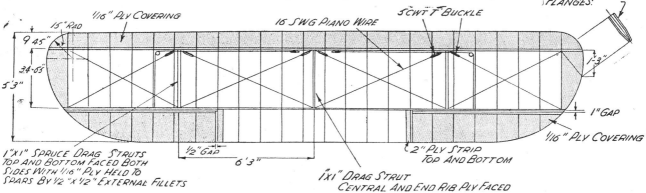

Fig. 2.—The general wing arrangement.

Labels on Fig. 2: 1/16" PLY COVERING · 15" RAD · 9·45" · 34·65" · 5'3" · 16 SWG PIANO WIRE · 5 CWT T BUCKLE · 4/16" PLY WITH 1/2"×3/16" SPRUCE FLANGES · 1·3" · 1" GAP · 1/16" PLY COVERING · 1"×1" SPRUCE DRAG STRUTS TOP AND BOTTOM FACED BOTH SIDES WITH 1/16" PLY HELD TO SPARS BY 1/2"×1/2" EXTERNAL FILLETS · 1/2" GAP · 6'3" · 1"×1" DRAG STRUT CENTRAL AND END RIB PLY FACED · 2" PLY STRIP TOP AND BOTTOM

POWER UNITS

Luton Anzani, 35 h.p. improved model £52 10 0
    dual ignition and impulse
       starter . . . £62 10 0
Sprite II, 25 h.p., with impulse starter £58 0 0
    dual ignition and impulse
       starter . . . £65 0 0
Carden-Ford, 30 h.p., 4-cylinder, radia-
    tor, etc. . . . £55 0 0
    with dual ignition . £63 10 0
Scott, 28 h.p., 2-stroke . . £53 0 0

on the rear face may need slight filing to accommodate 6W. Just inboard of the 5th rib from the wing-tip are the two pulley fittings 5W, and at the end rib is the outer drag bracing lug 7W.

The Rear Spar

The rear spar has the pair of rear lift strut attachment fittings 2W, the three drag bracing fittings 7W and 6W (two) on the front face; the 3 hinge fittings 4W and the pylon attachment lug 1W on the rear face. Note that the flanges of 2W on the front face may need filing to take 6W, as explained for the front spar.

All the fittings mentioned above may be bolted to the main spars. No fittings should be attached to the aileron spars at this stage.

Now place the drag struts in position and attach the six turnbuckles, or strainers, to the lugs of fittings 6W and 7W at the front spar. Cut 8 lengths of 16 s.w.g. piano wire, about 7 ft. long and fit these to the lugs on the rear spar. To do this make a loop 3 or 4 inches from the end with the aid of a pair of bull-nosed or round-jawed pliers, and turn the short end parallel and close to the main wire. Engage the lug of the fitting and slip a ferrule over the double wire (Fig. 4). The ferrule may be of the standard made-up wire type, or it may be made of a ½ in. length of steel tubing, preferably flattened to fit the two wires. Push the ferrule close to the loop, turn back the free end and cut off the surplus wire. Now make the loop at the forward end, by first slipping the ferrule on to the wire and engaging the eye of the turnbuckle end. Care must be taken to

Fig. 8.—Locking the bolts with a centre punch.

obtain the correct length of wire and this may be done by screwing out the turnbuckle so that about ¼ in. only of each thread is engaged. When the wires are tensioned, which should be done altogether, or at least in pairs, see that each turnbuckle has sufficient thread engaged at both ends. Small holes are provided in the turnbuckle ends for the insertion of a thin wire or pin to ascertain whether the threads are " in safety."

A warning may be issued here against over-tensioning of the bracings which sets up initial stresses in the spars and other members. As a rough guide the turnbuckles should be turned until the wire just straightens out and another further half-turn may be given.

Tensioning the Wires

Just prior to tensioning the wires. fix the drag struts by gluing and bradding

½ in. by ½ in. spruce fillets external to the ply faces and to the spar (Fig. 3). Tension all wires and check for rigging by measuring from the centre of the front spar to points along the rear spar at the drag strut attachments. Note that the end or wing-tip ribs act as the outermost drag strut. Alignment of the spars should also be checked by looking along them from tip to tip.

The ribs may now be fixed in position. Slide each rib a little to one side, apply glue to both faces of the spar and return the rib to its correct location. Bring the ribs up so that the bottom flanges fit tightly to the under-surface of the spar. A few brass gimp pins should be hammered through the rib verticals, or soldiers, to complete the join to the spars. Similarly attach the aileron spars, making sure that the 1 in. gap is uniform at all points—this may be facilitated by inserting pieces of

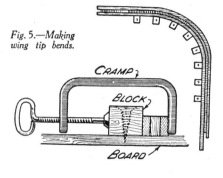

Fig. 5.—Making wing tip bends.

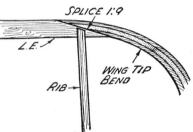

Fig. 6.—The wing tip splice.

wood 1 in. in thickness between the aileron and rear spar.

Next make the wing-tip bends. These are made up in two segments, the division being at the front main spar. The forward segment of small radius (15 in.) is made from 3 laminations of ½ in. by ³⁄₁₆ in. ash, the rear segment consisting of 3 laminations of ½ in. by ³⁄₁₆ in. spruce.

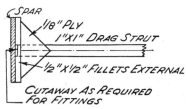

Fig. 3.—Details of the centre drag strut.

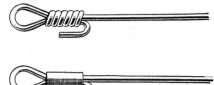

Fig. 4.—Loop ends of wire along bracing.

Making the Bends

To make the bends, set out both shapes on a board and screw a number of blocks to the inside contour. The laminations are glued and cramped to the blocks by means of small cramps. Leave until dry to set.

The leading-edge and trailing edge members are next fitted. The slots in the ribs will require some cleaning up to house these and lengths of cotton should be stretched across the span at the front and rear to ensure that all slots are in line. Any necessary adjustment should be made by cutting away the ribs.

Place the leading edge member (½ in. by ⅜ in. spruce) in the slots, glue to the small vertical members in the ribs and fix with one ⅞ in. brass gimp pin through the leading edge into each vertical. The trailing edge member (1 in. by ¼ in.) is similarly placed and glued into position and may be held by one small ⅜ in. gimp through each rib flange at the rear. If desired the joints may be further finished off by means of small semi-circular, or triangular, ply biscuits, fixed to the trailing edge and bottom rib flange.

Leading and Trailing Edges

Next cut the leading and trailing edge members ready for splicing. This should be done at a rib, the angle being roughly 1 in 9 (see Fig. 6). The rear segment is first fitted and in turn is scarfed at the front spar for receiving the front tip bend. Finally the front bend is cut to suit the leading-edge and rear bend scarfs and is glued in position. The front and rear splices may be made good by means of 2 or 3, ¾ No. 4 screws and one screw may be driven through the central scarf into the front spar.

Further shaping of the wing-tip bend

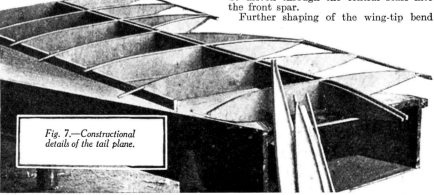

Fig. 7.—Constructional details of the tail plane.

Fig. 9.—A part-front view of the plane.

The Nosing Ply

The nosing ply may be fitted in separate lengths, or preferably in one piece over the 17 ft. parallel portion of the span. If it is to be fitted in one length, first cut a sufficient number of $\frac{1}{16}$ in. ply sheets to make a 17 ft. length. The necessary width may be found by measuring round a rib from the rear face of the front spar at the top to the rear face at the bottom. It is $22\frac{1}{2}$ inches. These pieces are then scarfed together as follows : Place a sheet of ply on a bench with a reasonably clean, sharp edge, bringing the edge of the ply flush with the bench edge. Then shoot with a plane held with a slight outward tilt so that the ply is given a feather edge, the tapering part being roughly 15 times the ply thickness, or in this case about 1 in. Repeat at the opposite edge but with the scarf in the opposite face. The joint is made by bringing two of the scarfed faces together (Fig. 11) and gluing. A wood strip should be tacked along the outer face, the tacks passing through to the bench or to another strip below. Strips of paper may be inserted between the wood strips and ply to prevent the glue from fixing them together. Remove wood and paper strip when the glue is set.

Curving the Plywood

The long ply sheet may be curved before fitting to the wing. This may be done by damping the *outside* of the ply ; leaving for a few minutes and then turning the ply over until the long edges meet. The ply may be tied in this position and left overnight. Tie with tape at several places and assist with long, stiff laths inserted under the tapes.

When the ply is brought to the wing nose, all ribs, the leading-edge stringer and the packing strips should be liberally smeared with glue. Fix the ply by gimp pins, or by wire staples, starting from the centre and working out towards both ends. If staples are used they should be removed when the glue is set.

If the leading edge ply is attached in separate lengths, each scarfed joint must coincide with a main rib. The ply edges are feathered before attaching to the wing, though the actual joint is made " in situ."

may now be done, the depth being carefully graded to merge into the thickness of the front and rear edge members.

We are now ready for attachment of the leading-edge nosing ply, but it is as well first to lock all bolts in the front spar. This is done by cutting the bolt (if necessary) almost flush with the nut and, with the aid of hammer and centre pop, making three centre pop marks round the thread, as shown in Fig. 8. Now run a length of $\frac{3}{8}$ in. by $\frac{1}{2}$ in. spruce along the gap above the front spar (Fig. 13), and fix to all ribs on the under-rib of the top rib flanges. This is for supporting the nosing ply. Strips of spruce, approximately $\frac{1}{2}$ in. by $\frac{3}{16}$ in. are then glued and tacked between all ribs, to the bottom face of the front spar and on the upper face of the $\frac{1}{2}$ in. by $\frac{3}{16}$ in. runner just fitted.

Before attaching the ply it is as well to take a straight edge, about 4 to 6 ft. in length, and to hold this against the rib

profiles in the vicinity of the leading edge, both above and below, to test for uniformity of contour. This should be done over the whole span and if there are any " high spots " the ribs should be cleaned down accordingly, or a little packing out may be done to ensure the correct shape along the span.

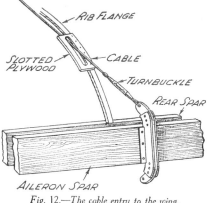

Fig. 12.—The cable entry to the wing.

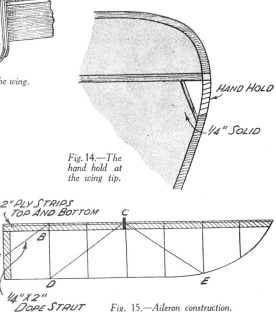

Fig. 14.—The hand hold at the wing tip.

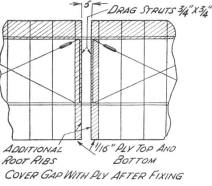

Fig. 10.—A plan of the wing centre.

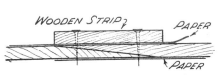

Fig. 11.—A scarfed joint in the plywood.

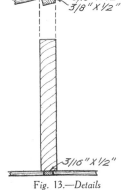

Fig. 13.—Details of the front spar.

Fig. 15.—Aileron construction.

Fig. 16.—Our Artist's impression of the Luton Minor.

A strip of wood is applied at each joint, with paper inserts, the tacks or staples being driven through the strip, ply and supporting member.

Positioning the Ribs

The position of ribs and other members may be pencilled on the outer face of the ply nosing to show where the pinning should take place.

A separate piece of plywood is fitted over each tapering portion of 3 ft. length running from the tip rib to the 4th rib. The wing-tip consists of 4 pieces of ply, two above and two below, the dividing line being the front spar. Before fitting these the diagonals, consisting of a ply web with $\frac{1}{2}$ in. by $\frac{3}{16}$ in. flanges, or alternatively of $\frac{1}{4}$ in. solid spruce, should be fitted. The tip ply is scarfed as before.

A hand hold may be made in the wing-tip by the insertion of a tapered piece of $\frac{1}{4}$ in. solid spruce, as shown in Fig. 14, the plywood stopping short at this member. The wing-tip bend may be bound with tape where exposed.

The Ailerons

We now come to the ailerons. Fig. 2 shows them covered with plywood but an equally good job, and lighter, may be obtained with fabric covering. If they are to be fabric covered a dope strut, AB of Fig. 15, of section about $\frac{1}{4}$ in. by 2 in. should be inserted as shown. The aileron lever bolts on the inside face of the rib at C, and stiffeners CD, and CE should be included. These may also be of $\frac{1}{4}$ in. spruce, tapering from the aileron spar depth to $\frac{1}{2}$ in. at the trailing edge. The ply webs in the intermediate ribs should be slotted to receive these stiffeners. Next fit trailing edge rib portions, i.e. aft of the rear spar, to form the aileron root, leaving a clear gap of $\frac{1}{2}$ in. between this and the adjacent main rib.

Strips of plywood, 2 in. in width should be fixed along the forward part of the aileron, top and bottom, and similar strips at the root.

The ailerons may now be cut away from the wing, the rib ends being cleaned up with a chisel and sand-paper. Note that if the aileron covering is ply, it is as well to attach the ply on one face before cutting away the aileron clear.

Aileron Hinges

The aileron hinges may now be fitted and should be so arranged that no appreciable sideways movement of the ailerons is possible. Fit also the 2 in. ply strips on the main plane ribs adjoining the aileron roots and fit packing strip—$\frac{1}{4}$ in. by $\frac{3}{16}$ in.—to top and bottom faces of the rear spar, between the ribs, over the aileron portion. No packing strip is necessary over the central part of the spar. Except for a general rubbing down with glasspaper and fitting the cables, the wing is now ready for covering.

LUTON MINOR

Price List of Completed Parts

Main plane, covered and doped	£50	0	0
Fuselage, painted	£36	0	0
Tail unit	£17	10	0
Undercarriage, with wheels and shock absorbers	£14	0	0
Controls	£2	0	0
Tanks	£3	10	0
Wing pylons and fittings	£1	0	0
Lift struts (streamline steel tube) and bracing	£6	10	0

Price List of Component Parts, Ready for Assembly

Set main plane ribs	£7	10	0
Main plane and aileron spars	£6	4	0
Fuselage sides made up (cost extra to materials)	£3	0	0
Fuselage made up, complete with decking (extra)	£24	0	0
Complete set fittings and controls made up	£20	0	0

Fig. 17.—The engine and engine mounting.

Fig. 18.—Showing the construction of the undercarriage.

cient to leave the cable free in all positions of the aileron.

Note if the cables tend to foul any parts of the ribs, the ribs should be suitably cut away and re-strengthened if considered necessary. This applies also to the drag bracing system dealt with earlier in these notes.

Two Additional Ribs

Figs. 10 and 19 show the modifications necessary if the wing is to be built in two halves. Two additional ribs are required, these being inserted $2\frac{1}{2}$ in. from each root, so as to leave a clear gap of 5 in. when the wing halves are placed together. 2 in. strips of $\frac{1}{16}$ in. ply are attached to the inside of these ribs, top and bottom. Close inside the root rib is the drag strut and close to this again is the fitting 7W to take the drag bracing.

The half wings may be joined either before or after covering. This is carried out by bringing the spar roots close together, carefully aligning the whole wing and bolting on the connection fittings 11W. This may best be done by fitting them to one half beforehand and carefully drilling the spars of the second half when in position.

Omit the two inner bolts in both bottom

The aileron balance cable connects across the bottom aileron levers. Attach a 10-cwt. turnbuckle to one of the levers and to the free end of this splice a length of 10-cwt. control cable (all cables should be of 10-cwt. flexible steel rope, 7 by 14, to specification 4W2). With the ailerons held, or clamped, level, the balance cable is run forward over the lower pulley of fitting 5W, right across the wing to the opposite fitting and out to the bottom aileron lever again, where it is spliced.

10 cwt. turnbuckles are fitted to the two top aileron levers, to which cables are spliced. These pass over the upper pulleys 5W, the inner pulleys 8W, pass through the

underside of the wing and connect to the controls in the fuselage. Make these cables of sufficient length so that about 5 ft. hangs below the wing and leave the ends bound but unspliced.

Cables for the Wings

Where the cables pass into the wings, slotted lengths of three-ply may be attached to the ribs, as shown in Fig. 12, to provide attachment for the covering material. The length of slot should be suffi-

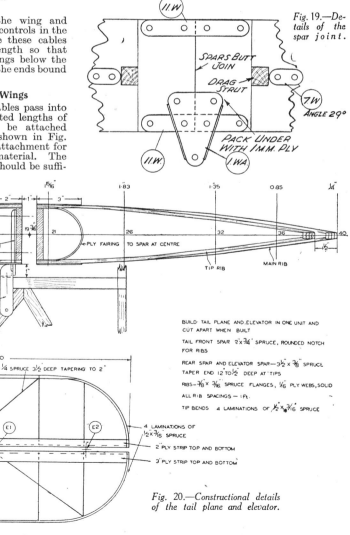

Fig. 19.—Details of the spar joint.

SPARS BUTT JOIN

DRAG STRUT

PACK UNDER WITH 1 M.M. PLY

7W ANGLE 29°

BUILD TAIL PLANE AND ELEVATOR IN ONE UNIT AND CUT APART WHEN BUILT

TAIL FRONT SPAR 2″ × ¾″ SPRUCE, ROUNDED NOTCH FOR RIBS

REAR SPAR AND ELEVATOR SPAR—3½″ × ⅜″ SPRUCE TAPER END 12 TO ½″ DEEP AT TIPS

RIBS—⅜″ × ⅜″ SPRUCE FLANGES, ⅛″ PLY WEBS, SOLID

ALL RIB SPACINGS—1 ft.

TIP BENDS 4 LAMINATIONS OF ½″ × ³⁄₁₆″ SPRUCE

Fig. 20.—Constructional details of the tail plane and elevator.

flanges till last, when the fittings 1WA are placed in position. When the wing is joined a strip of ply should be used for closing the 5 in. gap. This should be at least 7 in. in width and may be glued external to the root ply strips.

See that all bolts and turnbuckles are locked, as previously explained, and the wing is now complete except for covering.

Blue Prints

The "Minor" may be obtained, ready to fly, from the manufacturers, Messrs. Luton Aircraft Ltd., of Phœnix Works, Gerrards Cross, Bucks., the price varying from £180 upwards, according to the engine fitted.

A Method of Loop Splicing Flexible Steel Cables

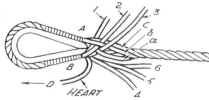

NOTE. STRANDS NUMBERED COUNTER-CLOCKWISE VIEWED FROM END OF CABLE

Fig. 21.—First half of No. 1 tuck. Cable serve at A and B with waxed thread. Cable bent round thimble heart turned back in direction of arrow D. No. 3 strand threaded under a. No. 1 strand threaded under b and c. No. 2 strand threaded under b.

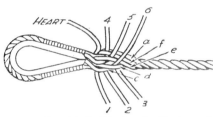

Fig. 22.—Second half of No. 1 tuck. No. 4 strand threaded under f. No. 5 strand threaded under e. No. 6 strand threaded under d. One tuck is completed when each strand has been threaded once.

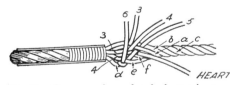

Fig. 23.—Commence of second tuck showing heart tucked in. In the 2nd, 3rd, 4th and the half tucks, the heart is laid along the cable and taken under a suitable strand (in illustration, No. 5 strand), thus forcing the heart into the centre of the splice. In the 2nd, 3rd and 4th tucks the strands 1, 2, 3, 4, 5, and 6 are taken under and over one strand (a, b, c, d, e, f, e.g. No. 3 strand is taken over b under c in 2nd tuck, over d under e in 3rd tuck, over f under a in 4th tuck. Half a tuck is made by threading alternate strands once. A complete splice consists of 4½ tucks. On completion of splicing loose ends cut off flush and served.

FIRST 3 TUCKS TO BE LEFT FREE OF SERVING

SERVING WITH WAXED THREAD

Fig. 24.—Showing the complete splice.

Messrs. Luton Aircraft also supply semi-manufactured sets of parts at £75 and complete sets of materials required for construction at £40, or the parts and materials may be obtained in component lots, i.e. wing, tail unit, fuselage, etc., for those who do not wish to put down the total cost initially. Messrs. Luton Aircraft have consented to reply to any queries, provided a stamped addressed envelope is enclosed, and to supply any materials, or small parts, and to carry out any welding that may be required. Furthermore they undertake to supply all types of engine and to allow a reduction to those who purchase both the sets of parts, or materials, together with the engine unit from them.

Those readers who desire to obtain a full set of blue prints, showing all parts drawn out to larger scale than is possible here, should write to Messrs. Luton Aircraft, Ltd., at Gerrards Cross. Five pounds is the cost of the complete set.

* * * *

"Errata." In the table of rib ordinates, given on page 9 of last month's issue, the second dimension in the second vertical column should read 4·55 instead of 4·2, and the dimension 0·5 at the foot of the same column should read 0·64.

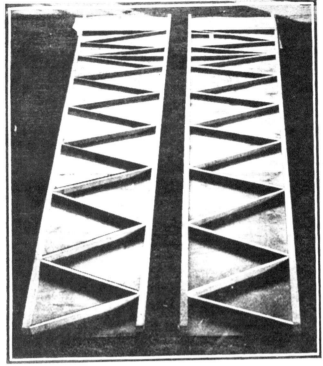

Fig. 25.—The fuselage sides.

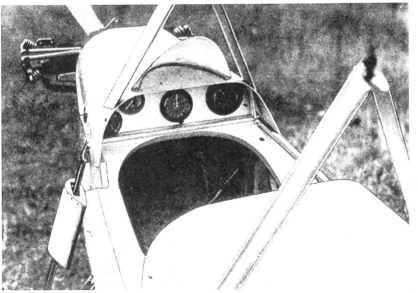

Fig. 26.—Showing the roomy cockpit.

Fig. 1.— A rear view of the plane showing its attractive lines.

Building the "LUTON MINOR" Light Aeroplane
PART III

Tail Plane and Elevator

IN the " Minor " construction the tail plane and elevator are made in one and cut apart afterwards. This method greatly simplifies construction and ensures that the two parts will match up properly when completed. The building of a fairly long component of short chord, such as either the stabiliser (fixed tail plane) or elevator, is not easily accomplished without the aid of an elaborate jig since the unit is very liable to twist and proper alignment is difficult. It is probably easier to build the two combined surfaces of the " Minor " than to build either one separately.

THE TAIL UNIT

Tail Spars

The rear tail-plane spar and the elevator spar are identical and are made of $\frac{3}{8}$ in. spruce, $3\frac{1}{2}$ in. deep, the lengths being trimmed to 7 ft. $10\frac{1}{2}$ in. The ends of the spars taper to $\frac{1}{2}$ in. deep at the tips, the taper being confined to the last 11 in.

The front spar is made from a piece of spruce 2 in. $\times \frac{3}{4}$ in., roughly 6 ft. in length. The two front edges are rounded off to form a " D " section (Fig. 2). Along the top and bottom faces of this spar notches are cut, $\frac{3}{16}$ in. deep, to accommodate the rib noses,

there being 5 notches top and bottom at 12 in. centres, commencing from the centre of the spar.

Tip Bends

The tip bends may be made next in readiness for the assembly. These are made in exactly the same way as the main plane tip bends, but one jig only is necessary. They are made up of 4 laminations of $\frac{1}{8}$ in. $\times \frac{3}{16}$ in. spruce, giving a finished section of $\frac{1}{2}$ in. $\times \frac{3}{4}$ in. The bends are made in one piece from 7 ft. lengths, the extra material being used to form the straight trailing edge (See Tail Assembly, Fig. 10.).

Tail Plane Ribs

The tail ribs are very simple units. One jig might be made up for all but the two tip ribs and slightly modified afterwards to deal with these two. Very few " buttons " or blocks are necessary for this jig.

PRICE LIST OF " MINOR " TAIL UNIT MATERIALS	£	s.	d
Tail plane, elevator and rudder spar spruce .		16	2
Remainder of spruce, as list above	1	11	3
18 sq. ft. plywood . .		6	0
Mild steel sheet, 16 s.w.g. (2 S.3), 1½ sq. ft. .		2	0
Complete set of materials as detailed above . .	2	15	0
Tail and rudder ribs, made up	2	5	0
Making up tail and rudder bends, extra to materials		10	6
Or all bends complete, including materials .	1	1	0
Complete set fittings (23) made up . . .	2	2	0
Tail unit made up, but uncovered. . .	17	10	0

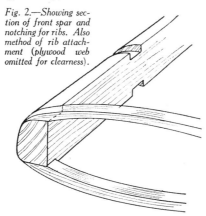

Fig. 2.—Showing section of front spar and notching for ribs. Also method of rib attachment (plywood web omitted for clearness).

MATERIALS REQUIRED FOR TAIL UNIT CONSTRUCTION
Aero Spruce
2 lengths, 8 ft., 3½ in. × ⅜ in.
1 length, 6 ft., 2 in. × ¾ in.
1 length, 4¾ ft., 4⅛ in. × ⅜ in.
10 ft. of 3½ in. × ¼ in.
120 ft. of ⅜ in. × 3/16 in.
90 ft. of ½ in. × 3/16 in.
5 ft. of 4⅛ in. × ¼ in.
Plywood
18 sq. ft. of 1/16 in. (1·5 m/m.) plywood.
M.S. Sheet (2.S.3)
1½ sq. ft. of 16 s.w.g.

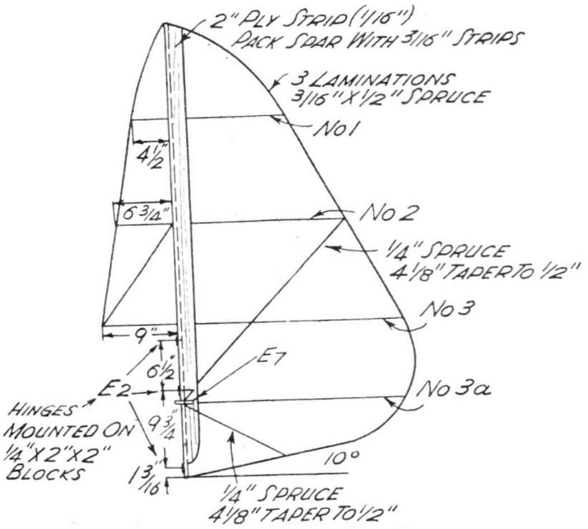

Fig. 3.—Details of the rudder.

Half ordinates are at the following distances in inches from the leading edge: $\frac{3}{4}$, 3, 6, 13, 21, 26, 32, 36 and 40, the chord being 40 in. The half ordinates are 1, 1·4, 1·75, $1\frac{15}{16}$, $1\frac{15}{16}$, 1·83, 1·35, 0·85 and 0·25 respectively. The hinge centre is at $19\frac{3}{4}$ in. from the leading-edge.

The rib webs are $\frac{1}{16}$-in. plywood cut to the shape of the rib, and are unlightened, the flanges being $\frac{3}{8}$ in. × $\frac{3}{16}$ in. or $\frac{1}{2}$ in. × $\frac{3}{16}$ in. spruce. In gluing up the ribs leave the front 6 in. unglued, as this will enable the flanges to be slipped over the front spar on assembly, at which stage the final gluing may be done (Fig. 4).

A gap of $1\frac{3}{4}$ in. is left at the centre of the rib, or more exactly at the $19\frac{3}{4}$ in. position, for the spars and hinge gap. This is best allowed for by cutting the ply webs in two separate lengths. The webs are also truncated $\frac{3}{4}$ in. at the leading and trailing edges to allow for the front spar and trailing-edge member. The central rib consists, of course, of the front half only, whilst the elevator central ribs, at the cutaway, are similar to the rear part of the main ribs, but are slightly attenuated.

The main ribs having been made up, the jig can be modified for the two outside ribs by cutting $1\frac{1}{2}$ in. off each end and slightly modifying the cambers accordingly.

Assembling the Tail Plane

Set out the three spars across two trestles, or a bench, and thread all ribs into their approximate positions. The two main spars may be clamped together with 1 in. blocks inserted between them. Fix all but the two end ribs by glue and brass gimp pins, the spacings being 12 in. in all cases. The two "cutaway" ribs are placed with the ply webs facing together.

Cut and insert the diagonal braces in the stabiliser. These are of $\frac{1}{4}$ in. spruce, $3\frac{1}{2}$ in. deep at the rear spar tapering down to 2 in. at the front spar. In fitting these members care should be exercised to ensure proper alignment of the tail plane by measuring, say, from the centre of the rear spar to the front rib attachments 2 ft. either side of the front spar centre.

Slots should be cut in the intermediate ribs for the diagonal braces to pass through. If small triangular fillets are finally inserted and glued between the rib flange and bracing member, this will considerably stiffen the elevator and provide a better job.

The tip bends may next be fitted by scarfing on to the front spar, screwing to the ends of the other spars, and fitting to the rear edges of the ribs, keeping the spacings 12 in. as before. The outer ribs may also be fixed at this stage.

Notes on making up fittings have already been given in the October issue of PRACTICAL MECHANICS, and will not be repeated. Note that the angle of fitting E5, which bolts to the fuselage for the front tail spar attachment, is $85\frac{3}{4}$ degrees—the plan angle of the fuselage at that point. Fittings E6, for the rear spar attachment, have an angle of $94\frac{1}{4}$ degrees, since these face in the reverse direction to E5. The tail fittings E1-6 are shown in Fig. 5.

The elevator levers, E1, are bolted to the elevator spar by 3-2BA bolts immediately outside the ribs. The diagonals, running from the levers to the end ribs at the trailing-edge may then be inserted. These may be cut from one piece of spruce $3\frac{1}{2}$ in. deep by about $2\frac{3}{4}$ ft. long, and taper to $\frac{1}{2}$ in. deep at the trailing edge. Similarly the small dope struts, $2\frac{3}{8}$ in. × $\frac{1}{4}$ in. spruce, may be inserted between the elevator lever root and the cutaway. These struts prevent bowing of the ribs bounding the cutaway, due to dope tension.

Strips of $\frac{1}{16}$-in. plywood are glued and tacked along the main spars, gluing also to the ribs and tip bends. Packing strips of $\frac{3}{16}$ in. deep × $\frac{1}{4}$ in. or $\frac{3}{8}$ in. spruce, will first have been glued along the two spars to fill in the spaces between the ribs. These strips are 2 in. wide, though a 3 in. strip may be used for the elevator. Cut away for the elevator levers and for fittings E4, though the latter are not yet fixed in position. It is better to leave the fixture of E3 and E4 until the tail plane can be tried in position on the fuselage, so as to make certain that they match up exactly with the corresponding fuselage fittings—E5 and E6 respectively.

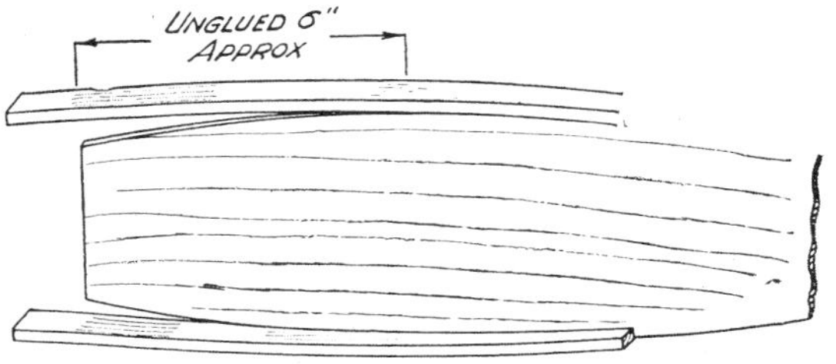

Fig. 4.—Front of tail plane rib left unglued for fixing to the front spar.

Elevator Spar Fairing

Finally, before cutting the two surfaces apart, a ply fairing is fixed to the elevator spar in the cutaway. Two small discs of $\frac{1}{4}$ in. ply, $3\frac{7}{8}$ in. deep × $3\frac{1}{4}$ in., are shaped to "D" form and are glued to the faces of the two ribs at the cutaway. Preferably the edges of these discs should be chamfered to provide a good gluing surface for the plywood fairing. The piece of plywood is then shaped and glued in position.

This small fairing considerably improves the appearance of the tail; it acts as a torsional stiffening device for transmitting loads along the elevator spar in the event of failure of one of the elevator cables, and it decreases the flight resistance of the aeroplane.

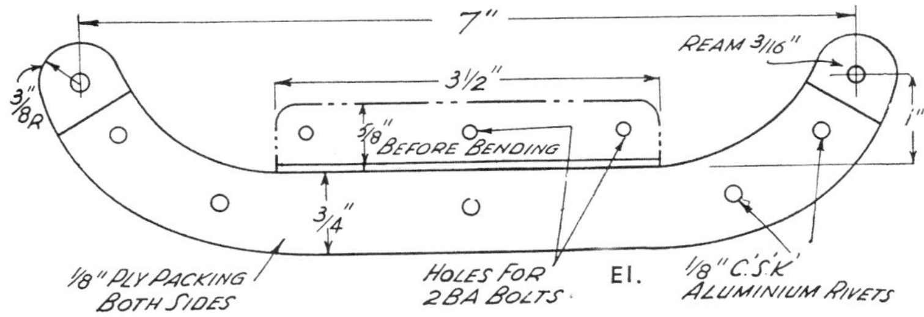

E1.

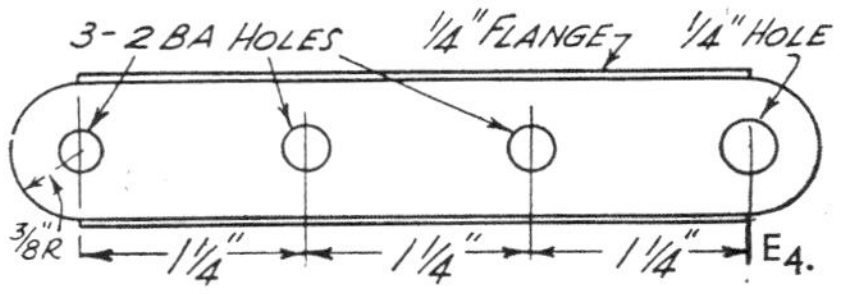

E4.

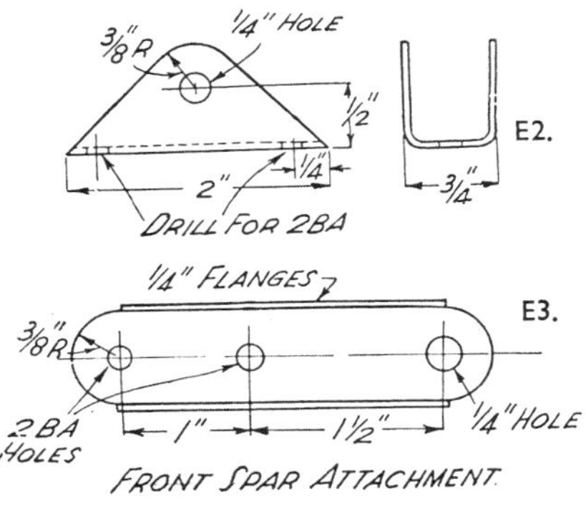

E2.

E3.

Fig. 5.—The tail fittings E1 to E6. Note E6 is similar to E5 with the following alterations. The angle of lug is $94\frac{1}{4}$°, dimension A is $\frac{1}{2}$ in. and dimension B $2\frac{1}{4}$ in.

E5. & 6.

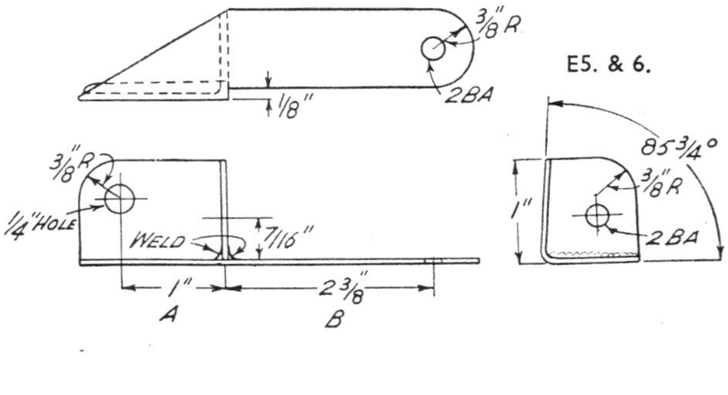

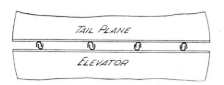

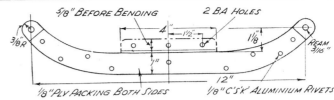

Fig. 6. (left).—Details of the hinges.

Fig. 8 (right).—The rudder lever.

Fixing the Hinges

The stabiliser and elevator may now be cut apart and the rib ends, together with the severed tip bends, are cleaned off. Fit the two outer hinges on the centre line of the elevator out spar, join these by a length of cotton and fit the inner hinges in alignment, close to the elevator levers. Similarly fix the outer tail plane hinges, taking care to match up with the corresponding elevator hinges, and by means of thread and offering up the elevator, the central

hinge positions may also be obtained.

Note that to prevent sideways movement of the elevator relative to the tail plane, the hinges should be arranged as shown in Fig. 6, $\frac{1}{4}$ in. pins, or bolts with the threaded portion removed, are inserted in the hinges and the component may be left in this condition for the time being. When final assembly is made these hinge pins will be fitted with washers and $\frac{1}{16}$ in. split pins.

The Rudder

Fig. 3 shows the assembly of the rudder. The spar consists of a piece of spruce, of $4\frac{1}{8}$ in. × $\frac{3}{8}$ in. section, $4\frac{3}{4}$ ft. long. It is shaped as shown in Fig. 7.

The rib ordinates are given in the table below. Except for rib 3A, which is the same as No. 3, but truncated at the front spar, they are different. This does not mean that three jigs are necessary. The rib shapes having been drawn out on $\frac{1}{16}$ in. plywood and cut to shape, the flanges, of $\frac{3}{16}$ in. × $\frac{3}{8}$ in. spruce, may be attached round the edges by means of glue and cramps. Slots for the spar can be cut when the ribs are set.

Assemble the ribs and spar, bolt on fitting E7, the control lever (Fig. 8) close above rib 3A, and insert the three diagonal members, taking care that the ribs remain perpendicular to the spar and that no distortion of the spar takes place. The front diagonal is a dope strut and may be either of thin spruce, say $\frac{1}{4}$ in. thick, taper-

Fig. 7.—The rudder spar.

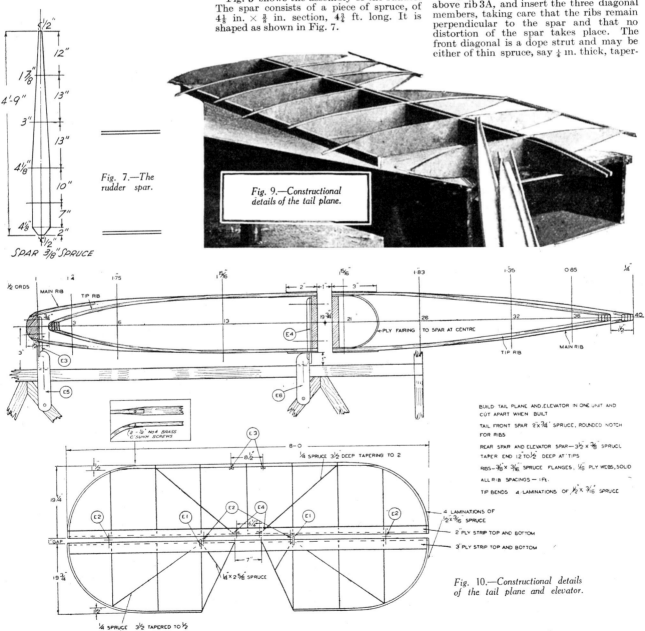

Fig. 9.—Constructional details of the tail plane.

Fig. 10.—Constructional details of the tail plane and elevator.

RIB ORDINATES

No. 1	Dist. from L.E.	1	2	3	4·5	6·5	9	12	15	16·5
	Ord. ins..	1·25	1·65	2·0	2·25	2·3	2·0	1·4	0·75	0·4
No. 2	Dist. from L.E.	1	2	4	6·5	9	12	16	21	25·5
	Ord. ins. .	1·65	2·45	2·95	3·37	3·4	3·25	2·63	1·55	0·4
No. 3	Dist. from L.E.	1	2	4·5	9	12	18	24	30	34·5
	Ord. ins. .	1·85	2·63	3·7	4·5	4·5	4·05	2·93	1·55	0·4

Rib flanges—$\frac{3}{16}$ in. $\times$ $\frac{1}{8}$ in. spruce. Webs—$\frac{1}{16}$ in. plywood.

ing from front to rear, or of square section $\frac{1}{2}$ in. $\times$ $\frac{1}{2}$ in.

Lastly the 2 in. wide plywood strips are glued to both sides of the spar, packing strips having been first inserted between the ribs, and the hinges bolted in position. The position of the hinges as given in Fig. 3 should be adhered to.

The tail unit is now complete except for covering and this will be dealt with in a later article.

The Author points out that the table of main plane rib ordinates given in the October issue of PRACTICAL MECHANICS contained a number of errors. (*Not ours.*—Ed.) It may have been noticed that the wing-tip rib chords did not agree with the wing layout and that certain points on the profile curves did not fair nicely into the curve passing through the remaining points.

We are therefore supplying an entirely new table herewith, and this should be used in place of the earlier table.

Where work has already been commenced on the ribs there is no need to scrap the main ribs (No. 1) provided the two points that fell outside the general curve have been ignored. The same applies to the tip ribs provided also that the chords have been corrected, but failing this it would be as well to make up the tip rib again.

Fig. 11.—A close-up of the engine.

DIST. from L.E.	RIB 1		RIB 2		RIB 3		RIB 4	
INCHES	Upper	Lower	Upper	Lower	Upper	Lower	Upper	Lower
3	3·125	1·98	2·75	1·64	2·4	1·44	1·9	1·09
6	4·5	2·57	3·9	2·15	3·31	1·76	2·62	1·37
9	5·3	2·76	4·62	2·35	3·69	1·94	3·04	1·5
12	5·9	2·83	5·12	2·44	4·25	2·04	3·27	1·55
18	6·5	2·85	5·575	2·5	4·54	2·03	3·31	1·44
24	6·475	2·76	5·5	2·33	4·40	1·87	2·97	1·2
30	6·03	2·53	5·05	2·13	4·00	1·63	2·25	0·98
36	5·27	2·2	4·36	1·89	3·25	1·33	1·47	0·7
42	4·22	1·77	3·49	1·5	2·37	0·99	0·73	0·39
48	3·06	1·32	2·5	1·08	1·46	0·63		
54	1·89	0·85	1·45	0·67	0·52	0·3		
60	0·7	0·38	0·43	0·26				
Chord	63		61·5		56·3		44	
L.E. Radius	1·2		0·96		0·72		0·48	

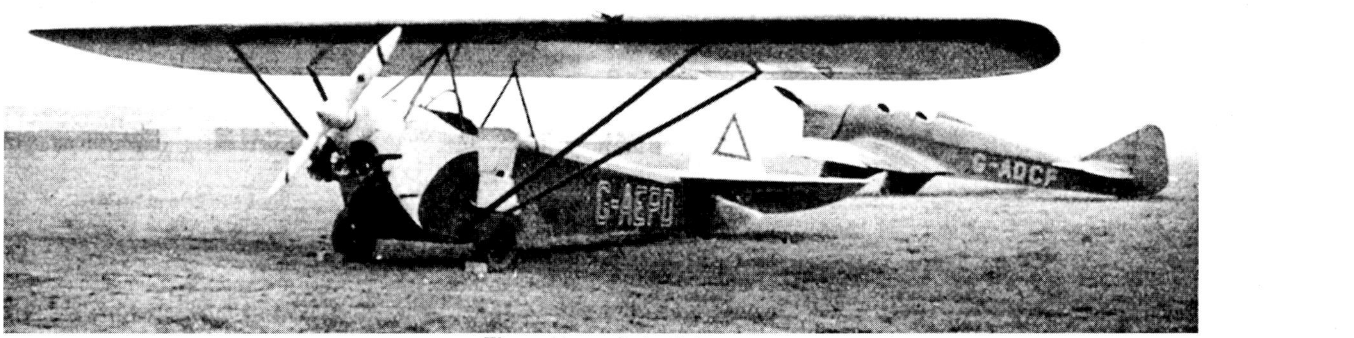

The machine ready for flight.

Building the "LUTON MINOR" Light Aeroplane

PART IV

Fuselage Assembly

THE fuselage of the " Luton Minor " is a plywood box structure of great robustness. It is of spruce girder construction, the spruce members being so triangulated that the plywood covering is not essential for load carrying, but acts as an additional safety factor, besides providing a very serviceable covering (Fig. 1).

Scarfing the Plywood

Construction is commenced by scarfing up the plywood for the two sides. It will be found that four sheets of $\frac{1}{16}$-in. ply are required for the full length, and these may be scarfed as complete sheets, or each sheet may be cut approximately in half before splicing in order to shorten the length of each scarf. The plywood is placed with the grain (outer) horizontal, but with the nose piece grain vertical. Fig. 3 (*a*) and (*b*), shows alternative ways of arranging the two sides from four sheets, depending on the size of the initial plywood boards, and, as already mentioned, the severance of the two sides may be made before or after scarfing.

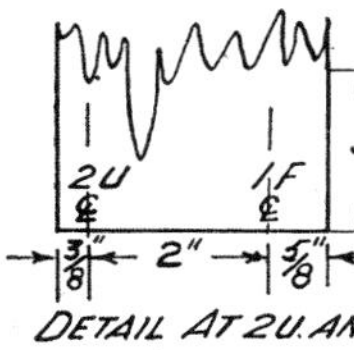

DETAIL AT 2U AND 1F

(Don't forget to place strips of paper on both sides of the plywood during scarfing to prevent sticking to the holding-down strips while the glue dries under pressure.)

After the glue is properly set, the splices should be cleaned up and carefully examined to ensure that no unglued gaps are left. If necessary, such faults should be made good.

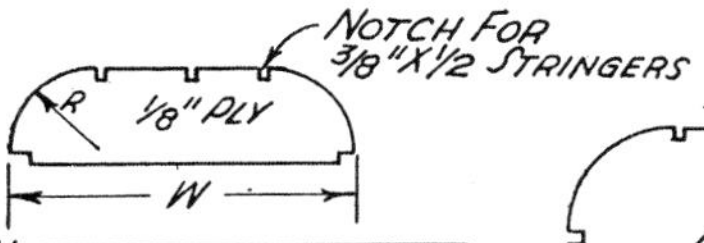

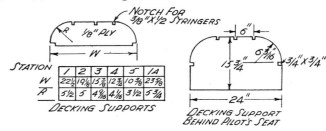

STATION	1	2	3	4	5	1A
W	22½	19⅛	15⅞	12¾	10⅜	23⅝
R	5½	5	4 9/16	4 1/16	3½	5¾

DECKING SUPPORTS

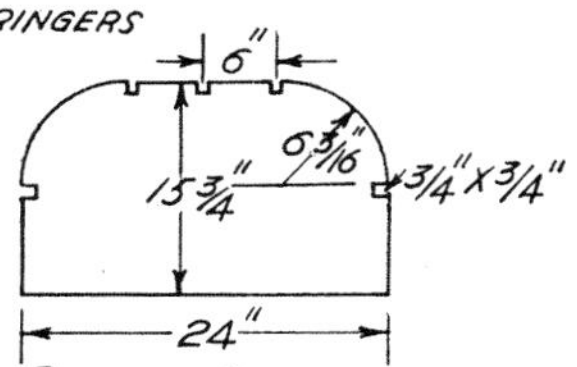

DECKING SUPPORT BEHIND PILOT'S SEAT

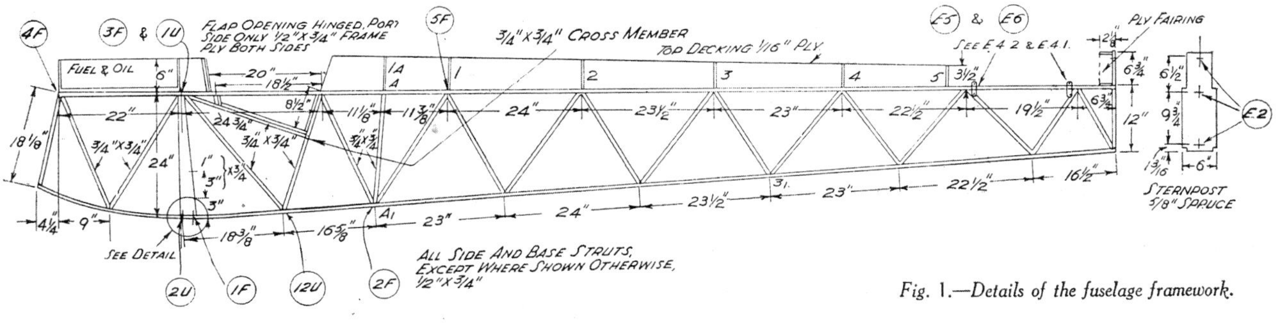

Fig. 1.—Details of the fuselage framework.

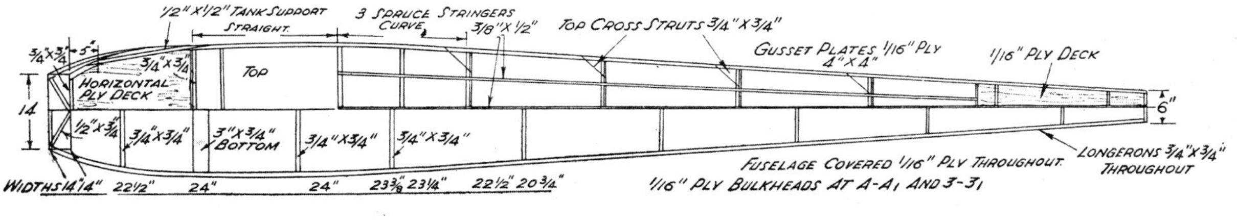

Fig. 2.—Photograph of the fuselage sides.

Making the Fuselage Sides

The next step is to carefully draw out the fuselage sides on the plywood, but leaving roughly 1 in. of ply beyond the outline at all edges. Before fixing the four main longerons they should be longitudinally sliced over the length forward of the heavy, 3-in. side members (Fig. 1). The two top longerons are sliced with a vertical cut so as to divide the section in two (see Fig. 5), whilst the bottom longerons are divided into four equal parts. The reason of this slicing, which is best done on a fine circular saw if available (or will be done by Messrs. Luton

Aircraft Ltd., upon request) is to assist in bending the longerons over the curved nose. Tie them temporarily with string to avoid damage.

The longerons may now be glued on to the plywood in the positions marked and temporarily tacked, or clamped, to avoid relative movement whilst the ply sides are turned over so as to rest on the longerons. Brass gimp pins, $\frac{5}{8}$ in. by 20 gauge, may now be driven in, at 1-in. to 1$\frac{1}{2}$-in. spacings, all along the length of the longerons, the heads being driven well home in the ply in order to produce sufficient pressure whilst the glue is setting. Note that no gluing should be done at the stage forward of the heavy undercarriage member, the longerons being left free over this length until the final boxing up of the nose portion.

The diagonal members are next cut carefully to length, inserted in position and glued and pinned as before. If pencil lines are drawn on the outside of the plywood, running the length of the centre lines of all diagonals, the pinning will be facilitated. As before fix no members forward of the heavy side strut.

When the glue is set, the surplus plywood at top and bottom edges may be removed and the edges made good by means of glass-paper. The two slab sides are now ready for boxing up (Fig. 2).

Boxing-up the Fuselage

First scarf up a length of plywood to cover the bottom of the fuselage from point A to the sternpost. The plan form may then be drawn on the ply, the width being 6 in. at the stern, increasing to 23$\frac{3}{8}$ in. at point A^1. The plan shape is perfectly straight from A^1 to the tail.

Now stand the two sides on their bottom edges, with the straight part (rear) close to the floor, the sides being 6 in. apart (outside) at the stern and increasing towards the front as shown in Fig. 1. The sides should be set parallel and perpendicular to the floor, or bench, on which they rest, checking being made by means of a large set square. The sternpost may be cut to shape (Fig. 1) and clamped in position, but not yet fixed.

Cut the cross struts for the fuselage bottom and place them in position on the floor and fix by means of plywood gussets, glued and pinned. The gussets are fixed on the inside of the struts and longerons. The method of gusseting is illustrated in Fig. 4. The arrangement at (b) provides a better job than (a) but takes a little longer. In both cases there is a cutaway for the side struts.

Bulkheads

Now cut the cross struts for the fuselage top at points A, and 3, together with the plywood bulkheads A,A^1 and 3,3^1. These latter should be carefully cut square, i.e. each corner making an angle of 90°, as they determine the fuselage sectional shape. The corners must be cut away for the longeron and it is better to cut out rather more

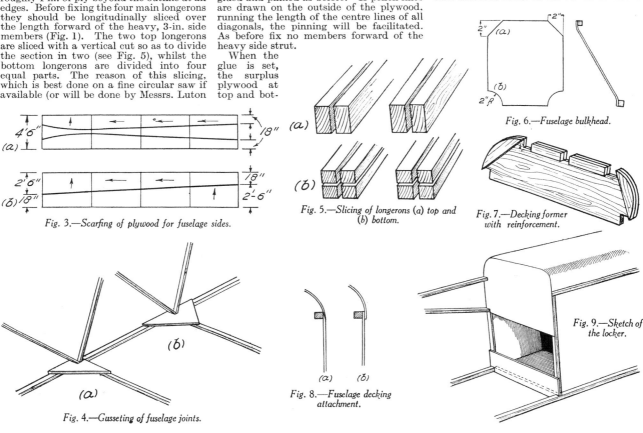

Fig. 3.—Scarfing of plywood for fuselage sides.

Fig. 5.—Slicing of longerons (a) top and (b) bottom.

Fig. 6.—Fuselage bulkhead.

Fig. 7.—Decking former with reinforcement.

Fig. 4.—Gusseting of fuselage joints.

Fig. 8.—Fuselage decking attachment.

Fig. 9.—Sketch of the locker.

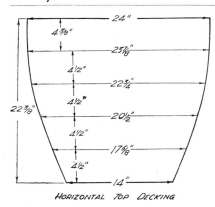

Fig. 10.—(*Above*) Horizontal top decking.
(*Right*) Fuselage nose under covering.

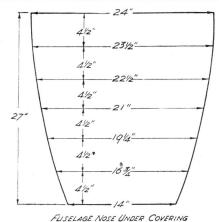

than is essential, say by cutting each corner with a circular arc of 2-in. radius (*b*) of Fig. 6, or by cutting a triangular piece 2 in. by 2 in., as at (*a*), which is equally good. See that the cuts are clean and not liable to start splitting of the bulkhead. Fix these two struts and bulkheads, gluing the latter to the bottom, side and top struts, the plywood being slightly curved at the top and bottom to lie vertically along the faces of the struts, as shown in Fig. 6.

Now turn the fuselage over so that it stands on the top edges, and check again for squareness, having first removed the stern-post member. Cut and fit the remainder of the top cross struts, to the rear of the pilot's seat position, fixing as before with gussets (Fig. 4). This is followed by the fixing of the plywood bottom, from the stern to the 3-in. undercarriage-support member.

Fuselage Decking

After cleaning off the bottom ply, turn the fuselage over again, and fix the stern-post in position. Mark out the decking formers on $\frac{1}{8}$-in. plywood, and cut them out, cutting also the notches to take the three longitudinal stringers and the longerons. Glue and pin the formers to the cross struts.

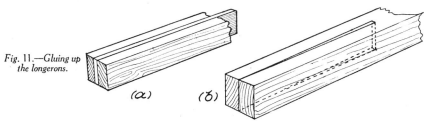

Fig. 11.—Gluing up the longerons.

The edges of the formers are reinforced with strips of spruce, say $\frac{1}{4}$ in. by $\frac{1}{2}$ in., or any other convenient size available. $\frac{1}{8}$-in. ply will do for these stiffening pieces (Fig. 7), pin and glue the stringers ($\frac{3}{8}$ in. by $\frac{1}{2}$ in.) in position, taking care that the top faces are in proper alignment, or difficulty will be

experienced in getting the decking ply to fit properly.

We now come to the fixing of the plywood decking to the rear of the cockpit. This may, if desired, be scarfed up into one piece before fitting, but a better job is likely to be obtained if it is fitted in two lengths of about 4 ft. as dictated by the positioning of the formers, since each scarf must coincide with a frame if the splicing is done " on the job." The decking ply should extend 1 in. down the fuselage side, and the joint may be either scarfed, (*a*) of Fig. 8, or lapped as at (*b*). If the former the fuselage side ply is planed to shape before the decking is laid on. The lapped joint is considerably easier and quicker for an amateur, and gives a very smart appearance if the edge is nicely cleaned off before painting. If the lapped joint is to be employed the ply formers should be left $\frac{1}{16}$ in. wider at each side.

Due to the double curvature of the decking between the cockpit back and point 1 the decking here must be scarfed on in two separate strips.

Fittings 2F and 5F should be attached at this stage.

The Locker

The bulkhead A,A[1] forms also the back of the locker. The floor consists of $\frac{1}{8}$-in. ply-wood, but should be stiffened up by an additional $\frac{1}{2}$-in. by $\frac{3}{4}$-in. strut across the middle of the floor, this being inserted, of course, before the plywood is fixed in position. The two sides of the locker are lined with $\frac{1}{16}$-in. ply, and a 6-in. strip of $\frac{1}{8}$-in. plywood is fitted across the front at the base (see Fig. 9).

The decking former at this point forms also the rear lining of the pilot's cockpit and extends down $8\frac{1}{2}$ in. to the extra $\frac{3}{4}$ in. by $\frac{3}{4}$

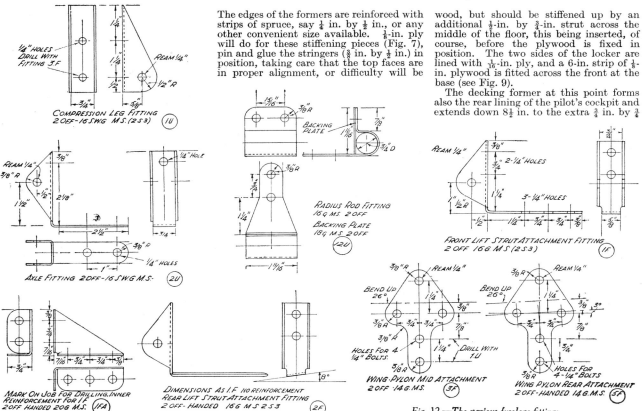

Fig. 12.—*The various fuselage fittings.*

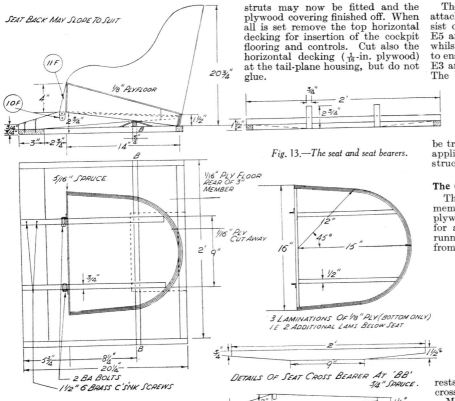

SEAT BACK MAY SLOPE TO SUIT
11F
10F
1/8" PLYFLOOR
4"
20 3/4"
2 3/4"
1 1/2"
3/4"
3/4"
3"
2 3/4"
14"
B

B
5/16" SPRUCE
1/16" PLY FLOOR REAR OF 3" MEMBER
1/16" PLY CUT AWAY
2' 9"
3/4"
B
5 3/4"
8 1/4"
20 1/4"
2 BA BOLTS
1 1/2" 6 BRASS C'SNK SCREWS

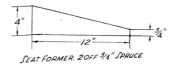

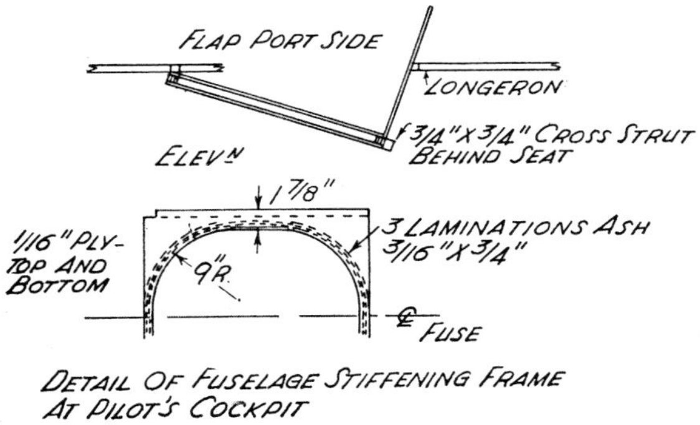

in. strut at the base level of the pilot's entrance flap.

Building up the Nose

First cut the horizontal ply decking to fit on the top longerons. This should be cut to the ordinates given in Fig. 10. The top longerons may now be pulled into shape, fit a strip of plywood, $\frac{3}{4}$ in. wide, along each saw-cut, and glue up the longerons with the ply strips in position (Fig. 11). Tack the top ply decking in position temporarily, but do not glue yet. Cut and fix the engine bulkhead, of $\frac{1}{8}$-in. ply, the bottom longerons being also pulled into position as before. *Note.*—Two plywood insertions will be required for the double cut and one of these will have to be halved to fit on either side of the other. If it is considered too laborious to fit these plywood insertions throughout the length of the saw-cuts, they may be omitted, but at least a short length of plywood, with the thickness tapered or feathered (Fig. 11 (*b*)) should be inserted when gluing up.

The remainder of the side and bottom struts may now be fitted and the plywood covering finished off. When all is set remove the top horizontal decking for insertion of the cockpit flooring and controls. Cut also the horizontal decking ($\frac{1}{16}$-in. plywood) at the tail-plane housing, but do not glue.

3/4"
2'
2 3/4"
1 1/2"

Fig. 13.—The seat and seat bearers.

2"
45°
15"
16"
1/2"
3 LAMINATIONS OF 1/8" PLY (BOTTOM ONLY) I.E. 2 ADDITIONAL LAMS BELOW SEAT
2'
3/4"
9"
1 1/2"
DETAILS OF SEAT CROSS BEARER AT 'BB' 3/4" SPRUCE.
3/4"
2"
1 1/4"
18"
5"
MAIN SEAT BEARER 2 OFF - 3/4" SPRUCE

PRICE LIST OF "MINOR" FUSELAGE COMPONENTS	
Complete set of materials, spruce, plywood, steel tube and sheet.	£8
Extra for making up the two sides	£3
Extra for making up complete fuselage	£24
Fuselage, complete with fittings and controls, and painted to customer's colours . .	£36
Set of fittings, made-up, controls, pulleys, etc. (33 fittings)	£4

The fuselage fittings may next be attached and all bolts locked. These consist of fittings 3F, 1U, 2U, 1F, 12U, E2, E5 and E6. Set the tail plane in position whilst fittings E5 and E6 are being attached, to ensure correct positioning, and fix fittings E3 and E4 at the same time (see Fig. 12). The bolt heads should be on the outside, and in no case should a bolt head, or a nut, come in contact with the timber, a large "penny" washer being inserted between the nut and wood. Where two or more bolts are close together the washers should be trimmed to prevent overlapping. (This applies throughout the whole of the construction.)

The Cockpit

The flooring forward of the 3-in. spruce member to the rudder bar is cut from $\frac{1}{8}$-in. plywood, notches also being cut to allow for all side struts and bolts. Additional runners of $\frac{1}{8}$-in. ply, 7 in. wide, will be glued from the rudder bar support to act as heel

4"
3/4"
12"
SEAT FORMER. 2 OFF 3/4" SPRUCE

FORWARD OF THE 3" MEMBER THE FLOOR IS OF 1/8" PLY- WITH ADDITIONAL 1/8" X 5" PLY RUNNERS UNDER RUDDER BAR PEDALS

rests. They should be screwed also at the cross members.

Make up the seat and seat bearers (Fig. **13**), screw the latter in position and attach the seat by means of the hinge fittings 10F and 11F (Fig. 15). The flooring round the seat may then be finished with $\frac{1}{16}$-in. ply, this being cut away at the middle where not required.

Cockpit Former

The purpose of this circular former is to strengthen the fuselage against torsion where it has been weakened by the presence of the cockpit opening. It acts also as an arm rest.

Obtain three strips of spruce, or preferably ash, $\frac{3}{16}$ in. by $\frac{3}{4}$ in., place together and bend into a hoop so that it just fits into the cockpit opening, the rear of the hoop bear- against the $\frac{3}{4}$ in. by $\frac{3}{4}$ in. central cross member behind the seat (already referred to), and the front coming just below the cross member between the top longerons forward of the cockpit (Fig. 14). Cut pieces of $\frac{1}{16}$-in. plywood to fit above and below the former. At the rear the lower ply will glue under the cross strut and at the front the top ply will glue also to the cross strut there. Remove the door by cutting through the ply with a sharp blade or chisel and clean up the ply edges.

FLAP PORT SIDE
LONGERON
3/4" X 3/4" CROSS STRUT BEHIND SEAT
ELEVN
1 7/8"
1/16" PLY- TOP AND BOTTOM
9"R
3 LAMINATIONS ASH 3/16" X 3/4"
℄ FUSE
DETAIL OF FUSELAGE STIFFENING FRAME AT PILOT'S COCKPIT

Fig. 14.—Fuselage stiffening frame at pilot's cockpit.

3/4"
3/16" HOLES
SEAT FITTING 2 OFF 18 G M S HANDED
11F
4"
BEND 90°
3/8" R
3/4"
3/4"
3/8" R
3/16" HOLES
3/4"
3/4"
3/4"
90° BEND LINES
SEAT BEARER FITTING 2 OFF 18 G M S
10F

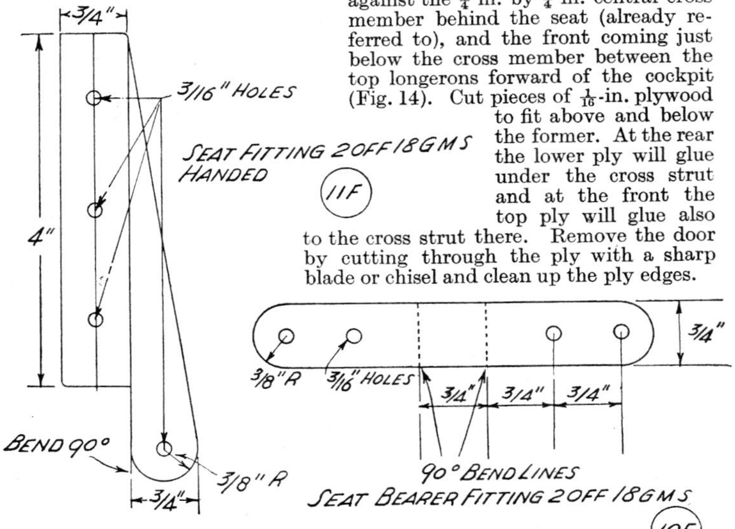

Fig. 15.—The hinge fittings for the cockpit.

BUILDING THE "LUTON MINOR" LIGHT AEROPLANE

PART V

Assembling the Undercarriage

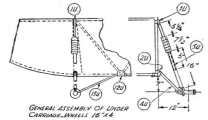

Fig. 1.—The undercarriage is of the split-axle type.

At the other ends of these 1-in. tubes cut slots $\frac{3}{8}$ in. wide × 1 in. deep, and weld the 16 s.w.g. inserts in position. Drill right through for $\frac{1}{4}$-in. bolts, $\frac{3}{8}$ in. from the end.

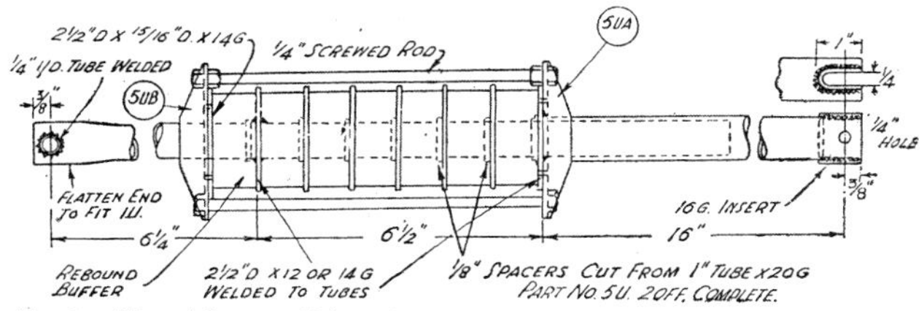

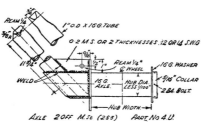

Fig. 2.—Thread fittings 5UA on the tubes and fix to the discs by means of two rivets.

THE "Minor" undercarriage is of the split-axle type with external compression legs for absorbing the landing shocks (see Fig. 1). The following materials are required :

- 1 M.S. tube, 36 in. × $\frac{15}{16}$ in. o/d. × 18 s.w.g. } Compression legs.
- 1 M.S. tube, 38 in. × 1 in. o/d. × 20 s.w.g.
- 1 axle tube, 14 in. × wheel hub diam. — $\frac{1}{100}$ in. × 16 s.w.g.
- 1 M.S. tube, 30 in. × 1 in. × 16 s.w.g. Axle extensions.
- 1 M.S. tube, 48 in. × $\frac{3}{4}$ in. × 17 s.w.g. Radius rods.
- 1 sq. ft. M.S. plate × 16 s.w.g. } Fittings.
- $\frac{1}{2}$ sq. ft. M.S. plate × 14 or 12 s.w.g.
- 10 aluminium separator plates, $2\frac{1}{2}$ in. diam. × 18 or 20 s.w.g.
- 36 in. — $\frac{1}{4}$ in. M.S. rod, plain or screwed.
- 14 aero rubber compression rings, $2\frac{1}{4}$ in. × 1 in. × 1 in.
- 2 wheels and tyres, 16 in. × 14 in.

Note.—All steel tubing to be 28-ton weldable (D.T.O.41), and steel sheet 28-ton steel (Z.S.3).

First make up four channel fittings, 5U/1 (Fig. 3), and six M.S. discs of 12 or 14 s.w.g. and $2\frac{1}{2}$ in. outside diam. Four of the discs will have $\frac{7}{8}$-in. holes bored centrally, and the other two have 1-in. holes. The latter are welded $\frac{1}{8}$ in. from the end of the two tubes, 1 in. diam. × 20 s.w.g. × $16\frac{1}{2}$ in. long. Now thread fittings 5UA on the tubes and fix to the discs by means of 2 rivets, countersunk in the disc face (Fig. 2).

Next weld one disc on each of two $\frac{7}{8}$-in. diam. tubes (20 s.w.g. × 18 in. long), the outer face of the disc being $6\frac{1}{2}$ in. from the tube end.

Cut 10 (5 for each leg) 18 or 20 s.w.g. aluminium separator plates, $2\frac{1}{2}$-in. outer diam. and $\frac{7}{8}$ in. inside, and also 12 $\frac{1}{8}$-in. spacers from the 1-in. diam. tube.

We are now ready to assemble the legs. Thread six rubber compression blocks on to the longer length of the $\frac{7}{8}$-in. tube, one of the small spacers being inserted in each compression block and one aluminium

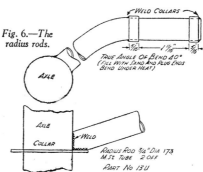

Fig. 5.—Details of the axles.

spacer between each two rubbers. Slide the smaller tube into the larger tube, as shown in Fig. 2. Thread a rubber block and spacer on to the small end of the inner tube and follow with an M.S. disc, riveted to 5UB.

Connect up by inserting two $\frac{1}{4}$-in. rods

through 5UA and 5UB. These rods may be either screwed rod, or plain rod with the ends threaded for $\frac{1}{4}$-in. B.S.F. nuts. The two inner nuts should be screwed well on at first and the whole is tightened up by means of the outer nuts. Lock up by holding each outer nut and screwing the inner nut out against the former.

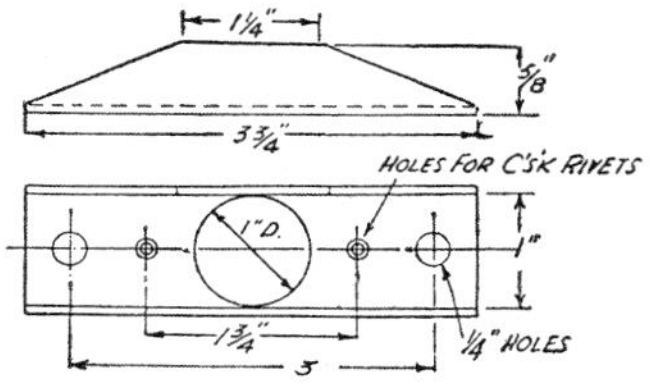

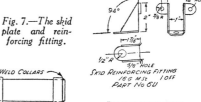

Fig. 3.—The channel fitting, four of which are required.

Now, and not before, the end of the smaller inner tube may be slightly flattened to $\frac{3}{4}$ in. and fitted with a $\frac{1}{4}$-in. inside diam. tube, welded in position.

A smart finish may be obtained by means of a plywood fairing (Fig. 4). This consists of two spruce formers, the top one of which is recessed to fit over fitting 5UB, and is held in position by means of screws through from the steel disc. The other former is threaded on to the 1-in. tube, on which it is an easy sliding fit, just below 5UA. The plywood covering, 1 mm. thick, may be glued to the lower former, but screwed to the top former for ease of removal.

We now come to the axles, 4U (Fig. 5). The length of each axle, at the centre line, is about 7 in., but will depend to some extent

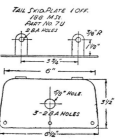

Fig. 7.—The skid plate and reinforcing fitting.

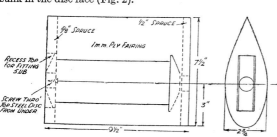

Fig. 4.—The plywood fairing.

Fig. 6.—The radius rods.

on the wheel hub width. One bevel cut is sufficient for both axles. The bevel end of the axle is drilled and filed to receive the 1-in. extension tubes, these being welded in position, top and bottom. Flatten the top ends of the extension arms to $\frac{3}{4}$ in., shape as shown, and drill for $\frac{1}{4}$-in. bolts.

Note that the axle tube should be not less than $\frac{1}{100}$ in. under the wheel hub. diam., and the wheel should be very free to rotate, or a seizure will undoubtedly occur when taking off or landing, with unpleasant results.

Cut a steel disc 2 in. larger than the axle in diam. and weld on the outer face to the axle, taking care to get the disc exactly perpendicular to the latter. Also cut a steel web to insert between the disc and axle extension tube. This may be made from a piece of mild steel, $\frac{1}{4}$ in. thick, or from two pieces of 12 or 14 s.w.g. steel plate. Weld along the three edges and drill a $\frac{1}{4}$-in. hole as shown.

A 16 s.w.g. washer, of diameter $\frac{1}{2}$ in. larger than the wheel hub, is threaded on the axle after the wheel, followed by a $\frac{5}{16}$-in. collar, which is bolted to the axle by a 2 B.A. bolt. When all is complete this bolt should be locked by riveting the head or by some other suitable means.

The axles and compression legs should be pinned temporarily in position, and carefully trued up. The radius rods, 13U (Fig. 6), are bent through 40 degrees, under heat, then cut to length and shaped. $\frac{5}{16}$-in. collars are welded, $1\frac{11}{16}$ in. apart, to match with the attachment fittings, 12U, and the lower end of the radius rod is welded to the axle and collar.

Apart from fitting up, the undercarriage is now complete.

The Tail Skid

Before fitting the tail skid, which is of spring steel and tracking, the skid plate 7U and reinforcing fitting 6U (Fig. 7) should be made. These fittings should be made together to ensure proper matching up. A spruce packing piece, say 3 in. × $\frac{3}{4}$ in., is glued between the bottom fuselage longerons at the stern, and a good job is made by gluing a further piece of $\frac{1}{16}$-in. plywood, 3 in. × 6 in. or so, across the top of the packing block and longerons. Fit 6U and 7U in position and drill the $\frac{5}{8}$-in. holes. A steel tubular sleeve, 1 in. long × $\frac{5}{8}$ in. o/d. × 17 s.w.g. is welded to fitting 7U and passes up through the packing block and into the $\frac{5}{8}$-in. hole in 6U. The sleeve is not fixed to

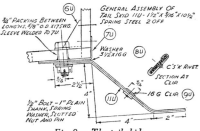

Fig. 8.—The tail skid.

6U, but should be just flush with, or slightly below, the top face. A $\frac{1}{2}$-in. bolt, 2 in. long with 1-in. plain shank, is welded to 6U. Fittings 6U and 7U may now be fixed in position by means of bolts.

The tail skid (Fig. 8) consists of two thicknesses of $\frac{3}{16}$ in. × $1\frac{1}{2}$ in. spring steel, bent to the required shape. This should be done by an experienced blacksmith, who will properly temper the springs after bending. (Luton Aircraft supply skids properly shaped, or will carry out the necessary work on customers' springs.)

The two leaves are held together by means of a small 16 s.w.g. clip, 9U, which is riveted to one leaf only with a countersunk rivet, leaving the other leaf free to slide over the former.

Insert a 16 s.w.g. washer, $3\frac{1}{2}$ in. in diam., between 7U and the skid, the whole being

tor should be placed in position to obtain the correct thickness of this fairing. It should nicely clear the similar fairing at the elevator gap. This fairing greatly stiffens

TAIL SKID MATERIALS

Spring-steel strip, $\frac{3}{16}$ in. × $1\frac{1}{2}$ in. × 21 in.
M.S. plate, 18 s.w.g. × 6 in. × $6\frac{1}{2}$ in.
M.S. plate, 16 s.w.g. × $3\frac{1}{2}$ in. × 10 in.
M.S. bolt, $\frac{1}{2}$ in. × 2 in. × 1 in. shank, with slotted nut.

CONTROL SYSTEM MATERIALS

M.S. tube, $\frac{7}{8}$-in. or 1-in. diam. × 18 or 20 s.w.g. × $5\frac{1}{2}$ ft. for control column, cross-tube, and rudder bar.
M.S. tube, 1 in. or $1\frac{1}{8}$ in. diam. × 17 s.w.g. × 2 in. for 3C.
M.S. tube, $\frac{1}{4}$ in. i/d. × $1\frac{1}{8}$ in. long for 1C.
M.S. tube, $\frac{1}{2}$ in. i/d. × $1\frac{1}{8}$ in. long for 6C.
M.S. plate, 16 s.w.g. × 1 sq. ft.
M.S. plate, 18 s.w.g. × 6 in. × 6 in.
M.S. plate, 12 or 14 s.w.g. × 9 in. × 3 in.
Aluminium pulleys, 2 in. or 3 in., 2 in addition to 6 wing pulleys.
10-cwt. flexible steel cable (aircraft).
10-cwt. turnbuckles, 9.
10-cwt. steel shackles, 18.
Aluminium tubing for fairleads, $\frac{5}{16}$-in. diam., 6 ft. length.

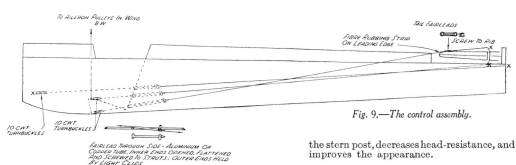

Fig. 9.—The control assembly.

the stern post, decreases head-resistance, and improves the appearance.

The Control System

The control assembly layout is shown in Fig. 9, the control column and rudder bar being shown in more detail in Figs. 10 and 11 respectively. The various items are shown detailed in Fig. 12.

The bend in the control column is done in order to move the hand-grip farther forward from the pilot's seat. The bending should be done with the tube red hot, it having been previously filled with sand and the ends plugged. Bend very carefully and avoid crinkling of the metal. When bolting the elevator levers to the ends of the cross-tube they should not be vertical, i.e. parallel to the control stick, but should slope forward so that the bottom hole in the lever is approximately 1 in. to the rear of the cross-tube centre line.

The aileron actuating cables run from the control column base, over pulleys at 5C and

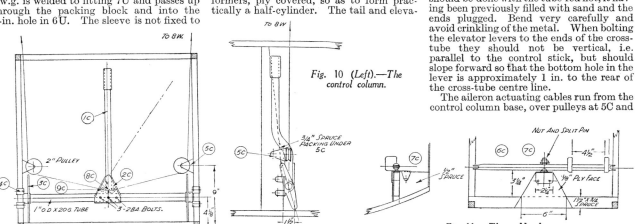

Fig. 10 (Left).—The control column.

Fig. 11.—The rudder bar.

up to pulleys 8W in the wing and thence to the *top* aileron levers via the outer pulleys. The aileron balance cable (already dealt with) connects directly across the bottom aileron levers via the appropriate pulleys ; 10-cwt. turnbuckles are inserted between the cables and both top aileron levers, and one bottom lever.

Turnbuckles attach to both ends of the rudder bar and to both ends of each elevator control lever. The cables pass out from the fuselage just to the rear of the pilot's seat, suitable fairleads being made from $\frac{5}{16}$-in. aluminium tubing and screwed to the two diagonal struts there. Short tubular fairleads may be similarly attached to the top of tail-plane ribs to prevent the elevator cables from rubbing the tail plane, and if necessary small fibre discs may be screwed to the tail leading-edge for the same purpose. The control cables should be threaded through all tubular fairleads before splicing has been done at both ends. Failing this it becomes necessary to cut open the fairleads along their length for insertion of the cable.

The pins holding the aileron cables to the link plates, 9C, should be provided with safety pins for ease of release for dismantling. The same applies at the rudder and elevator cable connections at the rear.

Types of Engine

Almost any type of engine of about 30 B.H.P. is suitable for use in the "Minor," provided the weight is not much greater than 100 lb. If the engine weight, including radiator and water in the case of water-cooled engines, approaches 150 lb. it becomes necessary to instal the wing tank in place of the fuselage fuel tank, and the pilot's seat may have to be moved back through a distance of 3 in. or so.

It is strongly recommended that engines should comply with the following brief specification :
1. Weight not exceeding 125 lb.
2. Maximum power not less than 30 B.H.P.
3. Revolutions at 30 H.P. to be not more than 3,000, unless drive is geared.
4. Dual ignition.
5. Reliability of a high order.
6. Air-cooled for preference.
The selection of the power unit to comply

PARTICULARS OF THE LUTON-ANZANI 35-H.P. ENGINE

The Luton-Anzani is an air-cooled V-twin, having 4 overhead valves with duplex springs per cylinder. A special shock-absorbing mounting is provided.
Capacity, 1,100 cc. Bore, 83 mm. Stroke 101·5 mm.
Lubrication by gravity to mechanical pump.
Weight—100 lb. single ignition.
　　　　105 lb. dual ignition.
Power—35 H.P. maximum at 3,150 r.p.m.
　　　21 H.P. at 2,000 r.p.m. normal cruising.
　　　28 H.P. at 2,600 r.p.m. high-speed cruising.
Price—complete with dual ignition, impulse starter, and airscrew hub　.　.　£65 10 0
single ignition, impulse starter, and airscrew hub　£60 0 0
"Minor" Anzani airscrew　£6 4 0

---

with this simple specification, and available at a reasonable price, is not altogether easy. Messrs. Luton Aircraft have tried out almost every type, and eventually it was decided to take the Anzani V-twin air-cooled engine as a basic power unit, to re-design certain parts that had given trouble, and to equip the improved version with dual ignition and an impulse starter.

The original Anzani engine was fitted to the winning machine in the 1925 International Light Aeroplane Competitions at Lympne, so that it is by no means a new and untried product.

Development of the Luton-Anzani 35-H.P. Engine

One of the main obstacles facing the constructor of an ultra-light aeroplane is the lack of suitable and reliable engines. Perhaps the chief cause of the apparent unreliability of small engines is the prevalent tendency of pilots to keep the engines running at speeds very close to their maxima. This is more than is expected from large aero engines, and certainly the small, relatively cheap engine should not be called upon to undergo such severe treatment.

It is true that light single-seaters can be flown successfully with an engine horse-power of 20, or even less, but the difficulty comes when a rapid climb has to be made in order to avoid some obstacle, and this is an important point that is seldom given sufficient consideration. Bearing in mind the low efficiency of airscrews of small diameter revving at high speed, figures of 20 and 30 H.P. should be regarded as the absolute minima for cruising and top speed conditions, and these should correspond to engine speeds of roughly 2,000 and 3,000 r.p.m., or preferably less.

The 34-H.P. Anzani air-cooled V-twin

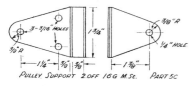

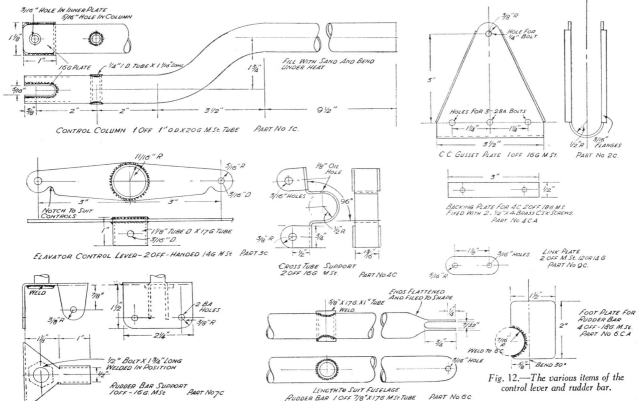

Fig. 12.—*The various items of the control lever and rudder bar.*

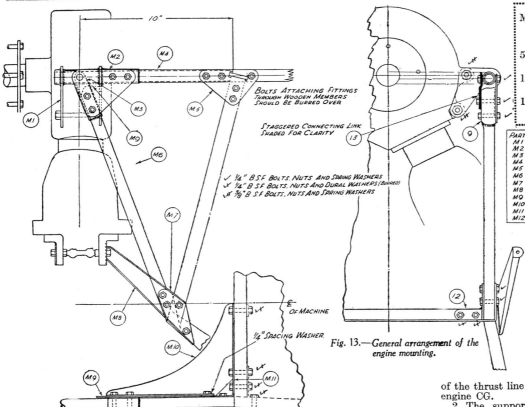

BOLTS ATTACHING FITTINGS
THROUGH WOODEN MEMBERS
SHOULD BE BURRED OVER

STAGGERED CONNECTING LINK
SHADED FOR CLARITY

✓ ¼" B.S.F. BOLTS. NUTS AND SPRING WASHERS
✗ ¼" B.S.F. BOLTS. NUTS AND DURAL WASHERS (BURRED)
✗ ⅜" B.S.F. BOLTS. NUTS AND SPRING WASHERS

¼" SPACING WASHER.

Ɛ OF MACHINE

Fig. 13.—*General arrangement of the engine mounting.*

MATERIALS REQUIRED FOR ENGINE MOUNTING (ANZANI)

5 ft. M.S. tube, ¾ in. o/d. × 17 s.w.g.

1¼ ft. M.S. tube, ⅞ in. o/d. × 17 s.w.g.

1 sq. ft. M.S. sheet, each 12, 14, 18, and 20 s.w.g.

PART No	DESCRIPTION
M1	HOUSING
M2	HOUSING PLATE. OUTER
M3	CONNECTING LINK
M4	TOP BEARER TUBE
M5	" " ATTACHT PLATE
M6	DIAGONAL "
M7	
M8	LOWER BRACING PLATE
M9	HOUSING PLATE INNER
M10	UPPER BRACING PLATE
M11	TOP CORNER FITTING
M12	BOTTOM " "

Engine Mounting

Since the Luton-Anzani engine has now been adopted as standard, the mounting for this engine will be described.

The following points should receive careful consideration in the mounting of any other engine :

1. Support the weight close to the intersection of the thrust line and vertical through the engine CG.

2. The supporting structure must be braced both vertically and horizontally to prevent rotation of the engine relative to the fuselage.

3. Attach the support members to nodes, or joints, in the fuselage structure, attach-

appears to meet with the above requirements and has been extensively used by Luton Aircraft, Ltd., in their " Buzzards," " Minors," and other light aeroplanes during the last few years. Unfortunately, although in many ways the Anzani " met the bill," the reliability of this engine has not been all that might be desired, and Luton Aircraft accordingly set out to overcome the weak points that their accumulated experience had brought to light.

It was decided, therefore, to completely redesign all working parts that had given trouble during the many flying hours with this type of engine, and as a result roughly half the working parts have been either completely changed or modified. After assembly the new engine was subjected to a systematic series of tests, lasting over several running hours, which culminated with 30-minute periods of continuous running under load at progressively increasing speeds, viz. 2,000, 2,250, 2,500, and 2,650 r.p.m.

The engine was examined after each test, and whereas previously certain adjustments, notably of the valve tappet clearances, had to be made after almost every flight, no modification has been found necessary throughout the whole of the tests, beyond slight adjustment after the initial settling down.

Although reliability was the chief quality sought, the running has been improved in other respects, and the smoothness is very noticeable. There is a slight increase in maximum power, whilst the slow-speed running is now particularly good, the engine ticking over at 100 r.p.m.

The Luton Anzani is now available with either single or dual ignition with impulse starter, and in the latter form a remarkably good unit has been made available at a **very**

moderate price. Existing Anzani engines can be modified to conform with the new specification.

PRICES OF MATERIALS AND PARTS

	£	s.	d.
Undercarriage materials (metallic) as specified .	1	0	0
Aero rubber compression rings, 14 . . .	1	0	0
2 wheels, tyres, and tubes, 4 in. × 16 in. . .	4	0	0
Complete set undercarriage materials, as above .	6	0	0
Pair axles, made up, complete . . .	2	10	0
Pair compression legs, made up, complete with rubbers	3	10	0
Pair radius rods, made up, ready to attach . .	1	0	0
Complete undercarriage, with wheels . .	11	0	0
Add for fairings . .		10	0
Tail skid spring steel. .		2	0
All tail skid materials, as detailed . . .		4	6
Tail skid made up, with clip		9	6
Fittings 6U and 7U made up		7	6
Control System, steel tube and sheet . . .		9	0
Pulleys, 8 at 1s. each . .		8	0
170 ft. 10-cwt. cable . .	1	10	0

	£	s.	d.
9 turnbuckles, 10-cwt. at 8d. each . . .		6	0
18 steel shackles, 10-cwt. . .		3	0
6 ft. aluminium tubing, ⁵⁄₁₆-in. diam. . . .		3	0
Complete set control system materials and pulleys .	2	15	0
Control column, cross-tube, and gusset plate, made up		18	0
Rudder bar and footplates, made up . . .		14	0
2 elevator levers . . .		8	0
Fittings 4C (2), 4CA (2), 7C, 9C (2), and 5C (2) .		18	0
Control system, complete, comprising last 4 items, 170 ft. cable, 9 turnbuckles, 18 shackles, 8 pulleys, and 6 ft. aluminium tubing . . .	5	5	0
Engine Mounting Materials, comprising M.S. tube, 5 ft. × ¾ in. × 17 g., and 1¼ ft. × ⅞ in. × 17 g., together with 1 sq. ft., each of 12, 14, 18, and 20 g. M.S. plate . . .		15	0
Complete set of fittings, tubes, etc. (24), made up .	3	7	6

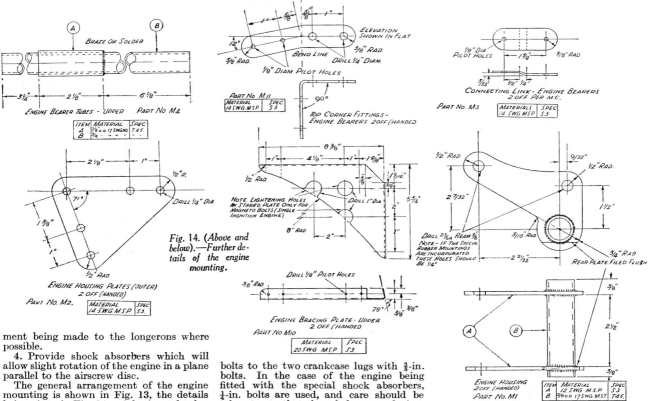

Fig. 14. (*Above and below*).—*Further details of the engine mounting.*

ment being made to the longerons where possible.

4. Provide shock absorbers which will allow slight rotation of the engine in a plane parallel to the airscrew disc.

The general arrangement of the engine mounting is shown in Fig. 13, the details being given in Fig. 14. A horizontal tube, M4, is fixed parallel with the top longeron, on to which sleeves a cradle, M1, which

bolts to the two crankcase lugs with ⅜-in. bolts. In the case of the engine being fitted with the special shock absorbers, ¼-in. bolts are used, and care should be taken to see that these bolts are only just tight. Fixing is then done by means of slotted nuts and split pins.

The engine weight is supported by side tubes, M6. The support tubes are held to

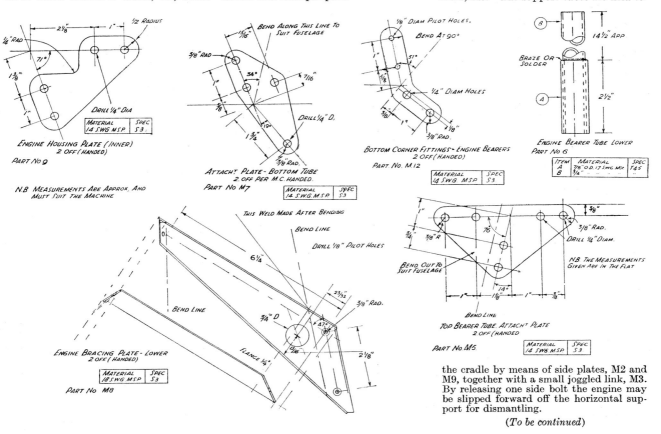

the cradle by means of side plates, M2 and M9, together with a small joggled link, M3. By releasing one side bolt the engine may be slipped forward off the horizontal support for dismantling.

(*To be continued*)

BUILDING THE "LUTON MINOR" LIGHT AEROPLANE

PART VI. Final Assembly

THE top bay is braced by plates, M10, whilst additional supports, M8, attach to the cylinder heads at the socket supports.

Engine controls of the motor-cycle handle-bar type are not recommended, and push-pull cables, consisting of a single high-tensile wire encased in a flexible steel casing, should be substituted. The air control in the carburettor, if fitted, should be removed, leaving only the one carburettor control and one magneto control.

The ignition should be coupled to the throttle so that the ignition is fully retarded when the throttle is closed and so that opening of the latter automatically advances the spark. Full ignition advance should be arranged for when the throttle is about one-quarter or one-third open.

The following note applies to the fuselage construction dealt with in the (January) issue of PRACTICAL MECHANICS:

Owing to possible slight variation in the fuselage plan shape, the dimensions of the decking supports, included in Fig. 1, should not be rigidly adhered to. The shape of frames 1A and 5 may first be made from the given dimensions, checking the widths with the actual fuselage, after which the intermediates may be made to suit. In each case the radius R should be equal to the height of the decking above the top longeron at the position considered.

The front fuselage bulkhead, to which the engine mounting is attached, should be made fireproof by means of a sheet of tinned steel. This should preferably be fixed before the top engine bracing fittings are set in position.

Engine Controls

It has already been mentioned that the carburetter air control, if fitted, should be removed, and that the ignition and throttle controls should be interconnected.

Fig. 1 shows the throttle arrangement and details for use with the Anzani engine, though they will probably be suitable with a little modification for other types of engine. Separate levers are employed for throttle and magneto, but the latter is arranged to be fully advanced when the former is roughly one-third open. The throttle lever then continues on alone. When the throttle is closed, a small projecting lug on the lever retards the ignition automatically.

Transmission is by means of solid high-tension steel wire within a flexible casing. The wire is held fast to the fork-end (15C) by means of a set screw, whilst the casing is similarly fixed to the support fitting (13C and 14C).

Adjustment may be made by careful positioning of the casing. First make sure that the throttle is fully open in the "open" position of the lever, and closed when the lever is fully back. Then note that the ignition is fully retarded when the throttle is closed, and fully opened when the throttle is approximately one-third open. The proper adjustment of the controls is essential for economical and correct running of the engine.

Petrol and Oil Tanks

The capacity of the petrol tank considered sufficient for all normal purposes is six gallons. This gives a supply of at least three hours for most light engines, and provided the engine is throttled back reasonably for cruising, the supply should be sufficient for a flight of almost four hours.

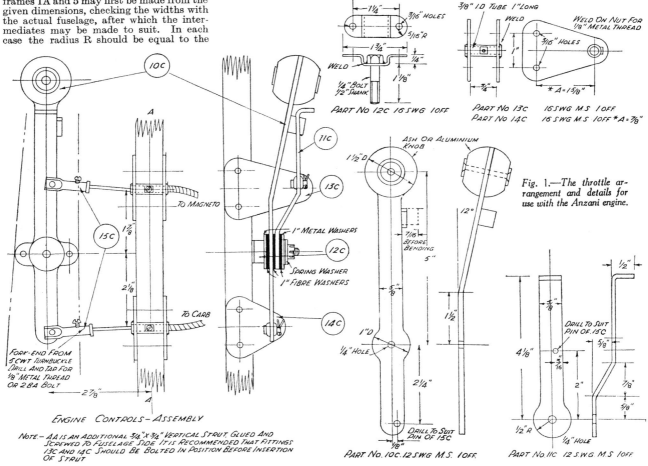

Fig. 1.—The throttle arrangement and details for use with the Anzani engine.

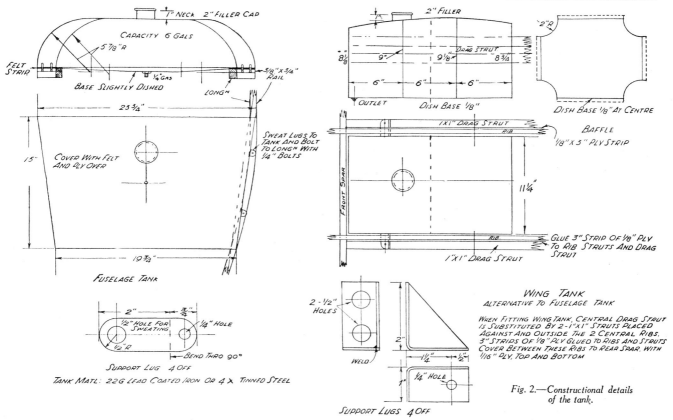

Fig. 2.—Constructional details
of the tank.

Normally the petrol tank is fitted in the fuselage, in the top decking forward of the cockpit. The tank is shown in Fig. 2, and rests on two spruce runners, ⅜ in. by ¾ in. The tank is placed with its front face just clear of the centre section drag strut, and in this position leaves just sufficient space for the instrument panel and instruments. The actual fitting of the tank might be left until almost the last, as the wing pylons may have to be adjusted slightly to give the correct wing position.

The tank is held in place by 4 lugs, which bolt to the longerons, but the fixing of these lugs to the tank should be left until later.

If, for reasons of balance, due to the fitting of a heavy power unit or other causes, it becomes necessary to install a wing tank, this should be made and fitted as shown in the alternative design. In this case the central wing drag strut is substituted by two drag struts, 1 in. × 1 in. each, situated just outboard of the two central ribs. Between the ribs and drag struts strips of ⅛-in. ply, 3 in. deep, are inserted and glued to ribs and struts. These considerably strengthen the structure. Four support lugs are sweated to the tank and bolt to the drag struts, on which the tank rests. Parts of the adjacent ribs will have to be cut away for this purpose.

Insert felt, or rubber, packing between the support lugs and the members to which they affix. The space between the ribs, and between the spars, is covered top and bottom with 1/16-in. plywood, the top covering not being fitted until the tank is in position. A piece of fabric should be cut to fit round the filler neck and on to the top plywood covering. This is doped in position to prevent spilt petrol from gaining entrance to the wing.

The tanks may be made of 22 s.w.g.

lead-coated iron, or good quality tinned steel (4X). The former is rather more expensive and is heavier, but it is non-corrodable.

The oil tank may be placed ahead of the petrol tank, but to one side of the centre section drag strut. It should be about 6 in. high, 6 in. wide and 5 in. deep, but the exact shape must be dictated by the space available. It is fitted with filler, and outlet at the bottom of the front face. If the engine fitted has an oil return system (the Anzani has not) a return pipe connection will be required near the tank top.

Pipe Connections

The pipes connecting the petrol and oil tanks with the engine should not be of copper piping without some form of flexible insertions, or failure due to vibration is certain to be experienced. They may be of any good brand of flexible tubing, although very good petrol- and oil-resisting rubber tubing is now available and a short length of this, say 4 in., inserted in each length of copper piping, and held in position by "Jubilee" clips is recommended as being eminently suitable for the purpose.

No long length of piping should be left unsupported, but should be held by means of a clip to any convenient point.

Balancing for Flight

The proper balancing of an aeroplane for flight is most important. It is necessary both for satisfactory flight and particularly for considerations of stability. In slow speed flight the centre of lift on the wings is in its most forward position, approximately at 0.3 chord from the leading-edge or about 18 to 19 in. in the case of the "Minor." The centre of gravity (C.G.) of

the complete aircraft, loaded, that is the point through which the weight acts, should be vertically below the centre of lift, or slightly in front. The limiting positions may be taken as 4½ in. in front and 1½ in. behind, greater diversion than this resulting in an unsafe machine.

When the fuselage is in rigging position, with the top longerons horizontal, the base of the landing wheels should be roughly 12 in. in front of the C.G.

Normally, the "Minor" is balanced for flight with an engine weighing about 110 lb. and a 6 gal. fuselage fuel tank. If a heavier engine is installed, balance may be obtained by fitting the wing tank, or by moving the pilot back about 3 in., or both. Alternatively an engine may be used of the correct weight, but having the carburetters situated too high to allow a sufficient head of petrol for gravity feed, when the aircraft is in the climbing attitude with the fuel tank about empty. In such a case the wing tank must be used and balance may be obtained by shifting the engine about 7 in. forward.

When making the C.G. check, someone should sit in the pilot's seat, or a weight of about 150 lb. should be placed 12 in. from the seat back. A weight of 24 lb., representing half the petrol weight, should be rested on the tank and a weight of about 5 lb. placed above the oil tank. The tail unit should be in position, as also should be the wheels, engine cowling, etc., but not the main plane.

The fuselage should be rested on a large plank of timber, which in turn rests on a steel tube, or other available circular rod. A few nails driven into the underside of the plank will retain the tube in position. The tube is then placed on top of any large rectangular block which is of sufficient height to raise the wheels just clear of the

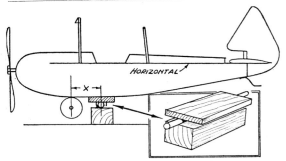

Fig. 3.—Method of checking for centre of gravity.

ground. This is shown diagrammatically in Fig. 3.

The position of the rocking tube should be adjusted so that the fuselage just balances, care being taken to see that the tube is equidistant from the axles on both sides.

The distance, x of Fig. 3, should be about 11 in. without the wing being in position, and certainly not more than, say, 2 in. either way.

The wing may next be supported above the fuselage by means of two trestles to which extensions have been clamped, Fig. 4. The wing should be so placed that the undersurface at the front spar is 2 ft. above the fuselage top longeron, and the wing incidence (obtained by setting the extension rails on the trestles) should be 3 degrees.

Set the leading-edge of the wing 18 in. in front of the C.G. as ascertained. (Note.—The wing weight will cause the C.G. of the complete aircraft to move 1 in. to the rear and so coincide with the wing C.P.)

Check the fuselage setting by means of a spirit level placed longitudinally and laterally. Check the wing incidence at both trestle supports. Check the lateral setting of the wings with a spirit level and check that the wing is at right angles to the fuselage axis by measuring with thread from, say, each wing-tip at the front spar to the centre line of the stern part. A plumb-bob dropped from the wing centre should

be vertically over the plan centre line drawn along the fuselage top.

Keeping the wing in this position relative to the fuselage, the front pylon struts, and the fitting, 6F (Fig. 5), may be fitted, together with the drag strut, the rear pylon and the rear fitting, 7F.

Holes may be cut in the top of the decking for the pylon struts to pass through and some cutting away will be necessary at the strut attachment.

The front end of the centre

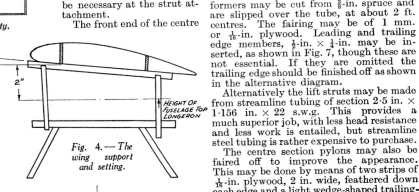

Fig. 4. — The wing support and setting.

drag strut attaches to the fittings 4F and 4FA, which should have been bolted in position before finishing off the top decking.

There now remains only the fitting of the main lift struts and bracing.

Fig. 6.—The main lift struts.

Main Lift Struts and Bracing

The struts are made of 1⅜-in. × 22 s.w.g. M.S. tubing. The end fittings, 13W, are shown in Fig. 6. The length of the struts is approximately 6 ft. 2 in. Bolt one end fitting in position, offer the strut up and cut to the required length. Slip the other end fitting in the tube, pin temporarily to the fuselage and wing fittings, and drill for the 2 B.A. bolts, taking care that the wing setting remains unaltered throughout.

The performance and appearance are improved by the fitting of plywood fairings to the main struts. Streamline shaped formers may be cut from ⅜-in. spruce and are slipped over the tube, at about 2 ft. centres. The fairing may be of 1 mm. or 1/16-in. plywood. Leading and trailing edge members, ½-in. × ¼-in. may be inserted, as shown in Fig. 7, though these are not essential. If they are omitted the trailing edge should be finished off as shown in the alternative diagram.

Alternatively the lift struts may be made from streamline tubing of section 2·5 in. × 1·156 in. × 22 s.w.g. This provides a much superior job, with less head resistance and less work is entailed, but streamline steel tubing is rather expensive to purchase.

The centre section pylons may also be faired off to improve the appearance. This may be done by means of two strips of 1/16-in. plywood, 2 in. wide, feathered down each edge and a light wedge-shaped trailing-edge member of spruce. The whole is

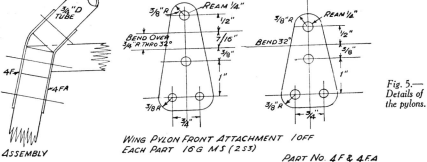

Fig. 5.—Details of the pylons.

bound tightly with strip fabric or tape and doped. (Fig. 8.)

After fixing the four main lift struts in position, and checking again for rigging, the drag and anti-drag cables should be inserted. They run from the base of one strut to the outer end of the other and vice versa.

Fittings, 12W, (Fig. 6), bolt to the inner pairs of bolts in 13W, and care should be taken to ensure correct matching up. Ten cwt. cable is used for the bracing, and 10 cwt. turnbuckles are inserted for adjustment.

Cockpit Flap Fastener

Details of this are given in Fig. 9. It consists of two steel plate arms, flanged at the lower edge for stiffness. They are

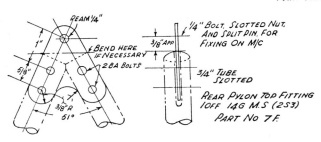

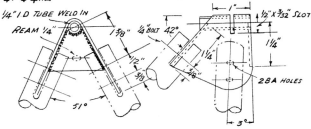

joined at the centre by a ¼-in. bolt, brazed to one arm, and an ash, or other suitable knob attaches here. The arms pivot about bolts 4 in. to either side so that when the knob is raised the outer ends come free from bolts attached to the longeron. Some sliding motion of the arms is permitted by an ¼-in. elongation of the pivoting hole. A small piece of M.S. plate may be let into the plywood on the fuselage side where the bolt head at the knob position rubs, and may be held in position by two small screws.

Fabric Covering

The usual method of wing covering is to make a "bag" which fits reasonably tight on the wing. This is then stretched over the wing, and sewn to all ribs, top and bottom, the stitching passing through the depth of the wing.

For light aircraft such elaborate work is not essential, though it may be mentioned that if the aeroplane is required for tropical regions it is recommended that the whole wing, tail unit, and even fuselage, should be entirely fabric covered to withstand the extreme heat.

A light, strong material, such as airship fabric, is better than the ordinary aeroplane fabric for light work, but it may be noted that many fabrics do not react favourably to dope and do not therefore give a satisfactory finish.

The fabric is cut into strips running from leading-edge to trailing-edge, the strip being sewn together along their edges with an ordinary (double) seam. It may be attached to the wing by dope, the substance used being applied to all wood surfaces that will come in contact with the fabric (ribs, leading and trailing-edges, etc.).

The fixing should be done in sections, for if too large an area is dealt with at once the adhesive will be dry before the fabric is properly positioned.

If the whole wing is to be covered, attach the fabric to the trailing-edge, pass it over the undersurface, round the leading-edge and back to the rear, finishing it off on the underside of the trailing edge. It is not necessary, however, to cover the forward ply-covered nose, and in this case the fabric may be attached first just above the front spar, passed round the trailing-edge and finished off below the front spar, the surplus material at the edge being trimmed off with scissors or a safety-razor blade after fixing.

The general tendency when fixing fabric is to concentrate the tightening in the fore and aft direction, but this in fact helps to produce sagging between ribs, giving that "lean" appearance. A better job is obtained when the fabric is pulled more in the spanwise direction.

A good finish is obtained by doping strips of fabric, or preferably, frayed tape, or again 2-in. notched tape, along all edges of the fabric. The same procedure is employed for covering the tail unit.

An important point to bear in mind before covering wings, etc., is the secure locking-up of all bolts within the structure. See also that the cables are properly in position and working smoothly over their pulleys.

Strips of fabric should be doped on to close the gaps between the wing and ailerons, and between the tail plane and

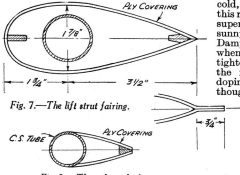

Fig. 7.—The lift strut fairing.

Fig. 8.—The pylon tube fairing.

elevator. These strips should be attached to the top surface of the wing, passing down through the gap and doped again on to the undersurfaces of the aileron, thus effectively closing the gap without upsetting the working of the control surface. Holes are cut in the fabric at the hinge positions (see Fig. 10).

Doping

There are two suitable doping schemes for light aircraft. The first, and most

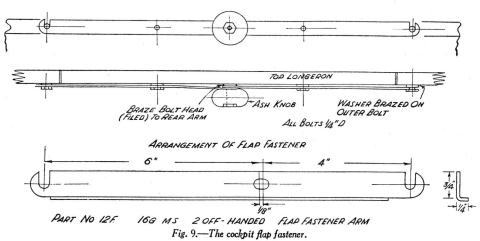

Fig. 9.—The cockpit flap fastener.

orthodox, is to apply at least two coats of red oxide tightening dope, followed by two coats of aluminium finishing dope. The second and probably better scheme for this type of work, is to apply four coats of tightening dope containing aluminium. Coloured finishing dopes may be used if desired, but they are roughly half as expensive again and do not allow of opening up and repairs so readily as the aluminium dope. It is recommended that colour should be confined to the fuselage, struts, and the ply-covered wing nose.

Most amateurs will have to apply the dope by hand, but a good finish can be obtained by following the simple rules as given, and even when a spray plant is available the first coat must be applied by hand to ensure its being brushed well into the interstices of the fabric.

The enemies of dope are dampness and

Fig. 10.—A strip of fabric connecting the top surface of the wing and the undersurface of the aileron.

cold, but more especially the former. For this reason the middle of the day is generally superior for doping operations, and a warm, sunny day should be chosen for preference. Damp and cold tend to chill the dope, when the appearance becomes milky. The tightening qualities are impaired, as also is the finished appearance. The minimum doping temperature recommended is 60° F., though preferably 70° F., and obviously humid weather should be avoided.

Well stir the dope several times during the period of application. Pour out small quantities for use, keeping the drum or main container closed. A 2-in. flat, stiff bristle brush is suitable, and should be cleaned in "thinners" immediately after use. If the brush should become solid, it can generally be made fit for use again by soaking in thinners.

Apply the dope liberally in patches of, say, 2 ft. by 2 ft., brushing first laterally and smoothing over in the fore and aft direction, working from one wing-tip towards the other. A period of 30 minutes or more should be allowed between coats. The fabric will no doubt go very "soggy" after the first coat, but there is no need for alarm, provided the fabric was reasonably tight to begin with, and all will be well at the finish.

If spraying is resorted to, it will probably be necessary to obtain suitable thinners for mixing with each dope used, or difficulty may be experienced in getting the spray gun to function correctly.

Painting

Before preparing for painting, go carefully over all bolts and make sure that they are properly and securely locked.

The fuselage, and the wing ply nosing if not covered with fabric and doped, should be painted both for protection and for appearance. Before commencing, the plywood should be well rubbed down with glasspaper, medium and fine, particularly at the scarfed joints. Any holes or indentations may be filled with stoppers, the surface being rubbed smooth when dry.

Best results are obtained if the plywood is first given a coat of primer, followed by at least two of undercoat and finally one or two coats of finishing paint, though the primer may be deleted if required for economy. Rub down after each coat with "wet and dry." Use plenty of clean, cold water, as this prevents the paper from becoming clogged and ineffective.

A good quality synthetic paint, suitable

MATERIALS REQUIRED FOR WING SUPPORT

12 ft. M.S. tubing, ¾-in. o/d. × 17 s.w.g.

25 ft. M.S. tubing, 1⅜-in. o/d. × 22 s.w.g.

or

25 ft. streamline tubing, 2·5 in. × 1·156 in. × 22 s.w.g.

30 ft. steel cable, 10 cwt.

4 turnbuckles, 10 cwt.

M.S. sheet, 16 s.w.g. 1 sq. ft.

PRICES OF WING SUPPORTS, ETC.

	£	s.	d.
Front and rear pylons, with fittings	1	0	0
M.S. tubing for pylons, 12 ft.		12	0
M.S. tubing for lift struts, 25 ft.	1	7	6
Streamline tubing for lift struts, 25 ft.	2	15	0
Strut end fittings, 8	1	16	0
Drag cable fittings, 8		12	0
Drag cable, 10 cwt. 30 ft.		6	0
Turnbuckle for drag cable, 4		2	8
Lift struts, fittings, drag cables, etc., made up	5	5	0
or with streamline tubing	6	10	0
Engine controls, complete with 13C and 14C		18	6
Petrol tank, fuselage or wing	2	5	0
Oil tank	1	5	0

for outdoor use, is recommended, there being a proper undercoat for use with each particular finishing paint.

Where the paintwork adjoins a doped surface, or another colour paint, the edge should be outlined with masking paper which may be cleaned off afterwards.

The inside of the cockpit should be painted also. The undercoating may be used here as it will give a matt finish. If possible the seat should be upholstered before painting.

Flight Adjustment

If every care has been taken to ensure proper setting of the wings relative to the C.G. the aircraft should be capable of steady horizontal flight with no force necessary on the control column. If, however, it is found that it is necessary to exert a continuous push or pull on the stick, then it is advisable to change slightly the setting of the tail plane, by respectively increasing or decreasing the incidence. To do this it will be necessary to make up a fresh pair of front tail fittings with the bolt holes raised or lowered by, say, ¼-in.

If this is insufficient to rectify the balance in flight, the fault is most probably to be found in the incorrect adjustment of the C.G. and this should be carefully re-checked.

In concluding this series of articles on the construction of the "Luton Minor" Messrs. Luton Aircraft Ltd. wish to point out the need for the employment of materials of the correct quality—inferior material will lead to accidents—and to the importance of careful workmanship. For a small fee, plus travelling expenses, Luton Aircraft will send an inspector to examine the work in progress and the importance is particularly stressed of having the airframe examined by a competent inspector before covering.

Those constructors who would like to be kept advised of developments in connection with this design, and to receive details of modifications, etc., are asked to send their names and addresses, together with a remittance of five shillings, to Luton Aircraft Ltd., Phœnix Works, Gerrards Cross, Bucks. For their own benefit *all* private constructors are asked to forward their names to Luton Aircraft and they will then receive notification of any structural or aerodynamic modification that may appear desirable from the point of view of safety. It is hoped that a "Minor" club

MATERIALS REQUIRED FOR COVERING, DOPING AND PAINTING

Airship fabric, 40 in. wide, 30 yards.

Frayed tape, or notched strip, 100 yds.

Aluminium tightening dope, 4 or 5 gals. or Red Oxide tightening dope, 2 gals. and Aluminium, or Coloured, finishing dope, 1 gal.

Primer for painting, 1 gal.

Synthetic paint, undercoat, 2 gals.

Synthetic paint, finishing, 1 gal.

	£	s.	d.
30 yds. airship fabric, 40 in.	2	0	0
100 yds. frayed tape,		7	6
or 100 yds. notched strip, 2 in.		12	6
5 gal. drum Aluminium tightening dope	3	19	6
4 single gal. tins Aluminium tightening dope	3	12	0
2 gal. Red Oxide tightening dope	1	12	0
1 gal. Aluminium finishing dope		17	0
Coloured finishing dopes, per gal.	1	0	0
Primer, for painting, per gal.			
Synthetic paint, undercoat per gal.	1	5	6
Synthetic paint, finishing, per gal.	1	6	6

will be formed shortly for the mutual assistance of all "Minor" builders and pilots.

Manufacturing Rights

Messrs. Luton Aircraft Ltd. have granted to each reader of PRACTICAL MECHANICS the right to construct one aeroplane of the Luton "Minor" type for his own use. All design and manufacturing rights are, however, retained by Luton Aircraft Ltd., and must not be infringed.

HOW TO BUILD THE 'FLYING FLEA'

NEWNES

PRACTICAL MECHANICS

OCTOBER

6D

Big Birthday Number!

BUILDING YOUR OWN AEROPLANE - THE "LUTON MINO

NEWNES

PRACTICAL MECHANICS

OCTOBER

6D

Building the Luton Minor

PRACTICAL MECHANICS

1'3

SEPT. 1959

G-AHE

CONTENTS

The Luton Minor Light Aeroplane

Mr. J. E. Corine, a "Practical Mechanics" Reader, Built the Luton Minor Light Plane in 5 Months From Our Articles, and Then Taught Himself to Fly After Four Hours' Dual Instruction

The finished Luton Minor built by Mr. J. E. Corine from our articles.

HAVING obtained the complete set of drawings and the description which appeared in this journal, I studied them very carefully. I realised the soundness of the design and the simplicity of construction, and accordingly ordered the complete set of materials from the makers. My only tools were a few wood chisels, hand brace, a few files, one small plane, a spirit level, a cold chisel, several cramps, and two saws, all of which can be obtained very cheaply.

Building the Minor

The fuselage was tackled first and completed without any trouble, very careful attention, of course, having been paid to detail so that when finished the nose of the fuselage was correctly aligned with the tail. Useful information and suggestions appeared in the articles in "Practical Mechanics" dealing with this component, as also were all other parts completely described in detail. If there was doubt at any point, I merely had to write to the makers explaining my difficulty to receive their practical advice by return of post. This service I found of very considerable help.

The tail unit, consisting of rudder, tail plane, and elevator, was dealt with next, again without any trouble, and then followed the main wing. All ribs were, of course, made in a jig. Being limited for space, I took the makers' advice and constructed the wing in two parts. This later improvement greatly simplifies construction without any sacrifice of strength and also solves the housing difficulty, as it takes only about fifteen minutes to dismantle and assemble for flight, there being no tiresome cables, etc., to be adjusted, with the exception of the aileron control. I strongly recommend this modification to all intending constructors.

All metal parts were first made in scrap tin, carefully marked and drilled on the job (if possible) to eliminate the possibility of holes being out of centre, or line, especially so in the longerons and diagonals. Petrol and oil tanks are of simple construction. The welding of the undercarriage is best carried out on the job and should be done by an experienced worker. Strict attention should be paid to avoidance of over-tensioning of the piano-wire bracing in the main wing.

Assembling and setting the wing, tail plane, elevator, and rudder (before covering) is a simple matter, the control cables being inserted during this period. The whole machine was built completely from the set of materials in the spare time of five months, and has since been inspected and pronounced airworthy by the airport chief ground engineer.

Successful Flight Trials

It was, indeed, a great day, as with mixed feelings of excitement and expectation, the machine was transported to the local airport. My friend, Mr. F. Dodd, who is an experienced pilot, promised to test the Minor for me. Everything was assembled in a very short time, a final examination was made, "Contact" shouted, and the engine (Luton Anzani, with impulse starter and dual ignition) fired the first time. After running-up for several minutes, a few short hops were carried out by Mr. Dodd, who then made a slight adjustment to the tail plane. The triumph was complete when we saw him circle the airport several times and make a perfect landing, reporting that everything worked splendidly. He has since completed over six hours' actual flying, subjecting the machine to very severe manoeuvres—certainly all that the amateur pilot will wish to perform. The Minor came through with flying colours.

A thorough examination of all parts was made after each flight and revealed that everything had stood up to the test, which was admitted by the Press and disinterested persons, including air-line pilots, to be very severe.

Learning to Fly

I now had complete confidence in the machine, and it was up to me to learn to fly as soon as possible. After obtaining four hours' dual instruction, so that I would know what to expect when on my own, Mr. Dodd started me off with taxying practice until I was able to maintain a straight course and felt quite at home in the machine. I then tried fast taxying with the tail up until this also became familiar. It was not possible to complete this part of the training in one day, and this enabled me to study my mistakes between the practice lessons.

My first time off the ground was very exciting. I climbed to a height of a few feet only and continued at this height to a pre-arranged mark in the airport, closed the throttle, and let the machine return to the ground, perhaps a little bumpy, but nevertheless on an even keel. After several similar short flights, we "called it a day." On the next occasion I was sent higher, but this time the machine had to be brought down by the use of controls. On these higher flights I was instructed to move the stick gently sideways, up and down, to familiarise myself with the movement of the controls. This I did and was surprised at the little movement necessary to bank, or turn.

Several days of straight flights were gone

Full Constructive Details of this Successful Light Aeroplane, Designed to Air Ministry Standards and Requirements, were Given in Our Issues Dated October 1937 to March 1938 Inclusively

through before I felt confident to do a complete circuit, but in the end this was accomplished without any difficulty, although I was naturally a little excited.

It is my honest opinion that this is the machine that the enthusiastic amateur has been waiting for, as building costs can be kept low and any part that is considered difficult to make can be supplied by the manufacturers at very reasonable cost, or sets of manufactured parts can be obtained from the makers.

I may state that I am more than delighted with the Minor. My flying time now runs into several hours in all kinds of weather and very high winds. It is delightful and easy to handle. The stalling speed is low, apparently between 35 and 40 m.p.h., the take-off run (over rough surface and long grass in my case) is 100 yards, and the petrol consumption about one and a half gallons per hour.

In conclusion, I would say that this machine has a wonderful future, and confidently recommend amateurs to get together and start building. It can be done by anyone who exercises a reasonable amount of care and pays attention to detail. I may also add that I have no connection with, or interest in, Luton Aircraft, Ltd.

PHOTOGRAPHS OF THE LUTON MINOR UNDER CONSTRUCTION, AND IN THE AIR

(Top Left).—The plane in flight and (right) the plane on the ground. (Centre) The engine, and below it, a further view of the stationary plane, whilst below is shown the construction of the tail.

(Bottom Left) The fuselage and chassis of the 'plane, whilst the other two photographs show the 'plane soon after taking off.

Build Your Own Aeroplane

A New Version of the Luton Minor is Being Produced

THE Luton Minor single-seater is already a well-proven machine. It was originally produced in 1938 and many examples were built and flown in various parts of the world. The construction was also serialised in PRACTICAL MECHANICS.

Fig. 1.—An artist's impression of the Luton Minor in flight.

Fig. 2.—It can be towed behind a small car.

Recently, Phoenix Aircraft Limited was formed to re-design and modernise the aircraft to present-day standards and to make it available for the "man-in-the-street" to build.

Heading the company is Mr. C. H. Latimer-Needham, for many years known in the field of light aircraft design, and Mr. A. W. J. G. Ord-Hume, one of Britain's most active amateur aeroplane constructors who built and flew his first aeroplane at the age of eighteen. Phoenix Aircraft Ltd., Cranleigh Common, Cranleigh, Surrey, has produced a new version of the Minor which is simple to build, safe and easy to fly and costs only 2d. per air mile for petrol to fly.

The Minor (Fig. 1) is a real aeroplane in miniature and is a parasol monoplane of all-wood construction. It is only 20ft. long and its wing span is 25ft. Lighter than a large motor cycle, it can cruise at 75 m.p.h. with its 37 h.p. Aeronca J.A.P. twin-cylinder engine, which uses only 2½ gall. of petrol an hour. Any engine up to 65 h.p. can be installed.

The Minor can take off in 80yd. and can land in 40yd. By removing the wings and placing them along the fuselage sides, the entire aircraft can be towed along the road on its own wheels behind a small car (Fig. 2). The Minor is small enough to go in a garage and can be built in a spare room without the use of costly or complicated tools.

Of fabric-covered spruce and plywood construction, the Minor costs £250 to make including the cost of the engine. The complete book of plans and instructions, specially written and prepared for the amateur who has little or no previous aircraft experience, costs £11 10s. which includes one year's subscription to and membership of the Popular Flying Association, whose address is Londonderry House, 19, Park Lane, London, W.1. Phoenix Aircraft will send a representative to give advice and help to any constructor who requires it. During construction the aircraft is carefully inspected by Popular Flying Association inspectors. When it is completed, it is thoroughly examined to ensure that it is properly made and then it is recommended to the Ministry of Transport and Civil Aviation for the issue of a "Permit to Fly."

Many constructors used the series of articles published before the war in this journal to build their Luton Minors, including Mr. A. W. J. G. Ord-Hume.

It is hoped that plans for the construction of the Luton Major will also be available.

THE LUTON MINOR
37 h.p. Aeronca J.a.p.

Fig. 3.—Three views of the Luton Minor.

BUILDING THE LUTON MINOR LIGHT AEROPLANE

The First Article of a Series Describing an Aeroplane that is Simple and Cheap to Build, is Easy to Fly, and Can be Towed Behind a Car and Kept in the Garage

THE prototype of this aeroplane first flew in 1937. It has been modernised and is the first post-war all-British aircraft which can be built and flown by amateurs. The Ministry of Transport and Civil Aviation has approved the Minor for operation under a "Permit to Fly," thus dispensing with the need for a Certificate of Airworthiness.

Aircraft construction is by no means difficult to master and it is quite within the capabilities of the average amateur who is reasonably good at metalwork and carpentry.

The Luton Minor was specifically designed for the amateur builder and pilot, thus simplicity and straightforwardness of construction coupled with maximum flight safety have been the overriding design consideration throughout.

Originally designed by Luton Aircraft Limited in 1936 as a safe, practical, personal aeroplane which was cheap to operate, many examples were built and flown in all parts of the world before the war by enthusiasts and today a number of these pre-war Minors are still flying!

Before the war PRACTICAL MECHANICS published a series of articles dealing with the construction of the Minor. The popularity of these articles was proved by the world-wide reception they were given which resulted in Minors being built in many countries.

Phoenix Aircraft Ltd., which has taken over the designs of Luton Aircraft Ltd., has modernised the Minor to bring it in line with present-day standards. Heading the design team is Mr. C. H. Latimer-Needham, the designer of the original Minor and many other successful light aircraft. The new Minor—the L.A.4a—is already being built in numbers by enthusiasts in Great Britain and such far away places as Australia.

The L.A.4a Minor is designed to be powered by the 37 h.p. Aeronca J.A.P. J.99 horizontally-opposed, twin-cylinder, air-cooled engine, although any engine up to 42 h.p. may be fitted with only small modification. With the J.A.P. engine, which uses only two and a half gallons of petrol an hour, fuel costs are only 2d. per air mile, with a cruising speed of 70-75 m.p.h.

By removing the wings and tail and fixing them to the sides of the fuselage, the entire aircraft can be towed on its own wheels along the road behind a 7 h.p. car. This enables the Minor to be housed in a shed or garage, thereby avoiding the cost of hangarage at an aerodrome.

The Minor will take-off in 80 yards, may be operated safely from a 200-yard long field and can climb at 450 feet per minute. The stalling speed is about equal to bicycling speed.

Phoenix Aircraft Ltd., in conjunction with the Popular Flying Association, operates an inspection and advisory service and will, upon request, send a qualified representative to give advice and even practical help to the constructor. The amateur, by availing himself of this service, can be certain of completing a perfectly airworthy aeroplane of his own for which he will be granted a Ministry of Transport and Civil Aviation "Permit to Fly."

PRACTICAL MECHANICS has obtained exclusive rights to publish the construction details of this delightful little personal aeroplane. However, since it would be impossible to reproduce the drawings to any useful scale, it has been agreed that we shall provide in this series of articles an illustrated and detailed step-by-step account of the construction. Readers who wish to build the Minor are advised to obtain the full set of plans from Phoenix Aircraft Ltd., whose registered address is Cranleigh Common, Surrey. They will then receive the full set of large scale, black-on-white drawings, which are fully detailed with most of the metal fittings drawn full size. The set of plans costs £11 10s., which is inclusive of a licence to build one Minor and one year's subscription to the Popular Flying Association—the founding and representative body in the United Kingdom of amateur constructors and operators of ultra-light aircraft.

This arrangement allows Phoenix Aircraft Ltd., to maintain a watching brief over constructors, so as to avoid unnecessary deviations and mistakes and to give the benefit of their experience. It is advisable that every constructor should be given the facilities of this advisory service so that he may receive copies of memoranda, issued from time to time, together with copies of any modifications and recommendations as issued by them.

Description

The Luton Minor is a single-seat, all-wood parasol monoplane designed specifi-

A partly constructed wing, photographed in the garden of an amateur builder of the Luton Minor.

cally for the amateur constructor who has little or no previous aircraft experience. It is an extremely simple aircraft to build and requires no special tools or workshop equipment.

The parasol wing layout has been chosen for its inherent pendulum-type stability, coupled with excellent view in flight, safe ground handling and also the simplest wing structure. There is no complicated cantilever main spar—the wing is in two separate 12ft. 6in. pieces, which bolt to tubular steel pylon struts above the cockpit.

The designers have steadfastly avoided all fabrications and assemblies which require the use of expensive tools or large workshop spaces. The structure of the Minor can be built in a large room or garage. Welding and brazing have been kept to a minimum and, if the amateur has no facilities for this, Phoenix Aircraft Ltd., undertake either to supply such metal parts ready made, or to weld up parts sent to them by amateurs.

Construction

The fuselage is of box construction with spruce longerons and bracing, with a covering of plywood. Aft of the roomy cockpit, the top decking is fabric covered, the fabric being supported on light spruce stringers and plywood formers. The fuel tank, holding 6½ gallons of petrol is mounted on the top longerons in front of the cockpit. The pilot's seat is hinged so that it tips forward to give access to the luggage compartment which has ample space for week-end baggage.

The undercarriage is of steel tube construction with rubber-in-compression shock absorbers housed in neat fairings. Wheel brakes may be incorporated if desired and a fully-castoring tailwheel is fitted. Metal fittings are all simple bent-up fabrications of mild steel sheet.

The wings have two spars each, comprising top and bottom spruce booms and a plywood shear web. The large-chord ailerons hinge directly on to the rear spar. Each wing is built in one piece, complete with the aileron, which is cut off after completion. This ensures perfect alignment without the need for a special aileron jig. The wing ribs are nearly all the same and are of open girder layout. Plywood sheet covers the leading edge and tips for durability and also to improve the airflow over the wing. The remainder is fabric-covered and cellulose doped. Attachment to the fuselage is by two centre-section pylons and two sets of parallel lift struts made of streamlined steel tubing.

Tailplane and elevators are also built in one piece and cut apart after completion. Construction is very simple and follows that of the wings. The fin and rudder are likewise simple wooden assemblies covered in fabric.

The pilot's controls are light and effective. The majority of the control cable runs are internal, examination being facilitated by inspection hatches. The cockpit is of ample size—the tallest and most well-built pilot will find all the controls within comfortable and easy reach.

Normally, the minimum of aircraft instruments are fitted, but for the sporting pilot, an artificial horizon and directional gyro can be incorporated.

The engine is attached to a simple cradle of steel tubing which is bolted to the front of the fuselage. Cowlings are of aluminium sheet and are all of single curvature thus dispensing with difficult shaping which can only be executed effectively with a wheeling machine.

Among those engines suitable, apart from the Aeronca J.A.P., is the Agusta G.A./40, the 40 h.p. Continental, the 32 h.p. Bristol Cherub and the converted 32 h.p Volkswagen.

Costs

The airframe of the Minor, excluding the engine, can be made for approximately £125. Aeronca J.A.P. engines are available for about £100 complete, plus £20 for the propeller. The total cost of the aircraft should not exceed £250 with the J.A.P. engine. This is much less than the cost of buying a small car having the same fuel consumption. Phoenix Aircraft Ltd. will supply the Minor, ready to fly, for £698 and can supply all parts, fittings and materials to order.

A partly constructed tailplane outside the garage where it was built.

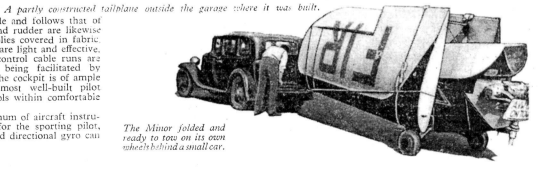

The Minor folded and ready to tow on its own wheels behind a small car.

Materials

All spruce and plywood used in the Minor should be of aircraft quality. Mild steel should be to specification S.510 or nearest equivalent (this is normal 28 tons/sq. in. steel). Steel tube must be of the aircraft specification stated on the plans. Brass aircraft gimp pins or brads are to be used for nailing. All wood-screws used are to be brass or cadmium-plated brass. On no account should steel brads, nails or screws be used—the moisture content of the wood will cause them to rust.

The glues used are of the synthetic resin type and the two recommended in the construction of ultra-light aircraft are Aerolite 300 (or 306) and Aerodux 185. Both are two-parts adhesives and the choice of which one to use is left to the constructor.

Fabrics and dopes will be dealt with later.

Sequence of Construction

It is recommended that the amateur should begin by building the tail unit. This will provide him with good practice and, should he make a mistake, it will not be too costly to rectify. As he gains proficiency so may he gain confidence and proceed to the mainplanes and fuselage.

It cannot be too highly stressed that the constructor should always use aircraft quality materials where specified (though not necessarily A.I.D. released) and must not resort to commercial materials for the sake of saving a few shillings, unless it is definitely stated on the drawings that such materials may be used for certain parts.

The essence of good work is quality rather than speed. The builder must take time over each part and aim to produce good work. By keeping in touch with a Phoenix Aircraft Ltd. representative, or a Popular Flying Association inspector, he can receive guidance, help and assurance that his work is satisfactory. If he is unable to avail himself of such assistance, he should seek the advice of a local licensed aircraft ground engineer who will usually be pleased to make helpful suggestions and give the benefit of his practical experience.

Tools and the Workshop

The constructor will require a dry work-

This Luton Minor was built by an R.A.F. officer for his own personal use and is shown here compared with a much larger aircraft.

room or garage in which to work. A firm bench with a woodworking vice and a metal-work vice is essential. An electric drill with a small circular saw attachment will save a lot of time and hard work. A steel-backed sanding disc, used in place of the circular saw, is useful for shaping blocks and general sanding off.

Ordinary carpenter's hand tools are sufficient for the woodwork involved. Make sure that the smoothing plane has a good sharp blade—if it is curved or chipped, buy a replacement. The plane is a most important tool in aircraft work—you will be doing some fine work with it—so protect the cutting edge when it is not in use. Cultivate the habit of laying the plane on its side on the bench.

Metalworking tools comprise a scriber, pair of dividers, centre punch, $\frac{1}{2}$in. cold chisel, pair of tin snips (two are preferable— one large and one small), a 12in. metal rule graduated in fractions and decimal inches, one or two steel squares (4in. or 6in.), a hacksaw, a good set of sharp twist drills up to $\frac{1}{4}$in. diameter and an assortment of hand files.

A small hand-operated guillotine, capable of handling up to 14 s.w.g. steel sheet, is a worth-while, although not vital extra. You will also require an office hand stapling machine and a good supply of staples.

Other essential items include a 3ft. straightedge (wood or metal) and a level. A builder's level would do if it is accurate, but a rigid straight plank of wood and a spirit level are much more useful. Two or three rigid trestles or saw horses will be needed—large wooden boxes may be used here.

Three lead plumb-bobs and a large angle square (a wooden "T" square will suffice) are required for truing up fuselage and wings.

Some planks of good straight commercial deal and a sheet of $\frac{1}{4}$in. or $\frac{3}{8}$in. commercial plywood will come in useful for the few jigs and fixtures which are required.

The Plans

A good deal of time—and often money—can be saved by carefully working through the plans before actually starting work. If you have a sound understanding as to how the aeroplane goes together beforehand it all becomes a logical sequence of events and this period of familiarisation is certainly not time wasted.

Lay the plans out on the floor or a large table. Follow each part through to final assembly. See where the various details go. This way you are also learning about the aeroplane you are about to start building and will eventually fly.

Building the 'Luton Minor'

BEGIN by building the rudder. This is a relatively simple component to make and will provide some good practice in aircraft carpentry and metalwork. If a mistake is made on the rudder, it is not going to be too costly to scrap it and start again.

Rudder Bow

Start by marking out the rudder bow on a flat table or bench at least 36in. × 48in. To do this, reproduce the rudder layout full size and draw in all the ribs and bracing. Check all the measurements against the plan.

Part 2 Deals with Building the Tail Unit

plane, rudder and wing tip if the piece of wood is about 4ft. long.

Fair each arc on your layout into the adjacent line by carefully adjusting the centre of the radius slightly until the arc sweeps accurately.

You have now marked out the outer edge of the rudder bow. Remember that the inner edge is ¼in. less all the way round, so now produce this inner shape, using the same centres but with each radius reduced by ¼in.

To this inside line, screw a number of wooden blocks ½in. thick by about 3in. × 1in. On the curves, these will have to be shaped slightly. In Fig. 1 the inner curve has been cut entirely

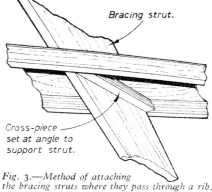

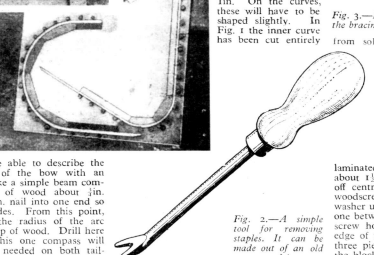

Fig. 1.—Two views of the jig for making the rudder and elevator bows.

As you will not be able to describe the necessary large arcs of the bow with an ordinary compass, make a simple beam compass. Take a piece of wood about ¼in. square and drive a 1in. nail into one end so that the point protrudes. From this point, set off with a rule the radius of the arc required along the strip of wood. Drill here to take a pencil. This one compass will describe all the arcs needed on both tail-

Fig. 2.—A simple tool for removing staples. It can be made out of an old screwdriver.

Bracing strut.

Cross-piece set at angle to support strut.

Fig. 3.—Method of attaching the bracing struts where they pass through a rib.

from solid wood, but it is not necessary for the amateur to do this.

Against these blocks will be set the strips of wood forming the laminated bow. To apply sufficient pressure during the setting of the glue, a simple method is to fit a number of "eccentric buttons" as can be seen in Fig. 1.

Cut these from ½in. thick commercial plywood or blockboard. You will need about fifty and they can be re-used for the other laminated bows on the Minor. Make them about 1½in. in diameter and drill them ⅜in. off centre to take a 1½in. long round-head woodscrew. Fix them to the layout with a washer under the head of the woodscrew and one between the button and the bench. The screw holes should be ⅞in. from the inner edge of the bow so that you can clamp the three pieces of 3/16in. thick spruce against the blocks by turning the buttons.

Fig. 4.—Details and dimensions of the rudder lever.

Radius 5/16"   Ream 3/16"dia   1½"   2"   1/8" continuous ply packing both sides   End of ply.

Radius 3/8"   Drill corners 1/8"dia. before cutting   Drill for 2BA. bolts   5/8" before bending.   1/8"

½"   Bend flange 90°   5/16"   Bend line.   1"

Typical section showing ply edges rounded   Radius 3/8".   3"   2½"   1/4"   6"

◆ = 1/8" csk. aluminium rivet.

The strips of spruce should not need steaming to shape, but to make a good job, saturate them in boiling water until they are supple enough to bend easily into the jig. On no account attempt to glue them whilst they are wet. Clamp the pieces by rotating the buttons, making quite sure that there are no gaps between the strips. Leave the wood thus for about a day to dry out thoroughly.

When dry, remove them (do not worry if they tend to straighten out somewhat) and line the jig with strips of waxed paper to prevent excess glue squeezed out of the joint from sticking to the bench. The waxed paper used to wrap bread is ideal for this job.

Using Aerodux 185 adhesive, glue the three laminations rubbing each to its neighbour to exclude air bubbles. Lift the three pieces and bend them together into the jig. Start at one end and clamp them up using the buttons. Do not tighten them haphazardly as this may result in gaps between the laminations.

Leave this overnight to set, then release the buttons and carefully lift the bow out, easing as necessary with the blade of a broad chisel. Shave the bow to the correct section.

Do not plane off excess glue—synthetic resin adhesives set very hard and will chip the cutting edge. If excess cannot be removed with a cloth whilst still wet, use a file when it is hard. The ordinary file makes an extremely useful wood finishing tool for aircraft work. Never use a rasp or Dreadnought on timber as this type of file tends to tear the grain.

Rudder Spar

Make the rudder spar from one piece of ¼in. thick spruce. When marking out a spar or similar beam, always draw the centre line first and then step off the positions of all ribs, metal fittings and so on. Mark off the widths at various stations along the centre-line.

Remove surplus timber with the saw—a power saw for preference. Do not cut closer than about ⅛in. to your line until you have gained experience. Cut away from the grain wherever possible to avoid the risk of splitting or lifting the surface grain. Finish off with the smoothing plane to the line of the layout.

The Ribs

Draw the plan of each rib on to the bench or a plank of wood with a hard pencil, again working from the centre-line. Set off the widths at the various stations and join the points thus obtained with a strip of thin wood bowed as necessary to give a fair curve. Drive in headless 1in. long brads at intervals of every 2in. to 3in.

Spring in the two rib capstrips and insert the cross pieces which fit each side of the spar (ribs F, E and D (Fig. 5) only have the cross piece behind the spar). These are glued in place. With scrap pieces of wood, wedge between the capstrips so that they form the accurate curved shape and touch all the nails.

Cut the webs from 1/16in. thick birch plywood with the grain running at right angles to the centre line (short grained) and glue them into place on top of the capstrips. With an ordinary office stapling machine, staple the plywood every 1½in. to the capstrips and the cross pieces. The rib is then secure enough to be lifted out of the jig and set aside to dry before cleaning up the edges and removing the staples. A simple tool can be made up from an old screwdriver for this, as shown in Fig. 2.

Only one rib is required from each jig.

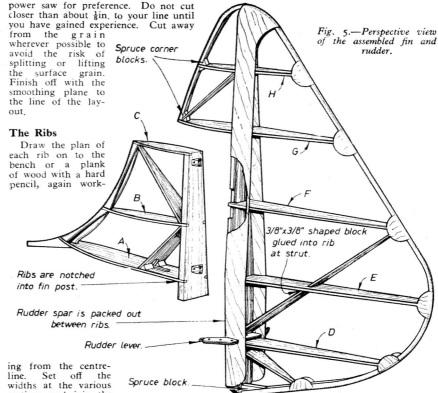

Fig. 5.—Perspective view of the assembled fin and rudder.

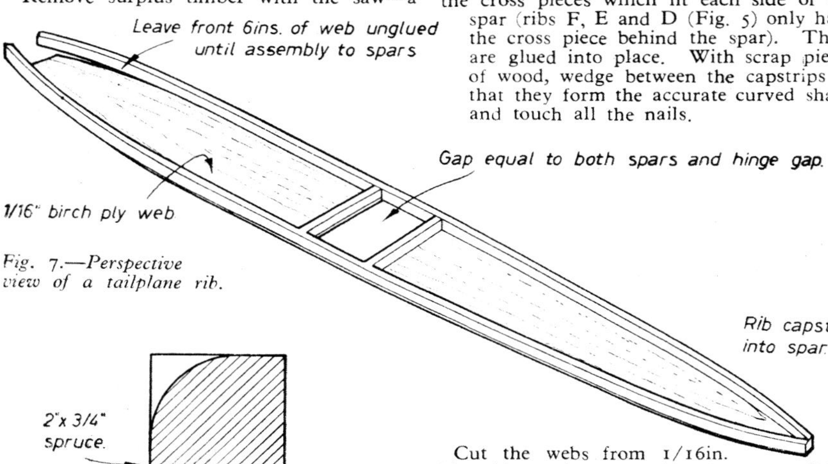

Spruce corner blocks.

3/8"x3/8" shaped block glued into rib at strut.

Ribs are notched into fin post.

Rudder spar is packed out between ribs.

Rudder lever.

Spruce block.

Thread the ribs on to the spar and glue and tack each one into place with ¾in. × 20 s.w.g. brass gimp pins making sure that they are in their correct positions on the spar and are also at right angles to it. Now fit the laminated bow which is fixed to the trailing edges of the ribs with semi-circular gussets of 1/16in. birch plywood. Only fit these gussets to one side of rib F until the diagonal bracing struts have been fitted.

To make these struts, first mark where they pass through the ribs by placing a strip of wood on the outside between the place on the spar and the joint of the rib trailing edge and bow. Cut a slot in the rib ply web for the strut at the appropriate place.

The strut itself is of ¼in. thick spruce, tapering from 3½in. width at the spar to ½in. at the trailing edge. Pass it through the rib slot from the same side as the gusset

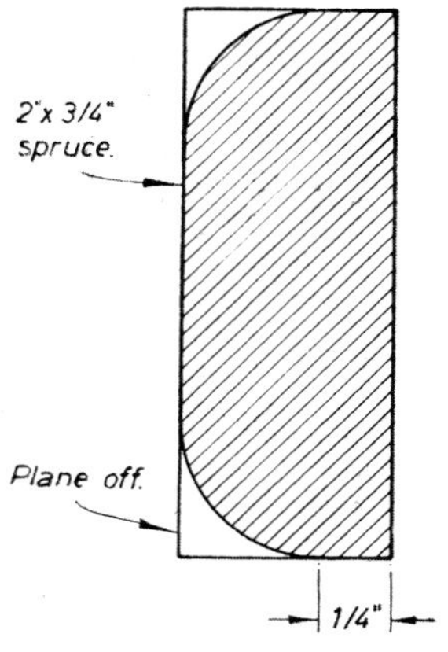

Leave front 6ins. of web unglued until assembly to spars

1/16" birch ply web

Fig. 7.—Perspective view of a tailplane rib.

Gap equal to both spars and hinge gap.

2" x 3/4" spruce.

Plane off.

1/4"

Fig. 6.—Section through tailplane front spar

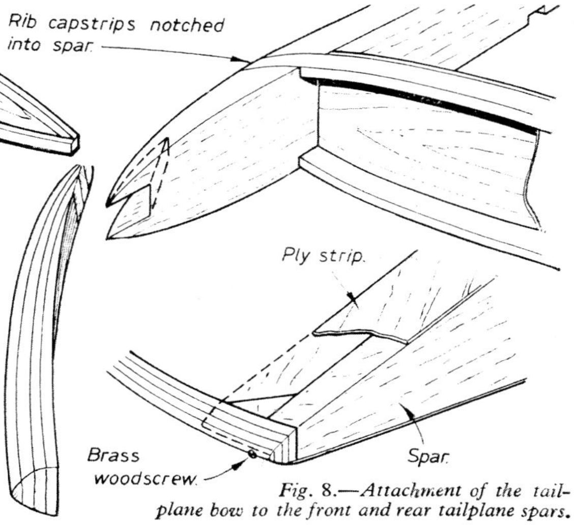

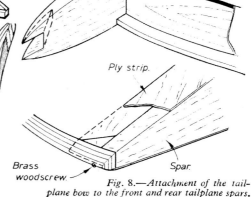

Rib capstrips notched into spar.

Ply strip.

Brass woodscrew.

Spar.

Fig. 8.—Attachment of the tailplane bow to the front and rear tailplane spars.

so that it can be brought in at the trailing edge as the forward end butts the inside face of the spar. Glue this and fit the remaining gusset to rib F.

Glue $\frac{3}{8}$in. $\times$ $\frac{1}{8}$in. spruce packing pieces to the strut where it passes through the rib, as shown in Fig. 3.

Hinge Brackets and Rudder Lever

These parts are all made of 16 s.w.g. mild steel sheet to specification S.510 or equivalent. Three hinge brackets are required.

Avoid scribing deep layout marks on metal.

Use a bench vice with smooth jaws (on some types the jaws may be unscrewed and reversed) so as not to mark the surface of the metal whilst it is being gripped for cutting and bending. It is quite easy to make smooth steel jaws and have them case-hardened. For this type of work, vice clamps or fibre jaws are of no use since some of the metal cutting will be accomplished with the cold chisel and hammer in the vice.

When chiselling metal, always keep the part being cut out in the vice and chisel the surplus off it rather than to clamp the surplus in the vice and remove the fitting

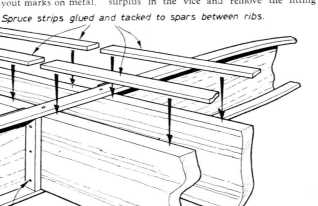

Spruce strips glued and tacked to spars between ribs.

Tack through rib vertical.

1″ gap between spars

Fig. 9.—Attachment of ribs to tail spars.

These scratches are a potential source of weakness and they can develop into cracks, especially if the steel is to be bent. The safest method is to use one of the special layout fluids such as "Spectrablue," which is a coloured spirit applied to the steel with a brush or swab. It dries almost immediately, producing a bright blue film which will show up the slightest scratch made with a scriber. It is possible to scribe a line by removing only the blue dye, leaving the metal showing in contrast. The resultant layout is very much like a blueprint and is much clearer to follow in cutting out. The dye is readily removed afterwards with spirit or cellulose thinners.

with the chisel. This latter way results in a distorted part which is useless.

Cut out the metal parts using a combination of the hacksaw, the cold chisel and the drill. If a bench guillotine or shear is available—and they do save much effort—again remember to work from your left so as to remove the surplus metal with the knife.

Until experienced in the use of these tools do not cut closer than 1/16in. to the layout line, cleaning off the rest with the hand file. Finish off with a smooth file and remove the burrs from each side. Drill any holes now, but do not open them up to full size until assembling them to the job. This is good practice for later when mating up

fittings to each other, discrepancies between holes must be avoided. Accordingly, drill the holes $\frac{1}{8}$in. at present.

Ideal protective treatment for metal parts is cadmium plating followed by a coat of chromate primer, but it is acceptable to give a good coat of metal primer and assemble them on the job with a chromate jointing compound such as "Duralac" or "Celloseal."

Later, when parts have been welded or brazed, it is important to remove all scale and dirt before applying such protective treatment. Sandblasting should be resorted to if the wire brush is insufficient.

From Fig. 4 it can be seen that $\frac{1}{8}$in. holes have to be drilled by the sides of the flange before it is bent up. This is to eliminate the possibility of fractures starting in the corners. Adopt this principle on all such fittings, whether they are bent up or not, and avoid sharp corners in a part which might induce stress cracks either in making or in service.

Bend up the rudder fittings, using hand bending bars, which can be held in the vice. It is important to maintain the correct radius of bend. As a guide, the radius inside a bend in 18 s.w.g. mild steel sheet should be 1/16in.; 16 s.w.g. should be 3/32in. and 14 s.w.g. $\frac{1}{8}$in. radius.

Avoid hammer marks on the fittings as they are bent. Form the bends with a mallet and a block of wood, using the end grain. Check with a square and a rule that the flange is at right angles and also that it is not rippled along its length.

Bolt the fittings to the rudder spar using 2 B.A. bolts, having a plain shank length of 0.4in. Put large duralumin "penny" washers on the other side of the spar and use self-locking stiff nuts.

Pack up the edges of the spar between the ribs with strips of 3/16in. × $\frac{3}{8}$in. spruce glued and tacked into place. Now glue the 2$\frac{1}{2}$in. wide strips of 1/16in. birch ply to each side of the spar. These plywood strips have the grain running longways (long-grained) and they are glued and stapled on. When the glue has set, pull out the staples and clean off the top and edges.

Complete the rudder by thoroughly sanding the laminated bow, the gussets and the edges of the ribs. Check to see that there are no brass brads or sharp edges protruding which might pierce the fabric covering.

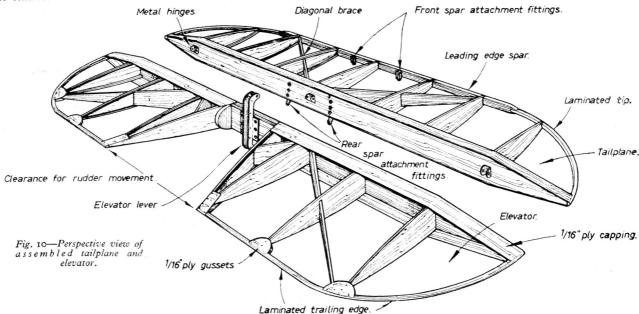

Metal hinges.

Diagonal brace

Front spar attachment fittings.

Leading edge spar.

Laminated tip.

Rear spar attachment fittings.

Tailplane.

Clearance for rudder movement.

Elevator lever.

Elevator.

1/16″ ply capping.

Fig. 10—Perspective view of assembled tailplane and elevator.

1/16″ ply gussets.

Laminated trailing edge.

Do not cover with fabric at this stage. The whole structure must be completed and put up for inspection before doing this. The assembled rudder is shown in Fig. 5.

The Fin

Remember that the rudder fits to this, so check that the fin leading edge will fair neatly into the curve of the rudder bow. The fin structure is of the same type as the rudder.

The lower rib A (Fig. 5) is of ¼in. thick spruce as are the two struts which taper from the full width of the fin spar to the width of the leading edge bow (see Fig. 5).

The leading edge is made from a curved 2in. wide piece of ⅛in. birch ply. Keep the grain as long as possible in this. Glue spruce strips ¼in. thick to each side of this and then pare with a spokeshave to the section shown on the drawing. Cut slots in the spruce to clear the ribs.

Bolt the two rudder hinges to the fin post so that there is a ¾in. gap between the top of the top fin rib and the under surface of the rudder rib G. Assemble the hinges so that there is a small amount of end float up and down of the rudder. This small amount of play applies to all the Minor control surfaces and reduces chances of seizure and eases their movement. It should be not less than 1/16in. Any excess of this within reasonable limits may be packed out with steel shims on assembly.

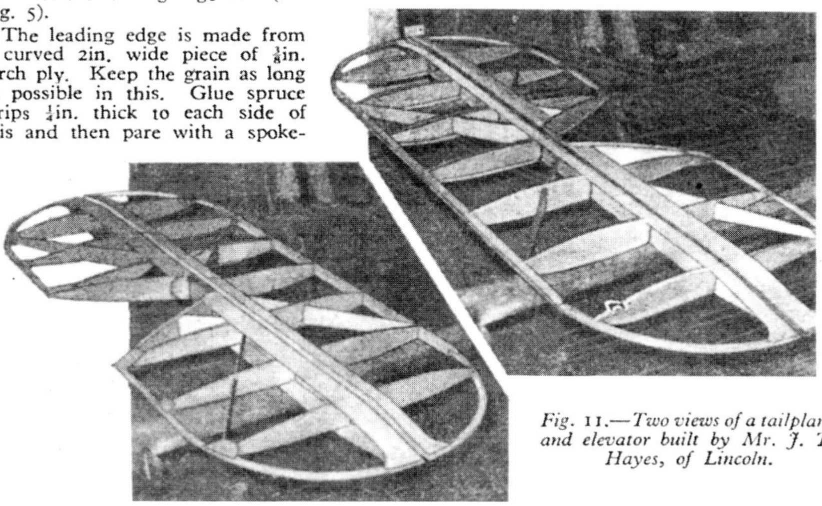

Fig. 11.—Two views of a tailplane and elevator built by Mr. J. T. Hayes, of Lincoln.

Tailplane and Elevator

The construction of the tail unit is completed by building the tailplane and elevator. In the Minor they are built together in one piece to dispense with the need for separate jigs. The two are cut apart after assembly to ensure accurate matching.

Begin by making up the metal fittings—the five hinges Pt. No. T.2, the two hinges Pt. No. T.7, the elevator lever Pt. No. T.1 and the front and rear spar attachments, Pts. No. T.3 and T.4.

Prepare the spars from best spruce and glue the reinforcing section to the centre of the elevator spar. They are all symmetrical about the centre-line. The front spar is also the leading edge of the tailplane and should, therefore, be shaped as shown in Fig. 6.

Make up a simple jig for the tailplane/elevator ribs on the same lines as that used for the rudder. All the ribs are the same except the outboard pair which may be built in the same jig with only slight modification. Cut a block of spruce 1¼in. wide to represent the gap for the spars and hinges, against each side of which is a vertical member (Fig. 7). The rib capstrips are of 3/16in. × ⅜in. spruce and the webs are of 1/16in. birch plywood. The direction of the grain should be vertical to the rib datum (short-grained). Leave the front 6in. of the rib webs unglued so that the capstrips can be passed over the front spar and into the notches provided.

Laminate up the bows for the tips.

Slide the ribs on to the spars, glueing and tacking them into place. Make sure that they are at right angles by checking with a square.

Place the structure on a level surface so that a twist will not inadvertently be built into it. Splice the tip bows into the front spar (Fig. 8) and fair them in neatly, shaping the tip of the front spar. Gusset the bows to the rib trailing edges.

Fit the diagonal bracing struts. These are made of ¼in. solid spruce tapering from 3⅝in. to ½in. at the trailing edge. These pass through the rib webs and are secured to the ribs by strips of ⅛in. square spruce tacked and glued into position. Where the members meet the spar, fit a shaped block to support the joint properly (Fig. 5). These may be made of ⅛in. square stock.

Make up the two spruce formers to support the "D" fairing to the centre of the elevator. Bolt on all the metal fittings, again assembling the hinges to provide 1/16in. end float.

The long plywood strips, top and bottom of both the tailplane rear spar and the elevator front spar can now be fitted together with the "D" fairing which is of 1/16in. plywood.

With a tenon saw, carefully sever the elevator from the tailplane and then clean up the rib ends on them both. Finish off with a thorough sanding. Store the completed tail unit, views of which are shown in Figs. 10 and 11, somewhere free from damp, dust and dirt.

In the next article of this series instructions will be given for building the wings.

The complete set of plans for the Minor costs £11 10s. from Phoenix Aircraft Ltd.

PRICE LIST OF PARTS FOR THE "MINOR" TAIL UNIT

	£	s.	d.
Rudder, fabric - covered and doped	9	18	0
Tailplane and elevator, fabric-covered and doped	20	10	0
Fin, fabric-covered and doped	4	2	6
Tailplane ribs, set	4	0	0
Tailplane bows, pair	2	15	0
Tailplane spars (three)... ...	4	10	0
Tailplane fittings	2	0	0
Rudder ribs, set...	2	15	0
Rudder bow	2	3	0
Rudder spar		19	6
Rudder fittings...	1	10	0
Fin-post, leading edge and ribs	2	5	0
Fin fittings	1	8	0

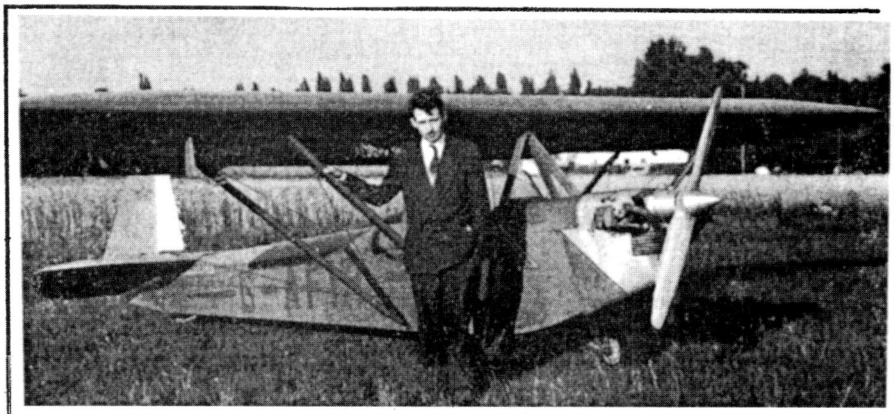

A LUTON MINOR TESTIMONIAL

SIR,—I have been most interested in the series of articles about the construction of the Phoenix Luton Minor Aircraft, which you are printing in your most excellent journal.

Since I have recently had the opportunity to fly a home-made Minor which the owner wished to sell, I thought that perhaps the impressions of a colleague and myself might be of interest to your readers.

It was with some trepidation that we set out to try the Minor, which we rather expected to be disappointing and probably under-powered with its two-cylinder J.A.P. engine. However, we were most agreeably surprised to find that it is so easy and simple to fly and that the engine is more than adequate.

In the Minor you feel that the aeroplane is part of you, and its quick, light controls make it a delight to fly. My first landing was far from perfect, but I found that the undercarriage was very forgiving and I did not bounce at all. I then found that by looking over the side I could easily see the wheel and judge my height to the inch, and several perfect landings seemed almost too simple to be true.

After less than half an hour each in the Minor, both my colleague and I had completely fallen for it, and our opinions were confirmed when we watched a Phoenix pilot put the Minor through its paces. Its turning circle beats anything that I have seen fly, and its manœuvrability in the hands of an expert is quite amazing. I am in no way connected with Phoenix Aircraft Ltd.—FRAZER MUSGROVE (Welwyn).

Building the 'Luton Minor'

(Continued from the October issue)

THE wing of the Minor is made in two halves which are joined together at the centre by fittings attached to the fuselage wing pylons.

Each mainplane is 12ft. 6in. in length and has a chord (width from leading edge to trailing edge) of 63in. The wing section is R.A.F. 48 (modified). This section has been chosen for its good lift/drag co-efficient and gentle stall characteristics.

3.—Commencing Construction of the Main Plane

Jig for the Ribs

This is best made from a panel of block-board about 5½ft. long and 1ft. wide. On to this, draw the full size layout of the rib, marking first the centre-line (rib datum), parallel to the lower edge. The bottom edge of the board must be quite straight.

Step off the ordinate stations, the first one (zero inches) being about 2in. from the left-hand edge of the board. Using a carpenter's square against the bottom edge of the board, draw in the station lines at right angles to the datum across the board.

With dividers, accurately step off the rib co-ordinates at each station, making doubly sure that the right dimension is set off at the correct station above and below the centre line.

Now mark in the position of the spars. The centre of the front spar is 9.45in. from the leading edge (station zero inches) and the rear spar is 34·65in. from the front spar centre.

Cut lengths of wood of the same section as the spar to represent the spars in the jig. The widths of these pieces should be equal to the spar thickness. Carefully glue and nail these into the jig at their correct positions.

From ½in. × 1in. strip wood cut a number of blocks about 1½in. long. These are required to hold the rib members in position

while the rib is being assembled and they are glued and nailed to the jig at each side of every member. On the capstrips, they should be placed at frequent intervals—a spacing of 4in. is advised. The rib verticals and diagonals need only be located by a block either side at each end. Make sure that the rib member is a snug but not tight fit between the blocks. Since all the main ribs must be of the same profile, it is recommended that one jig only be used.

Having finished making the jig, paint it with two coats of very hot linseed oil, letting the oil sink well into the wood of the jig. The oil is to prevent surplus glue from the rib sticking to the jig and preventing its easy removal. Remember that the boiling point of oil is very high and hot oil can burn your brush (and your skin) long before it begins to look really hot. Do not let oil contaminate aircraft woods—keep your timber well clear of oil, grease, dirt and dust.

This rib jig will make all the main ribs (Rib A). Separate jigs will be required for Ribs B, C and D but, as only two of each rib are needed, the jigs can be made using headless brads to locate the rib members. Note that the ribs which form the aileron

have a wider rear spar gap. Use the same jig, but pack out the gap to take the aileron spar. See Fig. 12.

A well made and accurate jig can save a lot of time and effort—especially when it comes to dressing the wing leading edge before ply covering.

The Rib Capstrips

These should not need pre-forming, although it is somewhat simpler to slip them in and out of the jig if they are so treated. To pre-form them, place a large shallow dish filled with water on a gas ring or stove so that about 12in. to 15in. of the end of the strip wood may be saturated. Boil the ends of all the strips for not more than five minutes.

Pre-form them to a slightly greater curve than is needed to allow for spring when they are dry. Clamp them up, as shown in Fig. 14, and leave at least overnight to dry out thoroughly. Do not try to accelerate drying aircraft wood by heating—this dries the timber quickly on the outside thereby making it brittle and can, in extreme cases, encourage rot. Air-drying is far better and much safer.

A lot of time can be saved at this stage

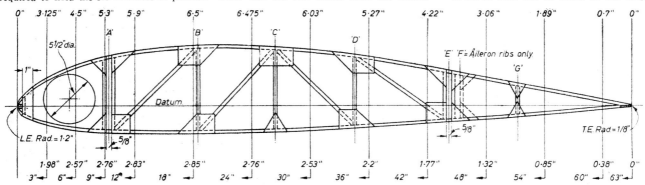

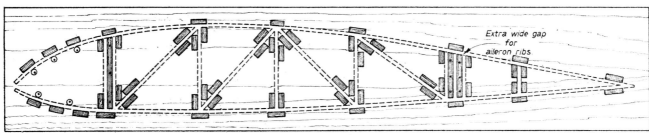

Fig. 12.—Rib construction and jig for assembling the ribs.

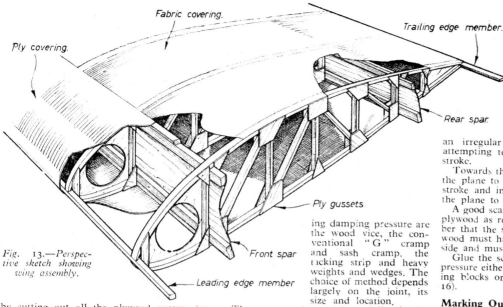

Fig. 13.—Perspective sketch showing wing assembly.

Labels on figure: Fabric covering. — Ply covering. — Trailing edge member. — Rear spar. — Ply gussets — Front spar — Leading edge member

by cutting out all the plywood gussets for the wing ribs. They are of 1/16in. thick plywood and there are only three basic shapes. The direction of the grain is not important. Cut out the nose webs from 1/16in. plywood. Trepan out the lightening hole either with a fly-cutter or by using a sharp pair of carpenter's compasses.

Slip an upper and a lower capstrip into the jig and cut the diagonals and vertical members. Cut all these members for the set of ribs. You will find that, by selective marking out, you will have very little waste rib stock, offcuts coming in useful for shorter rib members.

Gluing the Rib

Mix the adhesive for the ribs and begin gluing all the verticals and diagonals, ensuring that the joints are well glued but avoiding excess glue. Glue also the nose web and all the ply gussets, stapling them into place.

The rib is now sufficiently solid to lift from the jig. Turn it over, lay it on a flat surface and glue and staple the gussets to the other side. Build all the ribs in this fashion. If the parts are cut ready beforehand as suggested, it should only take about 30 minutes to assemble each rib.

Some of the gussets will have overlapped the edge of the capstrips in order to place them accurately on the rib joint. This does not matter as any excess may be removed when the glue is set.

A useful device for cleaning such surplus off the rib profiles is a metal-backed sanding disc fixed in a saw table. This will ensure that the rib edge is quite square. The sanding disc can be stuck to the metal face plate in the saw bench with a good contact adhesive. This sanding disc may also be used for trimming the mitres on the rib diagonals and will have many similar applications on the Minor.

The Spars

Cut and scarf together the plywood for the spar shear webs, leaving the plywood about ½in. wider than will be required.

The scarf joint is one of the strongest joints in woodwork if it is properly made. It consists of feathering the edges of the pieces of timber or plywood to be joined, one on the top surface and one on the under surface so that they may be superimposed upon each other, glued and clamped until set. Among the various methods of applying clamping pressure are the wood vice, the conventional "G" cramp and sash cramp, the tacking strip and heavy weights and wedges. The choice of method depends largely on the joint, its size and location.

The essence of a good scarf lies in the very accurate marking out so that the joint is the same length on both pieces of timber being joined.

To scarf plywood, first select a good

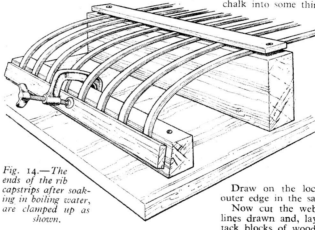

Fig. 14.—The ends of the rib capstrips after soaking in boiling water, are clamped up as shown.

planed wooden board about 1in. thick which is smooth, free from twist or wind and which has a straight edge.

Screw this to the end of the bench. Take one of the two pieces of plywood to be scarfed and lay it so that the edge is parallel and flush to the straight edge of the base board. Tack it into place at intervals with brads or staples, keeping the tacks at least 1½in. away from the edge (Fig. 15).

The width of the scarf for 1/16in. plywood should not be less than ½in. and preferably ⅝in. Pencil a line this distance from the edge.

Check that the blade of the smoothing plane is sharp. A 1½in. or 2in. steel plane is best to use, although a small bull-nosed plane will be needed later for certain scarfs cut when one piece of plywood is *in situ*.

Set the blade to remove only a thin shaving at a time and proceed to feather the edge of the plywood. If the plane is held at an angle of 15 to 20 deg. to the line of the scarf so that the wood is sheared off, a fine clean cut can be achieved. Since plywood is laminated, the various layers will show up as parallel bands as the edge is prepared. If the bands are not parallel, then the edge is not true; typical causes might be dirt between the ply and the base board, an irregular edge to the base board or attempting to plane off too much at each stroke.

Towards the completion of the edge, adjust the plane to remove even less wood at each stroke and increase the convergent angle of the plane to the edge.

A good scarf should show the layers of the plywood as regular parallel bands. Remember that the second, or mating piece of plywood must have its scarf cut on the reverse side and must be identical in width.

Glue the scarfed strips together and apply pressure either with "G" cramps and clamping blocks or by using tacking strips (Fig. 16).

Marking Out the Spars

Having prepared the four long strips of plywood—two for the mainspars and two for the rear spars—mark off a centre line corresponding to the rib datum along each one. Do this with a chalk line by well rubbing chalk into some thin string. Get two assistants to hold the line taut at each end and in contact with the plywood at the datum position. With forefinger and thumb, lift the string vertically at the middle about 3in. and then let go.

From this datum, mark off the position of the lower boom on one side and draw on the location of the bottom edge of the spar using a hard pencil and a straightedge.

Draw on the location of the top boom outer edge in the same way.

Now cut the web very accurately to the lines drawn and, laying it flat on the floor, tack blocks of wood about 6in. × 1½in. × 1in. at intervals of about 18in. along both sides. Lift out the plywood web.

Carefully select the wood for the booms from the best available spruce and diminish the thickness of the booms at the tip as shown in Fig. 17. Lay them in the jig and

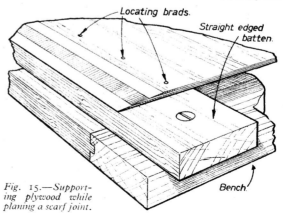

Fig. 15.—Supporting plywood while planing a scarf joint.

Labels on figure: Locating brads. — Straight edged batten. — Bench pack them out from the centre so that they are in close contact with the jig blocks. If necessary, the outer ends of the booms may be steamed to shape using boiling water. Let them dry thoroughly before gluing. Wherever the glue may come into contact with a wood jig block, insert a strip of polythene sheet or waxed paper.

Cut and fit all the vertical members and the root end block and lift strut angled block. The grain of all blocks in the spar is vertical with the exception of the angled lift strut block which has the grain parallel to its edges. The blocks should be a good snug fit in the booms.

Well glue the top surface of the booms and blocks and also the mating surfaces of the plywood web. Tack the web to the booms using $\frac{1}{2}$in. × 20 s.w.g. brass gimp pins at intervals of about 1in., staggering the pitch as shown in Fig. 18.

Leave the spar to dry and then carefully remove it from the jig. Repeat this for the other spars, remembering to make each pair handed—that is with the plywood web on the other side—so that both port and both starboard spars have the plywood webs facing aft.

Check the spars against each other in pairs to see that they are identical as regards depth and length.

Compression Struts

Each wing has two bays of wire cross-bracing so there is a main compression strut at the centre, one at the root end and one at the tip. The centre one is of box construction; the tip one is a spruce strut glued to the inboard face of Rib D and the root

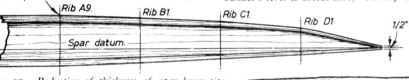

Diminish spar boom depth from here evenly on both top and bottom booms before bending.

Fig. 17.—Reduction of thickness of spar boom tips.

end one is a spruce strut to which is built the root end rib.

Make up all the metal fittings for the wings and, having marked their positions on the spars, drill through and temporarily bolt them in place. It is far easier to drill the various bolt holes at this stage as, once the wing is assembled, it is hard to line up the drill.

Mark the correct positions of all the ribs on the spars.

Wing Assembly.

Take two saw-horses or folding trestles which stand about 30in. high and set them about 8ft. apart. Lay the port wing front and rear spars upside down across the trestles with their plywood faces aft.

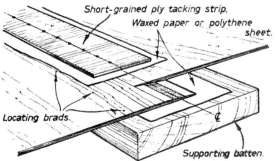

Short-grained ply tacking strip.

Waxed paper or polythene sheet.

Locating brads.

Supporting batten.

Fig. 16.—Gluing up a plywood scarf joint.

Thread all the ribs A to the spars, bottom surface up, and slide them approximately into their correct positions. Insert the aileron spar (which is made from $\frac{1}{8}$in. solid spruce) and then slide on the tip ribs B, C and D. Pack between the rear spar and the aileron spar with 1 in. thick packing.

Level off the wing on the trestles—a builder's level is useful here. To stop the wing slipping off the trestles, tack small blocks either side of the spars.

Glue all the ribs by sliding them to one side of the mark on the spar and thoroughly coating the spar and the rib vertical. Reposition the rib and, having seen that the rib capstrip is in firm contact with the bottom of the spar (uppermost) nail the rib to the spar through the verticals with $\frac{1}{2}$in. × 20 s.w.g. gimp pins. A convenient way of doing this which cuts out much thumb-hitting and tack-bending is to use a spring pin pusher (available at tool shops for about 5s.), finally knocking them home with the tack hammer. For nailing in awkward places, a pair of long-nosed pliers can be used to press the brad in.

The $\frac{1}{8}$in. thick plywood plates which cover the root end block and the lift strut fitting block may now be fitted, the latter

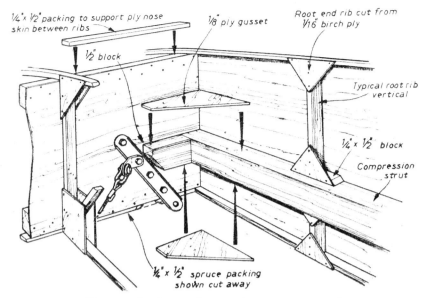

$\frac{1}{4}$" × $\frac{1}{2}$" packing to support ply nose skin between ribs

$\frac{1}{8}$" ply gusset

Root end rib cut from $\frac{1}{16}$" birch ply

$\frac{1}{2}$" block

Typical root rib vertical

$\frac{1}{4}$" × $\frac{1}{2}$" block

Compression strut

$\frac{1}{4}$" × $\frac{1}{2}$" spruce packing shown cut away

Fig. 19.—Attachment of compression strut at root end.

one being trimmed to fit each side of the rib.

Fix the compression struts, blocking and gusseting them into place (Fig. 19).

Bolting on the Metal Fittings

This is done next. Avoid over-tightening aircraft bolts as it is very easy to crush timber and distort fittings. Use a spanner of such a length that it is difficult to exert excessive torque. For a 2 B.A. nut, for example, a $2\frac{1}{2}$in. long spanner is ample; a $3\frac{1}{2}$in. spanner sufficiently tightens a $\frac{1}{4}$in. nut.

Do not hold the nut with one spanner and turn the bolt with the other. Always tighten up on the nut, using a fixed size spanner or ring spanner.

Use bolts of such a length that, when the washer and nut are in place, about $1\frac{1}{2}$ to 2 full threads protrude. The nut is then said to be "in safety." This applies with self-locking stiff nuts, lock nuts, plain nuts and castle nuts. When peening over bolts, support the head of the bolt with a heavy block of steel or a hammer head otherwise you may damage the structure surrounding the bolt.

Details for completing the wing construction and commencing the fuselage will be given next month.

Fig. 18.—How the rows of gimp pins on spar flanges, etc., are staggered.

Building the 'Luton Minor'

(Continued from page 75, November issue)

NEXT we deal with wire bracing. Thread string through the wing ribs between the bracing lugs for the wire bracing to determine the exact run of the wires. The material used for bracing is a hard, stiff wire commonly called piano wire. Form the ends of the wire as shown in Fig. 20. The sleeves are ¾in. long and are made of flattened copper tube. Soft-solder them to the wire—do not braze or silver solder them as the heat will affect the strength of the wire.

One end of the wire fits a 5 cwt. wire strainer or turn-buckle; the other takes an

Part 4 Concludes Construction of the Wings and Starts on the Fuselage

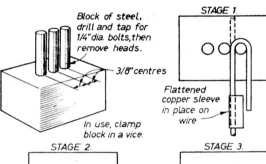

Fig. 20.—How to form an " eye " splice in piano wire.

aircraft shackle, both of which then pick up on the bracing lugs (Fig. 21).

Make each of the four wires in each wing in this manner, thread them through the wing ribs and then remove the guide string. Attach them to the lugs with shackle pins and 1/16in. split cotter pins. Leave the wires untensioned for the moment.

Use a large square to make sure that the spars at the root end are in line with each other. Since the wing is really a parallelogram, slight movement of the spars to

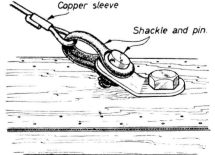

Fig. 21.—Attachment of bracing wires. The other end of the wire is fixed with a turn-buckle.

produce the desired rectangle can be accomplished by adjusting the tension of the wires.

When the wing is trued up, tension the wires just sufficiently to produce a low twang when they are plucked. Overtensioning of the wires can, in extreme cases, cause the splitting of the spar webs and any such pre-stressing of the wing is undesirable.

Wing Tip Bows

Make a simple jig for the laminations of the wing tip bows and, while the bows are setting in the jig, fit the leading and trailing edge members to the wing. Note that the aileron is not yet severed from the rest of the wing.

Make the root end rib. This is cut from 1/16in. or 1mm.

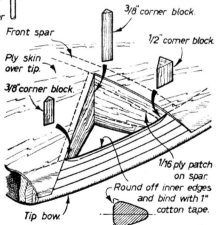

Fig. 22.—Details of the hand hold in the wingtip.

birch ply with a top and bottom capstrip of rib-stock. This is then built on to the spar roots and the drag strut as shown on the plan.

Clean up and fit the wing tip bows. Scarf the bow to the leading-edge member and also the trailing edge. Fit the drag-brace strut in the tip, the hand-hold member (Fig. 22) and also the diagonals which brace the aileron.

Cladding the Leading Edge

We now come to the ply-covering of the

wing leading edge. Remember that once this is done, any twist or warp in the wing will be locked in and the wing will not be true. Bearing this in mind, you are advised to make up three " L " braces, each about 6ft. high with a 2ft. or 3ft. base, to support the wing at right angles with the leading edge uppermost.

Screw the " L " braces to the floor so that one will support the wing at the root end, one at the centre drag strut and one at the tip. Fix to the braces short rigid cross pieces to hold the wing under the front spar. Hang the wing on to these with the top surface of the wing facing outwards.

Pack if necessary under the spar to bring the front spar level. Using " G " clamps and clamping blocks, secure the spar to the braces. Also clamp at the rear spar, packing out as necessary. This arrangement is shown in Fig. 23.

Hang plumb bobs over the front spar at the centre and also at the root and measure the distance between the plumb line and the rear spar where the line passes it. This distance should be the same for both lines; if it is not, then carefully pack between the rear spar and the support and re-clamp. When the measurements coincide, the wing is true and free from twist. Until the leading edge is completely covered, it is inadvisable to move the wing.

Take a straight edge long enough to touch at least three ribs and, working along the leading edge one rib at a time, try to rock the straightedge. Any irregularities in the profile will be shown either as high spots

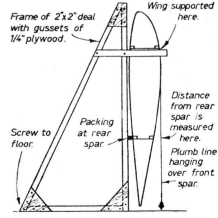

Fig. 23.—Brace the wing to the floor to check alignment before ply-covering the leading edge.

which can be pared away, or as low spots. These latter will require packing glued on and then shaping when dry.

This preparation of the front portion of the wing is very important as, if the ribs are slightly out of profile, the plywood covering will be lumpy. Not only would this be unsightly, but it would affect the performance of the finished aircraft.

Cover the leading edge in sections with separate pieces of plywood, scarfing them together on the job. Cut the plywood long-grained from 4ft. square sheets, half a sheet thus covering a 4ft. length of wing. Trim the sheet so that it can be scarfed on a rib and then pre-form the ply by folding it along the line of the leading edge, pouring boiling water over the outside and inside and clamping it between two planks of wood to the desired radius.

While this is drying, fit strips of packing to both sides of the front spar to support the plywood between the ribs (Fig. 19). Similarly, fit strips of packing on both sides of the rear spar over the aileron gap only. This is to support the fabric. Do not fit this packing to the rear spar over the main part of the wing.

Special clamps are available for pulling

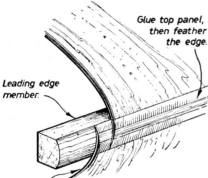

Glue top panel, then feather the edge.

Leading edge member.

Glue bottom ply before feathering the edge.

Fig. 24.—The joint between the top and bottom plywood panels covering the leading edge between ribs " C " and " D."

the plywood skin over the leading edge but, to save cost, it is quite sufficient to use webbing straps to apply pressure. You will need enough straps to pass over each rib which is to be covered with the ply panel being fitted. They will pass over the leading edge, round under the rear spar (which is padded with clean rag and scrap wood to prevent abrasion) and back up to the leading edge.

Starting from the under side of the wing, liberally glue the spar edge and the rib capstrips as far as the leading-edge member. Position the sheet of plywood and tack it to the spar edge with ½in. × 20 s.w.g. gimp pins, placed at intervals of about ¾in. Work up towards the leading edge along each rib

progressively, tacking to the ribs with tacking strips. Now glue the ribs on the other (top) side and the spar edge.

Loop the webbing straps over the leading edge, keeping them as close to each rib as possible, and tension them. Slide battens of wood between the plywood and the straps at each rib and force the plywood into intimate contact with the rib. Take care not to ruck up the plywood or cause " bubbles " in it. If the wood sounds hollow when tapped with the hammer, then there is a bubble or pocket which must be worked out. With tacking strips, tack between the battens through to the rib.

When the first piece has been completed, leave it overnight to dry before slackening off the webbing straps and removing the tacking strips.

Cut a scarf on the outer rib plywood for the next panel using a bull-nosed plane, a file or a chisel. The next panel should be scarfed on the inside before pre-forming to mate the first one.

The tip, where the wing diminishes in depth, must be covered in smaller panels; the last rib A to the rib C is done in one piece; the portion between rib C and rib D is covered in two halves, scarfed on the leading edge (Fig. 24). The tip of the wing, from rib D to the mainspar is covered again in two halves while the remainder of the tip is covered with two panels, one on top and one beneath. The grain of all the plywood should be spanwise.

Now build in the transverse stringers between the root end rib and the first rib A and ply-cover the root, top and bottom, using 1/16in. plywood, spanwise grained.

Carefully cut away the aileron and clean up the rib ends. No control cables are fitted yet.

The starboard wing is made in exactly the same way, but do not forget to glue the block into the mainspar which carries the pivot head. This and the anchor-unit plate must be fitted before the leading edge plywood is fitted.

Building the Fuselage

The method of building the fuselage which is described here is somewhat different to that shown on the plans. On these, the boxing up of the fuselage may present difficulties in aligning the two sides and bending in the bottom longerons at the nose.

The sequence of operations detailed herein has been adopted by Phoenix Aircraft Ltd. to eliminate these possible difficulties. The making of the necessary jigs for bending in the nose is strongly recommended as in

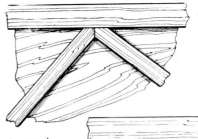

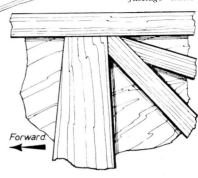

Forward

Fig. 26.—(Left) typical joint between bracing and longeron in fuselage sides and (below) joint of heavy under-carriage member and cockpit bracing struts in fuselage sides.

Port side. 2'6" 1'6" Cut. 1'6" 2'6" **Starboard side.**

Fig. 27.—Scarfing plywood sheets for the sides. Note how both sides may be cut from four sheets of nominal 4ft. width. Direction of the grain is important.

the long run time and effort will be saved and a better job achieved.

Fuselage Side Jigs

The first step is to make a jig to locate the longerons and various members in the fuselage sides, both of which are built flat. As the two sides must be dimensionally the same, but opposite handed, we advise the constructor to make a jig for each side in the manner described.

By making the two sides next to each other, time can be saved and measurements can be taken to both sides from one centre-line situated near the top longerons. This is clearly shown in Fig. 25.

Since the longerons at the nose end of the fuselage must be left at least 1ft. longer than will be required to aid bending, a clear space of about 17ft. × 4ft. 6in. will be needed. Ideally, use a level wooden floor and set out the jig as shown in Fig. 25. While wooden blocks must be used to locate the longerons, headless nails may be used to hold in place the various cross members. Do not bend up the bottom longerons in

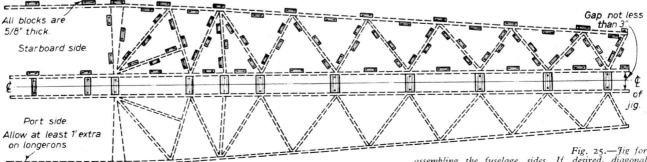

All blocks are 5/8" thick.

Starboard side.

Port side.

Allow at least 1' extra on longerons.

Gap not less than 3"

℄ of jig.

Fig. 25.—Jig for assembling the fuselage sides. If desired, diagonal bracing members may be located between headless nails. Longerons must be located in blocks.

Fig. 28.—*Photograph of the fuselage sides (picture by Mr. J. T Hayes, Lincoln).*

this jig, but just bring them parallel to the top ones as shown.

Cut and fit the longerons and spruce bracing struts, making sure that the joints are correctly formed as shown in Fig. 26.

Put a piece of polythene sheet or waxed paper under the joints and proceed to glue up each joint carefully and thoroughly. The farthest forward member to be glued at this stage is the heavy cockpit member which takes the undercarriage and lift strut fittings.

Plywood Side Skins

Now scarf up the ply sheets for the fuselage sides. Join the sheets as shown in Fig. 27. Scarf not less than 1 in 12 and, when set, well sand each side of the joints to remove any surplus glue. Cut the joined sheets as shown in Fig. 27 for the two sides. If desired, the sheets may be cut before scarfing to reduce the length of the scarf joints.

Place the long strip of ply skin over each fuselage side frame in the jig, allowing about ½in. overlap at the top longeron. Fix them temporarily in place with a few

brads and then pencil on the positions of the longerons and all members as a guide for stapling.

Remove the skins. Mix sufficient glue to glue up one side and remembering still not to glue anything forward of the heavy cockpit vertical member, apply glue liberally to the fuselage side frame. This is best done with a ½in. wide paint brush. Do not forget to wash it out after use in plain warm water.

With a moistened sponge, evenly dampen the *top* surface of the ply skin before gluing so that the ply will expand slightly and, when dry after gluing, will contract to form an even, smooth skin in the fuselage.

It is a common eyesore with ply-covered aircraft that, after a time and especially in damp weather, the ply distorts between structural members. This is even more apparent with flat surfaces and this slight moistening before fixing will considerably retard this tendency.

Fitting the Skin

Enlist the help of an assistant and carefully position the ply skin on the frame. Starting at the top longeron by the heavy cockpit member, begin stapling the ply. Hold the stapling tool at an angle of about

45° to the centre-line of the member and staple at intervals of about ¾in. Work one bay at a time progressively aft.

To keep within the setting time of the glue, especially in warm temperatures, it may be necessary to glue only a 4ft. length at a time. If this is done, allow an overlap of the next glue application to avoid a possible gap. Repeat this procedure for the other fuselage side.

While the glue is setting, draw out on the floor the plan of the top of the fuselage from the stern-post as far forward as the cross member which is situated 119½in. from the stern post. Screw blocks of wood to the floor to locate each side of the longerons. The sides will be placed between these blocks inverted so that the fuselage is upside down for the next stage in assembly.

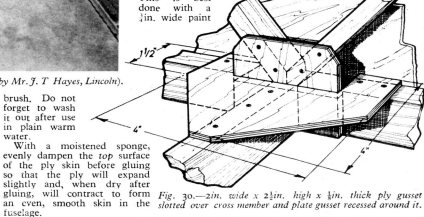

Fig. 30.—*2in. wide x 2½in. high x ⅛in. thick ply gusset slotted over cross member and plate gusset recessed around it.*

Remove the two sides from the assembly jig and plane off the surplus ply overlapping at the longerons. Do not as yet trim the excess from the unglued portion forward of the undercarriage member.

Filling Gaps

Examine carefully for any gaps in the gluing along the longerons and bracing. If construction has been done correctly, there should be no gaps but, should any be discovered, force glue under pressure into the gap with a polythene cake-icing syringe.

Check the two sides together and see that the top longerons are flush and free from lumps of dried glue. Sand each joint on the inside of each side. Ideally, use an orbital sanding tool but, if you use a rotary sanding disc in an electric drill, exercise caution as they cut quickly and can remove the base wood in addition to the dried glue.

Remove all the staples with the special tool described in Fig. 2 (October issue).

Fitting Cross Struts

Set the two sides upside down in the plan jig (Fig. 29).

Remember that you now have the fuselage upside down and mark on the positions of all the cross struts in the fuselage bottom (uppermost) as far as the one 109½in. from the stern post.

Clamp the rear fuselage sides to two straight-edged boards (Fig. 29) and cut and fit the cross members. To support and strengthen these butt-joints, make and fit ⅛in. plywood saddle gussets as shown in Fig. 30. The saddle gussets at the cross member which takes the 1/16in. ply bulkhead in the rear fuselage will not be fitted until this bulkhead has been installed as they will need to be shaped to suit. Do not screw the cross members to the longerons.

(To be continued)

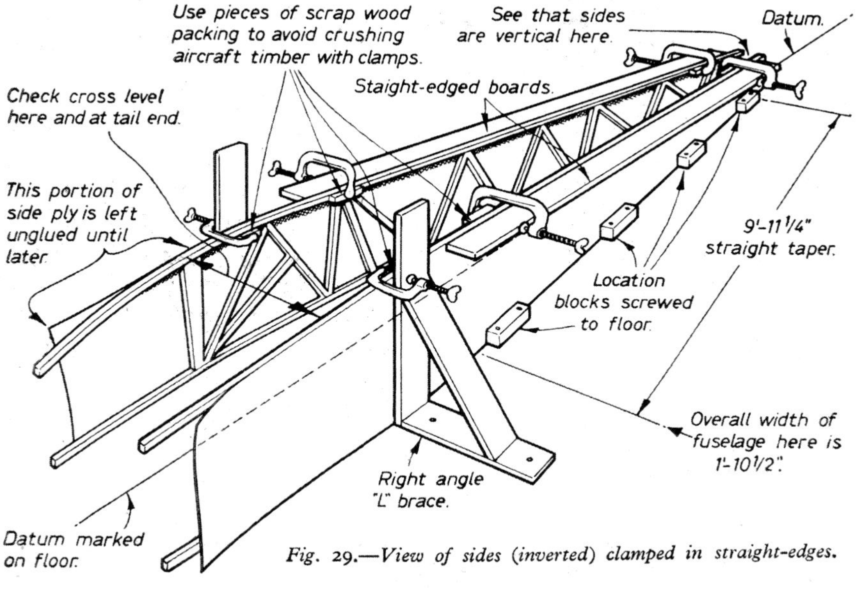

Use pieces of scrap wood packing to avoid crushing aircraft timber with clamps.

Check cross level here and at tail end.

See that sides are vertical here.

Staight-edged boards.

Datum.

This portion of side ply is left unglued until later

9'-11¼" straight taper.

Location blocks screwed to floor.

Overall width of fuselage here is 1'-10½".

Right angle "L" brace.

Datum marked on floor.

Fig. 29.—*View of sides (inverted) clamped in straight-edges.*

Building the 'Luton Minor'

(Continued from the December issue)

WITH the cross members fitted in the bottom rear fuselage, cut and fit those at the top longerons (which are lowermost). Also fit the diagonal struts which pass between the sides. Before gluing these in, however, check the alignment of the fuselage sides—all the cross members should be at right-angles to the centre-line drawn on the floor.

The Bulkhead

To complete the structure of the rear fuselage, cut and fit the bulkhead which runs diagonally across the fuselage elevation. The top and bottom cross members which take this should be shaped as shown in the detail on Fig. 31. Before doing this check that the fuselage sides are square. Note that the bulkhead will not be rect-

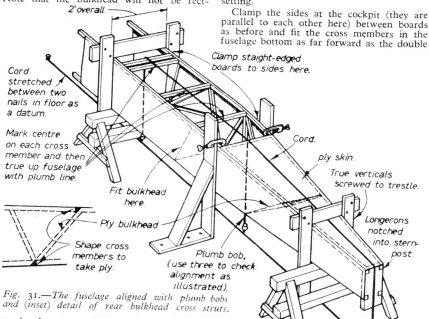

Fig. 31.—The fuselage aligned with plumb bobs and (inset) detail of rear bulkhead cross struts.

angular but trapezoidal as the fuselage is tapered, the top edge being shorter than the lower.

The plywood skin can now be fitted to the fuselage bottom from the stern post as far forward as the cross member, 109½in. forward, again moistening the ply. The direction of the grain of the lower ply should be longways.

When stapling plywood to the cross members, get an assistant to support the centre of each member with the flat of a heavy hammer or a heavy block. Failure to do this may crack the member and will certainly result in gaps between the member and the ply skin.

Tack a few strips of scrap wood diagonally across the unbraced forward halves of the fuselage sides to prevent them moving.

Set the fuselage on two trestles with extension pieces as shown in Fig. 31. Stretch a thin cord between two nails in the floor to represent the fuselage centre-line. The illustration depicts the correct method of aligning the fuselage. Remember that the rear end is rigidly boxed and thus alignment is achieved by adjusting the posi-

tions of the sides at the front end so that their distances from the centre-line are equal. Plumb-bobs are used to determine the right setting.

Clamp the sides at the cockpit (they are parallel to each other here) between boards as before and fit the cross members in the fuselage bottom as far forward as the double

members which take the undercarriage and lift-strut fittings.

Cut a scarf joint on the edge of the bottom ply at the cross member (the end of the ply fitted previously) and to this scarf and fit the ply skin as far forward as the double cross-struts, stopping on the front one of the two.

Remove the fuselage, turn it up the right way and realign it between the uprights on the trestles. Again clamp the top longerons at the cockpit between boards. Cut and fit the cross members at the top longerons and also the bulkhead at the rear of the pilot's seat. Note that this bulkhead again is not rectangular, the lower dimensions being slightly greater.

Part 5 Continues Construction of the Fuselage

Curved Cockpit Former

The next job is the making of the curved cockpit former which is made *in situ* and serves to stiffen the fuselage over the cockpit area.

It is made from three laminations of 3/16in. × ¾in. ash, 7ft. long. Glue them together flat, then spring the three pieces into the cockpit, gluing them to the sloping strut which passes down the sides of the cockpit. Cut and fit the cross member at the front of the former and glue and clamp the bow to it at the centre where the former is flattened for 3in. Keeping the edges of the strips flush with the top of the strut in the fuselage side, screw the strips to this member using 1½in. long countersunk brass woodscrews ⅛in. in diameter. Also screw the bow to the last diagonal strut in the fuselage before the cockpit bulkhead, cutting the ends of the strips flush with the rear edge of this member.

The curved seat-back lower former, which forms part of this cockpit stiffening former, can be made separately, using a simple jig into which the two laminations of ⅛in. × ⅜in. spruce are glued and bent and joined at the centre to the ⅛in. × ¾in. cross strut. Glue on one ply web, allowing enough ply to glue on to the cockpit former at the sides and the shaped 1in. × ¾in. cross strut at the back.

After this has set, glue this former into place across the rear end of the cockpit former.

Now cut and fit the 1/16in. plywood diaphragms which fit on each side of the cockpit former, one on the top, one below, so that the ply overlaps the edges of the fuselage strut. This is illustrated on the plan.

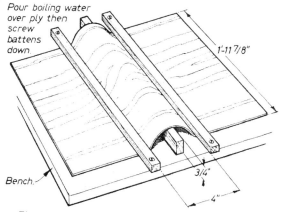

Fig. 32.—Pre-forming floor ply for seat cross support

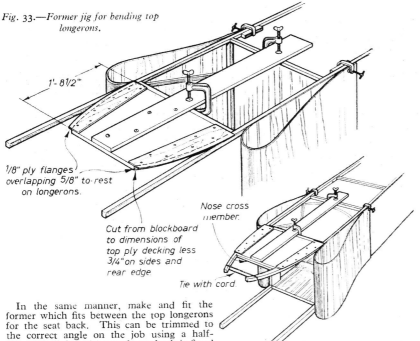

Fig. 33.—Former jig for bending top longerons.

1'-8½"

1/8" ply flanges overlapping 5/8" to rest on longerons.

Cut from blockboard to dimensions of top ply decking less 3/4" on sides and rear edge.

Nose cross member.

Tie with cord.

In the same manner, make and fit the former which fits between the top longerons for the seat back. This can be trimmed to the correct angle on the job using a half-round file before the actual seat-back is fitted later on.

Fit the cross member between the top longerons at the front of the cockpit and also the wedge strip between it and the former cross strut.

Make the special seat support cross member and glue and screw it to the bottom longerons using one 1¼in. × ¼in. countersunk brass woodscrew each side. Glue it also to the bottom ply skin.

Cockpit Floor

The cockpit floor may next be fitted and it is advised that this be done in two sections—from the bulkhead as far forward as the next cross member as one section and then the second section as far forward as the front undercarriage cross member.

Both sections are of 1/16in. ply with the grain fore and aft. The rear section is supported forward of the bulkhead by a ¼in. × ¼in. member glued to the bulkhead between the longerons.

The second section (which is overlapped 1in. on to the first) has to be pre-formed to fit over the special seat support cross member. Do this by clamping the ply as shown in Fig. 32 and pouring boiling water over it. When dry, glue and tack it into place.

This completes the fuselage except for the bending in of the longerons at the nose. This is an important job and care must be taken not to crack the longerons. Begin on the two top ones by making an internal former of blockboard as shown in Fig. 33. Fix this to a straight board which is then clamped to the cross members as shown.

Fold back the unglued forward plywood skins and tie them to the fuselage sides out of the way, taking care not to fold them so tight that they split.

Thoroughly soak one longeron in boiling water for several minutes and then, holding it with a glove, carefully begin to bend it. Do not hasten the bending, but work it slowly, applying more boiling water as necessary. Bring in both longerons in this manner and tie them together with cord at the front end where they overhang. Do not remove the blockboard former.

The lower longerons present a slightly more difficult job. Remove the fuselage

from the trestles and set it on the floor between the " L " braces as shown in Fig. 34.

Make the jig for bending in the lower longerons (Fig. 35) using softwood and commercial ply. Note how the longerons are located against blocks on the inner profile and are held down in place by cross-beams screwed into the blocks. The dimensions for the profile base may be taken from the fuselage bottom nose skin measurements.

The lower longerons will need steaming and boiling water saturation before and during bending and ideally a shallow tray should be placed under them which is filled with water heated by a gas jet. If this is done, take care that the gas jet is centrally placed under the tray and is not near the longerons where local heating might affect the wood.

When the longerons are supple (after about ten minutes in boiling water), remove

the water tray and position the jig.

Check that the jig is in the right location fore and aft and also about the centre-line of the fuselage.

Bending Lower Longerons

Bending each longeron into place in the jig will require the services of an assistant who must press downwards on the longeron immediately forward of the heavy fuselage side member. This is to avoid concentrating all the bending forces at the forward corner of this member which might crack the longeron.

The cross-beams which hold the longerons down against the inner profile blocks are fixed with 2in. long screws so that they can be gradually tightened, drawing the longerons down into place. This permits periodic applications of boiling water as they are screwed down. Again tie the protruding ends of the longerons with cord.

Leave the fuselage set thus for about two days to dry out. Do not try to accelerate the drying by applying direct heat.

The Side Ply

If the jig for the lower longerons has been made right, and the cross-beams are the correct length, it is now possible to glue and staple on the side ply from the undercarriage heavy member forward without removing the jigs for the upper and lower longerons. Before doing this, however, check with a spirit level across the top longerons at the cockpit and again at the nose to see that there is no twist in them. If there is, it can easily be packed out now. Likewise check across the lower longerons at the nose so that the engine bulkhead will be perfectly rectangular.

Once the side skins are in place and the glue set, the jigs may be removed from the nose, leaving the cords in place to prevent any tendency for the side to spring open.

Fit the cross members between the top longerons at the front together with the horizontal plan bracing struts.

With the fuselage horizontally level, drop a plumb-bob over the nose cross member to the lower longerons and in this manner mark the position of the nose cross member in the lower longerons which is set 4¼in. ahead of the top one to give the angled bulkhead.

The side members for the engine bulkhead are next fitted making sure that the ends are correctly mitred to butt against the longerons.

A full set of plans costs £11·10·0 from Phœnix Aircraft, Cranleigh Common, Cranleigh, Surrey.

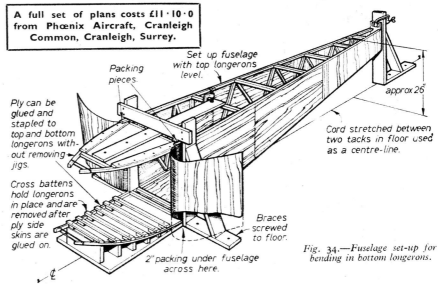

Packing pieces.

Ply can be glued and stapled to top and bottom longerons without removing jigs.

Cross battens hold longerons in place and are removed after ply side skins are glued on.

Set up fuselage with top longerons level.

approx 26'

Cord stretched between two tacks in floor used as a centre-line.

Braces screwed to floor.

2" packing under fuselage across here.

¢

Fig. 34.—Fuselage set-up for bending in bottom longerons.

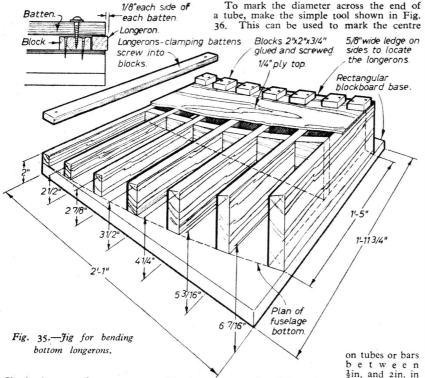

Fig. 35.—Jig for bending bottom longerons.

Check the nose for squareness with the rest of the fuselage and then fit the inverted "V" struts in the front.

Fit the ⅛in. ply engine bulkhead, invert the fuselage and fit the rudder bar support and the ¾in. × ¾in. cross member in the nose floor. Scarf on the bottom ply skin from the undercarriage member to the engine bulkhead. The grain of this skin should be at right-angles to the fuselage centre-line.

The forward cockpit floor is made of ⅛in. birch ply with the grain running across the width of the fuselage and is lapped on to the rest of the cockpit floor, terminating on the rudder bar support.

The two ¾in. square members in each side of the fuselage forward of the heavy undercarriage member can next be fitted.

These struts, if they are straight, will tend to draw the curved side ply flat, giving an unsightly appearance. To avoid this, the struts should be curved to match the side, the degree of bowing being about 1½in. at the middle. Either steam the struts on the bench, or make each strut out of two pieces of ⅜in. × ¾in., laminating them together on the job and packing them out against the side ply from the centre.

The primary structure of the fuselage may now be completed by gluing in the 6in. long ash block at the tail end which takes the tail-wheel leaf-spring and temporarily fitting the tailplane table. This is of 1/16in. plywood supported at the stern post by ⅜in. × ¾in. spruce cross member between the longerons.

Metal Fittings

The next step in making the fuselage is to complete all the metal parts shown on Sheet 3 of the plans, the engine bulkhead fittings on Sheet 11 and the wing pylon fittings on Sheet 10.

Some of these parts are made from steel tubing and a few basic points relating to tube work should be understood.

To mark the diameter across the end of a tube, make the simple tool shown in Fig. 36. This can be used to mark the centre on tubes or bars between ½in. and 2in. in diameter by sliding the tool along the end of the tube. The bisector then allows the marking of the diameter.

The diameter of tubing can be measured by clamping it lightly between the smooth jaws of the vice and measuring the distance across the jaws next to the tube with a rule. Alternatively, of course, use a caliper rule.

If the tube be clamped horizontally in the vice so that its top edge is flush with a straightedge placed across the jaws, a centre-line may be drawn on the tube using a rule and scriber.

Where a relatively long tube is being worked at each end, complete one end first and then insert a long bolt or steel rod through any bolt hole in the finished end. This can then be sighted on from the other end using an engineer's square to ensure perfect alignment of the two ends.

Next month's instalment continues with the construction of metal fittings and carries on with the rear decking, etc.

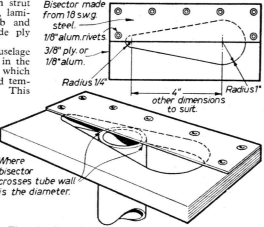

Fig. 36.—Tool for marking the diameter on a tube or circular bar.

AIRCRAFT BUILDING BY AMATEURS

MONOPLANE FOR £250

FROM OUR AERONAUTICAL CORRESPONDENT

The first British ultra-light aircraft since the war designed specifically to be built by amateurs with little or no previous aircraft experience has been produced by Phoenix Aircraft, Ltd., of Cranleigh, Surrey. They are a new firm formed to design and develop light aircraft for sport and pleasure flying.

The aircraft, known as the Luton Minor, is a single-seat monoplane of all-wood construction developed from a pre-war type. The airframe, without the engine, can be built for about £125. Suitable engines, costing about £100 with the airscrew, are available, and with a 37 h.p. Aeronca J.A.P. engine the total cost of the aircraft, the manufacturers say, should not exceed £250. Plans and instructions to build the Minor cost £11 10s., which includes a year's subscription to the Popular Flying Association.

If the wings and tail are removed and fixed to the sides of the fuselage the aircraft can be towed on its own wheels by a car. It is small enough to be kept in a garage. With the J.A.P. engine fuel costs are claimed to be only 2d. an air mile.

WING SPAN OF 25FT.

Only 20ft. 9in. long and with a wing span of 25ft., the Luton Minor can take off in 80 yards and land in 40 yards. Empty weight is 390lb. and gross weight 627lb. The range in still air is 180 miles. Top speed is 85 m.p.h., cruising speed 75 m.p.h., and stalling speed 28 m.p.h. The aircraft is of fabric-covered spruce and plywood construction, and any engine of up to 65 h.p. may be fitted with small modification.

During construction the Minor will be inspected by representatives of the Popular Flying Association. After completion it will be examined to ensure that it has been properly made and then recommended to the Ministry of Transport and Civil Aviation for the issue of a permit to fly. The manufacturers are prepared to send a representative to give advice and help to any constructor who requires it; the only charge for this service will be travelling expenses.

Building the 'Luton Minor'

Part 6.—Completing the Fuselage and Attaching the Tailplane

Tube Bending

WHEN bending a tube, due to the fact that it has no resistant central core, the tube will tend to flatten at the bend. This results in an increase of the axis at right angles to the bend and a corresponding decrease in the axis in the plane of the bend.

However, by bending the tube round a block of the same radius as the desired bend and having a groove in it equal to the tube diameter, this deforming can be resisted to a large extent. Special tube-bending machines are available which almost eliminate deformation of the cross-section of the tube.

Thin tubing is the hardest to bend, for the inner radius tends to buckle. Some expensive machines are made which make use of a "mole" which is a shaped rod

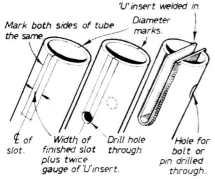

Fig. 37.—*The three stages in marking out, cutting and finishing a tube fork-end.*

slipped inside the tube and which follows up the bend, ensuring a smooth, uniform section.

Thin steel tubes can be bent using a well-greased spring whose outside diameter is the same as the inside of the tube.

Other methods include the use of a fusible alloy or low-melting-point metal which fills the tube, is bent with the tube and then flowed out by immersing the bent tube in boiling water or oil.

The method which the amateur can best adopt is to plug one end of the tube with wood, pack the tube tightly with sand (it must be *dry* sand) and plug the other end. The tube is then heated with a torch or blow-lamp and bent over a radiused former. Make the former of durable wood such as oak.

Alternatively, the amateur may enlist the assistance of a co-operative plumber and his tube-bending machine. Remember to use the right bending former and follower for the diameter being bent.

Slotting Tubes

To slot the end of a tube as, for example, to take a "U" insert, mark out the full width of the slot from the centre-line of the tube on each side (Fig. 37) and drill a hole to mark the termination of the slot.

Now cut with the hacksaw and finish off with a thin flat file to size. On large-diameter tubes, it is better to hold the saw at an angle and cut each slot individually, eliminating the chance of inaccurate cutting of the other side.

Fig. 38 shows the right method to employ when flattening the ends of tubes symmetrically or asymmetrically. If tubes are to be closed completely flat at the end, always heat the tube red hot first. Crush the end, using a block of wood, end-grain on. Never hit direct with the hammer.

When cutting a narrow slot in a tube as, for example, to weld in a single 16 s.w.g. plate, use two hacksaw blades together in the saw. Cut carefully, for one blade will be slightly tighter in the frame than the other.

Use a hacksaw blade with the right number of teeth per inch when cutting tubing. Very thin tubes can be sawn by keeping the hacksaw at a tangent to the surface all the way round by rotating the tube as it is cut. Remove the internal burrs

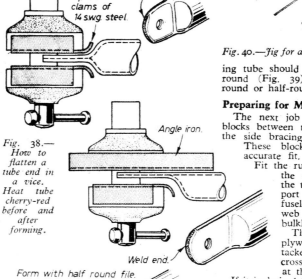

Fig. 38.— *How to flatten a tube end in a vice. Heat tube cherry-red before and after forming.*

Fig. 39. — *How meeting tubes are carefully filed to a snug fit before welding.*

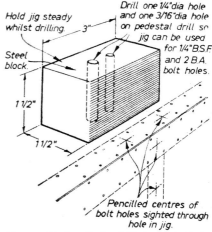

Fig. 40.—*Jig for aligning drill when boring holes.*

with a half-round smooth file.

Where one tube meets another, the meeting tube should be filed to a snug fit all round (Fig. 39). This is done with a round or half-round bastard file.

Preparing for Metal Fittings

The next job is to glue in the corner blocks between the fuselage longerons and the side bracing at the engine bulkhead. These blocks must be a true and accurate fit.

Fit the rudder bar which pivots on the support bracket bolted to the top of the rudder bar support cross-member in the front fuselage and the ½in. spruce web between it and the engine bulkhead.

The top decking of 3/32in. plywood can now be glued and tacked into place on top of the cross-member and plan-bracing at the nose.

If it is desired to cover the plywood structure of the fuselage with madapolam fabric to preserve and strengthen it (this is strongly advisable in very hot or humid climates), the fabric should be applied to the sides and bottom at this stage. Instructions for doing this will be given later on. In any case, it is recommended that a 2in. wide serrated edged fabric tape be doped to the lower corners along the fuselage length, around the edges of the stern-post and engine bulkhead and along the top longerons from the engine to the seat-back to seal the edges against moisture and preserve the wood.

Apply two coats of red oxide tautening dope along the corners; then apply the tape with another liberal coat of dope as described further on. This is done *before* any metal fittings are bolted on.

Drilling Bolt Holes

The bolt holes through the fuselage members for the attachment of the metal fittings must be drilled accurately. Ideally, an electric drill should be used. Back up the member being drilled with a flat piece of scrap wood so that the drill passes through into it. This way, the drill will not tear the surface grain as it breaks through.

A useful jig can be made to ensure perfect alignment of the drill. This is shown in Fig. 40. The jig is placed over the pencilled location of the hole and the drill bit carefully centred through it.

All bolts in the fuselage pass from the outside inwards and all nuts are on the inside. Where no fitting backs on to the inside, make use of large duralumin "penny" washers to avoid crushing the timber. Trim them to fit if necessary, but always see that the trimmed edge is smooth and straight otherwise the nut will pull it into the surface grain and cause damage. Unless otherwise specified, mild steel hexagon-headed cadmium-plated bolts are used with a plain shank of such a length that no more than one thread-pitch shall come into contact with the wood through which they pass. Use self-locking stiff nuts except where otherwise stated.

Begin assembling the engine mounting bulkhead brackets, the wing pylon fittings, the undercarriage and lift-strut brackets and the fish-plates which join the fin-post to the stern-post. Fit also the reinforcing gusset, Pt. No. 8F, having first drilled the solid ash block to take the tailwheel leaf spring. The shield plate, Pt. No. 9F, is also fitted.

Assemble and fit the control column and

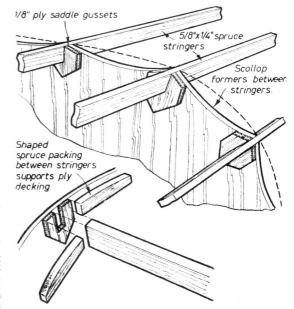

Fig. 41.—Control column and bracket assembly.

its bracket (Fig. 41). Do not fit the swivelling aileron cable pulleys and their brackets to the fuselage sides until the wings are fitted later.

The Rear Decking

Cut out all the decking formers from $\frac{1}{8}$in. plywood (grain vertical) and fix these in place to the fuselage cross struts. Cut notches for the stringers in the first one (immediately above the bulkhead at the rear of the cockpit) and the last one (at the forward end of the tail-plane table). Lay in the spruce stringers and, keeping them straight, mark where they touch each of the other formers and cut notches.

The curved seat-back former must be fitted next. Leave the ply protruding above the longerons at least 8in. at the centre and then spile off the developed curve of the decking. Do this with a batten of wood held against the first two decking formers as shown in Fig. 42.

Cut the curved ply back to this line and mark the positions of the stringers. Do not notch the ply here—the ends of the stringers are supported behind the ply by the special saddle-gussets.

Glue all the stringers into place and fit the saddle-gussets (Fig. 43). Strengthen the seat-back ply on the aft side with shaped pieces of $\frac{1}{8}$in. thick spruce which will also provide a larger gluing surface for the curved rear decking of plywood which is fitted next.

Bend a sheet of fore-and-aft grained 1/16in. ply over the decking and tie it with string round the fuselage whilst marking the shape with a pencil. Leave plenty of spare on the front and rear edges which can be trimmed off later. Cut a scarf on the fuselage side plywood where the decking skin will meet it, transfer the exact location of the scarf to the skin, remove it and cut the scarf on the port and starboard sides of it. Remember that this skin will be scarfed on the "inside."

Glue it on, stapling the ply to each stringer, starting from the top centre one.

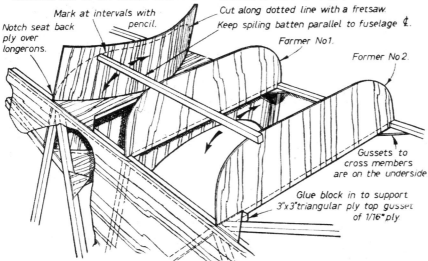

Fig. 43.—Attaching the stringers to the curved seat back former.

Strap the ply round the fuselage to avoid unevenness due to the spring of the ply. Use tacking strips to apply setting pressure to the scarfs at each side.

When the glue has set, trim back the excess ply to the correct line and scollop the rear edges between the stringers as shown on the plan. This can best be done with a very sharp modelling knife followed by a rub with a piece of glass-paper wrapped round a cardboard or metal tube of the right diameter.

Finish off by scolloping all the decking formers (except the last) in the same manner between the stringers. This will prevent the edges of the formers from showing through the fabric covering. Likewise carefully sandpaper each stringer to remove the sharp corners. This can be done before fitting them if preferred but, if so, remember not to radius the edges over the front portion of the stringers to which the ply deck is glued.

Tailplane Attachment

The front tailplane attachment fittings are now offered up to their correct locations on the rear top longerons. The tailplane decking is not yet fitted, so pack under the top flange of the fittings with scrap 1/16in. ply.

Fig. 42.—How to mark out the curve of the seat back former.

Drill and temporarily fit the two front fittings, making certain that a line stretched between them is exactly at right angles to the fuselage centre-line.

Put on the tailplane and bolt the two front spar lugs to the fuselage fittings. Now position the rear spar fittings and mark their locations. Remove the tailplane and drill the bolt holes for these rear brackets. Take off the four attachment brackets, cut and fit the tailplane table and, when set and trimmed to size, finally bolt on the brackets.

Make the inspection panel in the port side of the fuselage at the tail and position the tailplane again. Offer up the elevator and mark the location of the slot in the tailplane table through which protrudes the elevator lever.

The bracket which locates the leading edge of the fin and the top elevator cable pulley is next fitted to the last decking former. Fit the fin, ensuring that it is vertical to the fuselage. This is best checked with a spirit level across the longerons and a plumb bob.

Cut the slot for the elevator lever in the fin base rib.

Now make the cockpit seat (Fig. 44) and temporarily fit it to the brackets on the seat rails screwed to the cockpit floor.

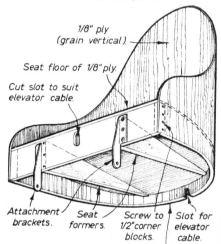

1/8" ply (grain vertical)

Seat floor of 1/8" ply.

Cut slot to suit elevator cable.

Attachment brackets. Seat formers. Screw to 1/2" corner blocks. Slot for elevator cable.

Three laminations of 1/8" short-grained ply glued to seat ply to support seat all round.

Fig. 44.—The pilot's seat. It is hinged by the attachment brackets to allow access to the luggage compartment behind the seat.

The Undercarriage

Start by making the main leg-axle assembly. Flatten the end of the leg tube and spile the shape of the interpenetration with the axle tube. This is shown in Fig. 45. Repeat the spiling for both sides of the axle tube and cut out the oval-shaped hole using a drill, a rat-tail and a half-round file. Work carefully so that the leg tube is a snug fit inside the axle holes. See that the angle is correct and weld all round, top and bottom. Now measure off the length of the leg and complete the top end where it picks up in the fuselage brackets. The collar assembly and brake-drum back-plate (if brakes are to be fitted) are welded together. Thread the assembly on to the axle and weld it to the axle *from the brake-drum end only*.

Shape the inboard end of the axle tube where it connects to the tension strut assembly.

Set up the leg on the bench. Take a piece of ¾in. × 17 s.w.g. T.45 tube to make the radius rod, bend the end and form it for attachment to the fuselage lug. File the other end to a snug fit between the axle tube and the axle collar assembly and tack-

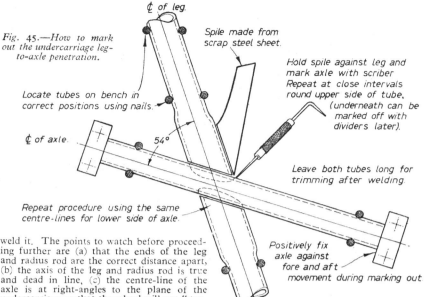

Fig. 45.—How to mark out the undercarriage leg-to-axle penetration.

Locate tubes on bench in correct positions using nails.

₵ of leg.

Spile made from scrap steel sheet.

Hold spile against leg and mark axle with scriber. Repeat at close intervals round upper side of tube. (underneath can be marked off with dividers later).

₵ of axle.   54°

Leave both tubes long for trimming after welding.

Repeat procedure using the same centre-lines for lower side of axle.

Positively fix axle against fore and aft movement during marking out.

weld it. The points to watch before proceeding further are (a) that the ends of the leg and radius rod are the correct distance apart, (b) the axis of the leg and radius rod is true and dead in line, (c) the centre-line of the axle is at right-angles to the plane of the undercarriage so that the wheel will not "toe-in" or "toe-out," and (d) that the angle formed by the leg and the axis of the leg frame is ninety degrees.

The tie tube is next filed to shape and tack-welded into place. Since the tube is larger in diameter than the radius rod, this end should be slightly flattened to avoid a bulge at the join. Repeat this procedure for the other, opposite-handed, undercarriage frame.

Welding Up the Frame

If the constructor enlists the services of somebody else to weld up the undercarriage, tell the welder the gauges of the various tubes to be welded.

In welding up the side frame, preheat the tubing if possible to minimise distortion. After the welding is complete and before cooling off, pass the welding torch up and

down each tube by the weld with a "warm" (not welding) flame to relieve the stresses set up in welding. Never quench a welded part. This makes the metal dangerously brittle. A strong weld is cooled slowly.

The remainder of the undercarriage parts are now made up. As soon as possible after welding tubular parts, flush them out in boiling water and strong detergent and, when dry, fill them with a good metal primer paint and stand them to drain overnight. If parts are to be cadmium-plated, flush them out in oil to prevent corrosion until the plating is done, and then paint the insides.

Special Phoenix undercarriage rubbers are used in the tension strut. These should be assembled to the tubes using talcum powder or french chalk. The completed undercarriage can now be assembled to the fuselage.

(To be continued)

Building the 'Luton Minor'

Wing Support Pylons

THESE are ¼in. dia. 17 s.w.g. with bolted attachment plates at the top. The front spar undersurface is 24in. above the top fuselage longerons. Make up the front pylon first. This consists of three tubes—the two side ones being identical in length. Time can be saved if the lower ends of the front and rear side pylon struts are completed first with the "U" piece welded in.

Set up the fuselage with the top longerons level fore and aft and also level at right-angles to the fuselage centre-line at the cockpit. This is known as the "rigging position." All rigging and measurements will be taken with the aircraft trestled in this manner.

Take a pair of 3ft. wide trestles and screw and clamp extension pieces to them to support one wing (either will

Part 7—Wing Pylons; Wheel Brakes; Control Cables, etc.

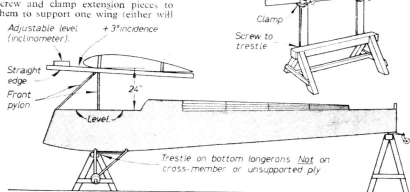

Fig. 46.—Setting the wing incidence prior to making the rear pylon on the job.

do) in its correct position and connect the front spar fitting to the front pylon (Fig. 46).

Make certain that the wing is at right-angles to the fuselage. This is most accurately done by establishing a fuselage

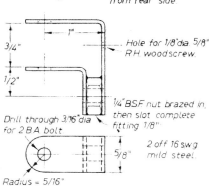

Fig. 48.—The cable adjuster brackets which are bolted to the seat rails.

centre-line on the floor and transferring the front wing spar line to the floor, using plumb-bobs, cords and tacks. Using the ratio 3 : 4 : 5 unit triangle system, work with the longest units possible to keep within the centre-line lengths, i.e., a 3ft. unit giving 9ft. along the spar line from the intersection and 12ft. along the fuselage side, the third side being 15ft. Measure with steel tape or wire.

Hold a straightedge against the lower surface of the wing spars and, with an adjustable level, set the wing at an angle of incidence of 3 deg. (Fig. 46). Fix the wing trestles in this position and, without altering this setting or that of the fuselage, make up the rear pylon on the job. Watch carefully to see that the centre-line of the pylons is exactly on the centre-line of the fuselage.

When the pylons are completed, remove the wing, dismantle the pylons (do not forget to label each strut) and paint or plate them before reassembly.

Wheel Brakes

If wheel brakes are to be fitted, it should be done at this stage. Fit the undercarriage and bolt on the brake assemblies. Do not fit the wheels yet. Each brake assembly is marked "Port" or "Starboard" and it is imperative that they be assembled to their respective sides.

It is advisable to use 5 cwt. flexible stranded aircraft control cable for the actual operating cables. Cut lengths for each side

and silver-solder a nipple to one end of each wire. Thread the wire through the brake assembly from the outside (wheel side) leading it through the cam return spring and passing it out of the assembly through the hole provided. Run the wire into a large-diameter Bowden outer sheath and, avoiding sharp bends, run cable and sheath up the radius-rod on the forward side, lashing it at intervals with waxed thread or plastic adhesive tape.

The cable and sheath enter the fuselage through a small oval hole in the bottom skin 3in. inboard from the radius-rod fitting (Fig. 47). Fig. 48 shows the two small brackets which locate the cable adjusters and are attached to the inside faces of the seat rails at the front. The run of the cables is shown in Fig. 47. The brake pedal assembly which bolts to the rudder pedestal is illustrated in Fig. 51 and detailed in Figs. 49 and 50.

The forward end of the brake cable wire is looped around a cable thimble, tightly bound for a length of 1in. with 22 s.w.g. copper wire and soldered. A small shackle then connects it to the pedal lever.

Now fit the wheels. If they foul the brake shoes, unwind the small star adjusting wheel

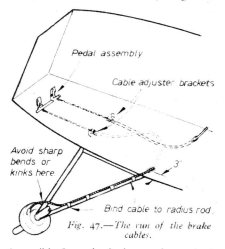

Fig. 47.—The run of the brake cables.

(accessible from the brake attachment back plate side) until the shoes have contracted sufficiently to permit the wheel to slip on. By adjusting the star wheel, tighten the shoes so that the wheel is almost impossible to turn. Now slacken off three "notches" on the star wheel. The length of the operating cable is now adjusted on the seat-rail cable adjusters to take up any slack.

The tailwheel assembly is next made and

fitted. The leaf-spring for this can be made from a 1934-type Austin 7 rear spring. This will have to be softened for drilling and then re-tempered.

The standard tailwheel for the Minor is the 5in. Phoenix type which has double shielded ball-races.

Attach the tailplane and elevator to the rear fuselage and bolt on the fin. Fit the rudder. To ensure perfect and accurate alignment, the attachment of the hinges to the fin may be left until this point. The rudder should swing freely without any tendency to bind. A minimum of ¼in. gap should be left between the fin top rib and the underside of the rudder rib.

The Control Cables

The control cables in the fuselage are now made. The cable used is pre-formed flexible wire rope to specification W.9. Each control cable will have both ends looped to form an eye around a heart-shaped brass thimble.

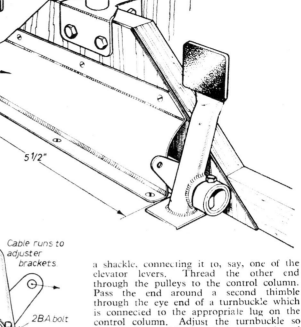

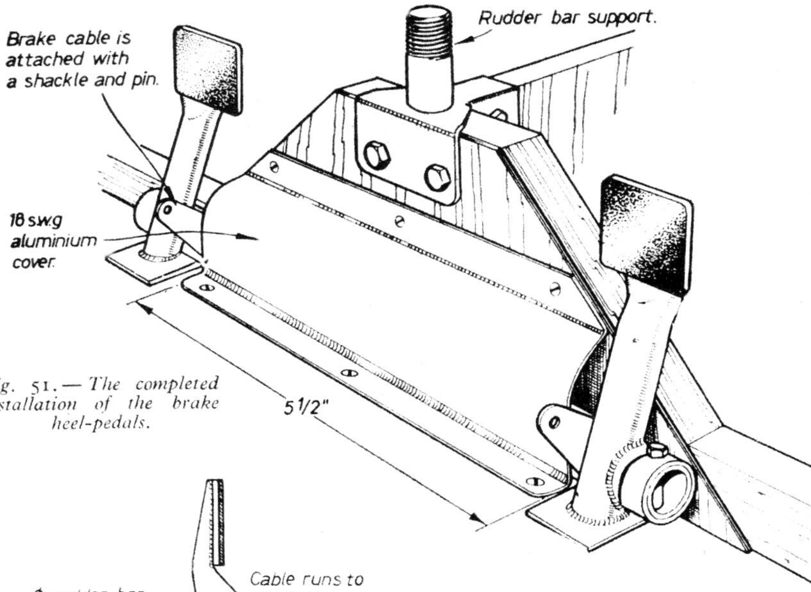

Fig. 51. — The completed installation of the brake heel-pedals.

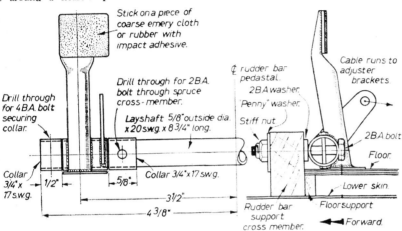

Fig. 50.—Assembly of the brake pedals.

One end of the cable will be spliced to a turnbuckle for adjusting its tension in service, and the other end will be attached to its respective fitting with a shackle through the spliced eye. All the fuselage cables have their turnbuckles situated in the cockpit. Remember to thread the end of the cable through the turnbuckle eye before making the splice at that end.

Making a Sleeved Splice

To avoid splicing an eye end, which demands skill, the end of the cable is inserted

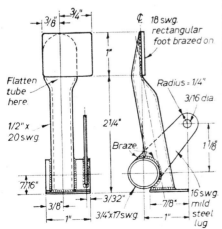

Fig. 49.—Brake pedal details. Two are required (right and left handed).

through a 3in. length of 3/16in. o.d. × 20 s.w.g. copper tube which has first been annealed and flattened to an oval section in the vice. The cable end is doubled back and threaded back through the tube. The thimble is put in place and the cable drawn taut. Make sure that the centre-mark denoting the length of the cable (explained farther on) is in fact central. Using a mallet and a wooden block, dress the copper sleeve to the wire.

Lightly clamp the splice vertically in the vice and heat with the soldering iron until it is possible to flow solder down through the sleeve around the wire. When it is thoroughly tinned and still molten, again dress the tube with the mallet. Take care not to spurt hot solder in your face. Avoid excessive heat in soldering as this would affect the strength of the cable.

Clamp the splice vertically in the vice so that about ⅜in. of the copper sleeve is firmly held in the jaws. Using either a hand-vice or a pair of smooth-jawed parallel grips, hold the other end of the sleeve again ⅜in. from its end and carefully give one and a half full turns, twisting cable and sleeve into a spiral. Unclamp and re-tin with the soldering iron. Trim the spare end back to the end of the sleeve. This splice is very strong and does not need to be pre-stretched before use.

Finding Cable Length

Fix the pilot's controls in the central or neutral position (stick vertical, rudder bar central) and clamp strips of wood across the tailplane and elevator, fin and rudder to hold them central. Make a loop in one end of a piece of the cable and tie it with thread. Pull this tight around a thimble and insert

a shackle, connecting it to, say, one of the elevator levers. Thread the other end through the pulleys to the control column. Pass the end around a second thimble through the eye end of a turnbuckle which is connected to the appropriate lug on the control column. Adjust the turnbuckle so that the last visible thread pitch at each end is five full turns inside the barrel. Holding a rule against the turnbuckle, screw it up so that the turnbuckle is ½in. shorter than the previous setting. This additional ½in. length of the cable must be allowed to counteract the shortening by approximately ¼in. at each end when the cable is twisted in the sleeves. Pull the cable taut around the thimble and tie back as before. Mark the cable at the centre of the thimble with paint (Fig. 52). Remove the cable, untie the ends and proceed with forming the eye end splices as detailed earlier.

In making the control cables for the rudder, do not forget to thread each cable through a length of ¼in. o.d. copper or tungum tubing to form the fairlead through the fuselage sides before making the second eye end to each.

Lead the elevator cables into position, using thin string or thread and connect them up. Operate the elevators, using the control column, and see that the cables do not foul any part of the structure throughout the full range of movement. Should they touch any fuselage members, try rerouting the cables or, if this does not rectify it, screw 2in. × ½in. strips of ⅛in. thick red fibre to the members as rubbing pads. No unsupported cable should be in such close proximity to any part of the airframe that any possible whip in the wire could bring it into contact with objects which might cause damage to, or be damaged by, the moving cable. If any doubt exists, make use of a fibre pad.

See that the slots in the pilot's seat are large enough to prevent cable-fretting.

Fit the rudder cables and shape the fairleads. Secure the ends of the fairleads with clips, as shown in Fig. 53, having first made sure that the cable runs in a straight line, in side elevation, between the rudder bar and the rudder lever. It is a mistake to lubricate the fairleads with oil or grease, as dirt will collect and act as a grinding medium inside the tubing, thus accelerating wear to both cable and fairlead.

Operate the rudder and check functioning. Should the cables tend to touch the fuselage

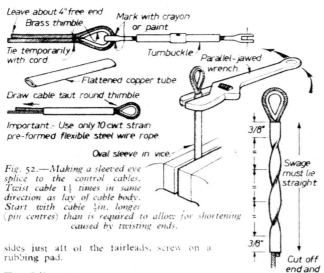

Fig. 52.—*Making a sleeved eye splice to the control cables. Twist cable 1½ times in same direction as lay of cable body. Start with cable ½in. longer (pin centres) than is required to allow for shortening caused by twisting ends.*

sides just aft of the fairleads, screw on a rubbing pad.

The Lift-struts

The four lift-struts are made from 22 s.w.g. streamlined mild steel tubing, section 2.5in. × 1.250in. Each strut is approximately 7¼in. in length and has a screw adjustment at the lower end.

Start by cutting the streamlined tubing into four pieces 6ft. 2in. long and form the lower ends. The threaded blocks are 1½in. long, 1.19in. in diameter and are bored and tapped ½in. B.S.F. A local garage should be able to make these up; alternatively they are available from Phoenix Aircraft Ltd., together with the actual adjustable eye end, which is turned from ¾in. square bar.

The strut end is slotted on both sides of the minor axis and on the forward side of the major axis and dressed round the threaded block. Weld the block into the strut "rosette" fashion. The 22 s.w.g. mild steel closer plate is then edge-welded to the angled cut. *This must be done accurately.*

Braze in the two short 3/16in. dia. bore tubes which locate the bolts for the bracing wire fitting, Pt. No. 12W. This assembly is illustrated in Fig. 54.

Now make up the top fitting which picks up on the spar fittings. This is made separately from the strut and comprises a wrapper plate, a web and two gussets, all made of 16 s.w.g. mild steel plate, and a ½in. × 17 s.w.g. steel tube. The steps in the making of this fitting are illustrated in Fig. 55. Connect these fittings to the lift-strut attachments on the wings.

Fitting Lift Struts

Set the fuselage in the rigging position with the wheels clear of the ground and, with the aid of an assistant, offer up the wings, bolting the root-end fittings to the centre pylon fittings and supporting them just beyond the lift-strut attachment fittings with the trestles modified with extension pieces.

Place a straightedge across the ribs on the top surface parallel to the main-spar and, using a spirit-level, see that each wing is horizontal. No dihedral is employed in the

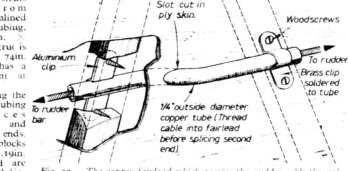

Fig. 53.—*The copper fairlead which carries the rudder cable through the fuselage side. Bends must be gradual and smooth.*

Minor rigging, since there is ample pendulum stability.

Temporarily bolt the lift-struts by their lower ends to the fuselage fittings and adjust the eye ends until about ⅜in. of thread is showing. By holding each strut against its respective top strut fitting, it is possible to mark off the exact length of the strut. Remove the struts and the top fittings from the wing brackets. Cut the struts to length and mark the positions of the bolt holes. Press the top fitting into the strut end and drill the four holes, using a 3/32in. drill.

Refit the struts to the wing and fuselage. The top fitting, being a tight fit in the strut end, should not move although it is not bolted through. With strut and fitting thus located and accurately aligned, drill the four holes 3/16in. dia. and bolt through, using shaped packing washers under the bolt heads and nuts. The bracing wire lug is also bolted on.

Remove the struts and unscrew the eye ends. Flush out the struts, using boiling water and detergent, afterwards rinsing in hot water. When dry, replace the eye ends, having first screwed on a ½in. B.S.F. thin lock nut, and paint the inside of each strut by filling and swilling with metal primer followed by overnight draining.

The final operation is to drill a ⅛in. dia. drainage hole behind the threaded block at the lowest part of the closer plate.

Once more fit the struts and make up the 10 cwt. cable cross bracing between each pair of struts. Each wire has a turnbuckle at its lower end and a shackle at the top. Make these in the same fashion as the control cables—they are equally important.

The Aileron Control Cables

The cable from the bottom lever of each aileron runs over the respective front spar root end pulley down into the cockpit through a small hole in the curved cockpit former, round the swivelling pulley and to the inverted " V " lever in front of the control column pedestal.

The two top aileron levers are connected by a balance cable which is made in two lengths joined with a double eye end turnbuckle to one side of the centre-section. This off-centre join, reached through a small inspection door in the undersurface of the port wing, facilitates dismantling.

The position of the hole in the cockpit former for the operating cable is found by stretching a cord *outside* the fuselage side from the pulley in the wing to the fore and aft location of the inverted " V " lever marked on the fuselage side. This must be a straight line and, when established, it is a simple matter to mark off where the cable passes through the cockpit former. A fibre grommet or rubbing pad must be provided at this hole. To improve the appearance, the fibre may be fitted to the undersurface of the former, a clearance hole being provided in the top ply.

The complete rigging system and control runs will be illustrated later on.

The complete set of plans for the Minor costs £11 10s. from Phoenix Aircraft Ltd., Cranleigh Common, Cranleigh, Surrey.

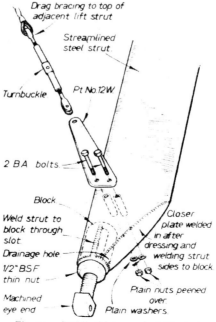

Fig. 54.—*Detail of lower end of lift struts.*

Fig. 55 (Right).—*Upper end fitting for lift struts.*

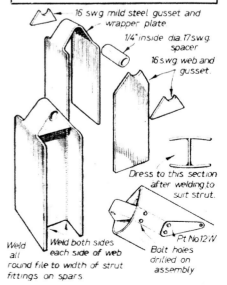

Building the 'Luton Minor'

The Instrument Panel

THIS is made either from 14 s.w.g. aluminium sheet, flanged top and bottom, or from ¼in. thick plywood with long grain. The normal instruments are, in order of precedence, the airspeed indicator (A.S.I.), altimeter, engine speed indicator (tachometer or E.S.I.), oil pressure and oil temperature gauge. A most useful addition to this basic panel is a turn and slip indicator.

Two other vital items are the engine ignition switches and the compass. The former should be of the approved aircraft

Part 8 Deals Mainly with Engine and Instruments

Fig. 56.—The Aeronca J.A.P. engine fitted to an amateur-built Luton Minor.

pattern or the Phoenix Key-Switch. The large P.8 or P.11 bowl compass is bulky and difficult to install in a convenient place in the Minor. Ideally, a dash-board mounted compass should be used, or the miniature E.2A type.

The cut-outs in the panel for the instruments will be varied to suit the instruments which the constructor intends to fit. Use only serviceable instruments and position them on the panel, as shown on the plan. All instruments are available from Phoenix Aircraft Ltd.

The panel is attached to the fuselage sides and also at the centre to the overtank cowling using special rubber mountings. The panel should be fitted, only the two side attachments being used at present.

The Firewall

Paint the top decking from the instrument panel location

KEY to Fig. 57

1 Airspeed Indicator pipelines (³⁄₁₆in. o.d alum.) taped to pylon side struts, both then passing into the starboard wing.
2 Tachometer (engine speed indicator).
3 Oil pressure gauge, 0 to 100 p.s.i.
4 Oil temperature gauge, 0 to 50 deg. C.
5 Turn & bank indicator (vacuum-operated from venturi mounted on starboard side of fuselage and connected to it with rubber hose).
6 Altimeter (sensitive).
7 Airspeed Indicator, 20-100 knots, 20-120 m.p.h.
8 Ignition switches (twin).
9 Port magneto earth cap lead.
10 Starboard magneto earth cap lead.
11 Double earth lead, united at front.
12 Aluminium clip.
13 Short lengths of reinforced rubber hose wired on.
14 The Altimeter connection is left open.
15 Attachment of fuel feed pipe to petrol tank.
16 Aluminium clip.

17 Fibre split grommet fixed with 4 B.A. screws.
18 Oil temperature thermometer bulb connection.
19 Ball joint and socket.
20 Throttle layshaft assembly.
21 Throttle connecting rod.
22 Throttle hand lever.
23 Horizontal coil in fuel pipe.
24 Petrol inlet to Fuel Filter.
25 Fuel Filter.
26 Flexible fuel hose to carburetter with "banjo" connection
27 Tachometer drive connection to engine.
28 Oil Pressure pipeline connection to engine.
29 Dress the firewall over engine mounting fittings.
30 Oil Temperature capillary tubing.

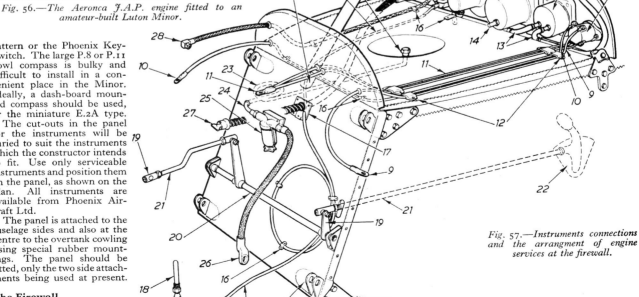

Fig. 57.—Instruments connections and the arrangment of engine services at the firewall.

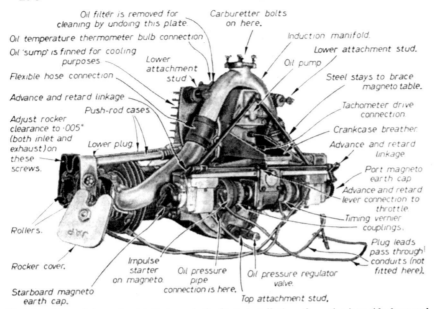

Fig. 58.—*Some of the engine details shown to facilitate installation; the engine is upside down and viewed from the rear.*

forward using a good petrol-resistant enamel. Paint also the engine bulkhead. Pay particular attention to the corners (which should be fabric-taped) where oil seepage and contamination mostly occurs.

Make the firewall using 22 s.w.g. mild steel sheet, flanging it as shown on the plan. This firewall should be plated or painted to resist corrosion. An alternative material for the firewall is stainless steel sheet or a laminate of two pieces of 18 s.w.g. duralumin with asbestos cloth between.

Screw the firewall to the bulkhead with ⅜in. r.h. brass woodscrews along the top cross-member and through the flanges to the side and bottom members. Dress the metal to fit over and round the engine mounting fittings.

A Tiger Moth-type fuel filter is bolted on and holes bored for the petrol feed pipe, the oil pressure pipe, the tachometer drive and the ignition switch leads. These last-mentioned holes are drilled to take rubber grommets. Cut the slot for the throttle rod. Make and fit the throttle torque shaft and levers assembly which bolts through the firewall and bulkhead side members with 2 BA bolts.

The throttle hand lever is now made. This is bolted on the port side of the cockpit and connected to the shorter of the two levers on the torque shaft with a ⅜in. × 20 s.w.g. mild steel tie-tube in such a manner that, with the throttle hand lever back in the farthest aft position, the short torque shaft lever is vertical.

The Engine Mounting

The engine mounting must not be fabricated except by a fully qualified and approved welder. The constructor should seek the advice of his nearest licensed aircraft engineer or Phoenix Aircraft Ltd.

The special rubber mountings should be pressed into their housings before fitting it to the fuselage. In doing this, press on the outer tube of the rubber mounting, not on the inner one as this will tend to shear away the rubber bond between the two tubes.

The mounting is fitted to its attachment brackets on the fuselage using four ⁵⁄₁₆in. dia. mild steel bolts, plain washers, castle nuts and split pins. Note that the holes in the fuselage fittings and the engine mounting legs should be reamed out to size on assembly. Use a corrosion-inhibiting sealing compound on assembly.

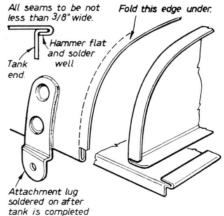

Fig. 59.—*Details of the petrol tank construction.*

The Engine

The Aeronca J.99 J.A.P. engine is a twin-cylinder, horizontally-opposed air-cooled unit and is normally supplied with the carburetter and exhaust pipe removed, wooden blanking plates being fitted over the openings on the engine. Plug blanks are fitted in place of sparking plugs and no oil is in the engine. The motor may be stood on sacks or a mat on the ground upside down if the oil filler cap is first removed. Do not attempt to lift the motor by the push-rod cases, magneto table or induction pipes. The correct way to lift it is by holding it under the cylinder heads and by the propeller hub. Two people can quite easily lift the engine. As it will have to be turned the right way up for attachment, allow ample room to turn round with the engine in the work-shop.

Fitting the Engine

First of all place a weight on the tailplane as, without the wings on, the aircraft may tend to be nose heavy with the engine in place.

Remove the three engine stud nuts and washers and place them on the top decking where they can easily be reached.

With the aid of an assistant, offer the engine up to its mounting and carefully insert the engine studs evenly in the three mounting

bushes. It may be necessary to employ a third person to prevent the aircraft moving backwards as the engine is pushed into place. Without releasing the weight of the engine, place the washers on the studs and start the nuts. These can then be tightened up, the bolts drilled and ³⁄₃₂in. dia. split pins put in.

Wiring the Switches

The ignition switches are now wired up using 5mm. rubber-covered multi-strand ignition cable. This is the only type of wire which should be used and it is obtainable from any large garage or direct from Phoenix Aircraft Limited.

The two lower connections on the switches are for the two earth leads. These run side by side from the switch, along the top decking and through the two rubber grommets off-centre in the firewall. They are connected to a convenient part of the engine—the lower rear bolt of the magneto drive gear housing is ideal. Allowing a reasonable amount of slack (2in. is ample), join both cables together and insert them in a single ignition eye terminal, soldering the wires at the end. This then passes under the selected earthing bolt and its lock washer. The two top switch connections are attached to the earth-caps on their respective magnetos—the left hand top lead to the left hand magneto and the right lead to the right magneto. The connections at the magneto must again be soldered eye terminals. The wires should be secured to the top decking with small aluminium clips. Ideally, the wires should be inserted through lengths of Systoflex sheath, obtainable from electrical stores and garages, and then clipped into place.

The Engine Instruments

The oil pressure pipeline is next fitted. This must be a flexible hose as, if it is made of rigid copper, vibration will soon fatigue it and a pressure oil loss is serious. The hose may be either a suitable motor part or of the Super-flexit aircraft pattern. Make sure, when buying, that the end connections will fit the engine and the pressure gauge. Do not make up non-standard adaptors of any sort as they are a source of weakness and will not pass the inspector who is soon to check over the aircraft. Clamp this oil pipe to the top decking in such a manner so as not to strain it at either end.

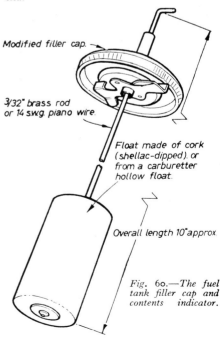

Fig. 60.—*The fuel tank filler cap and contents indicator.*

If an oil temperature gauge is fitted, the thermometer bulb is screwed into the base of the engine sump by removing the blanking plug provided. The instrument is supplied as a unit comprising panel dial, a length of sealed fine copper capillary tube and the bulb. On no account attempt to cut or shorten the capillary tube. If breakage occurs, or the capillary is crushed, it is impossible to repair and the instrument must be discarded completely.

Fit the instrument to the instrument panel and pass the capillary tube and bulb through a hole in the top decking. Clip the capillary to the underside of the deck and pass the tube out through the hole for the tachometer drive cable (the hole will need slightly re-shaping to allow this tube and the tachometer drive to pass through). Form an 8in. dia. coil of the surplus tube and clip this to the firewall with three aluminium clips fixed with 4 BA screws passing right through the bulkhead. Allow generous radii for all bends.

Note that the highest oil temperature which will be reached will be in the region of 30 deg. C., so select a gauge which has this range represented by a reasonable segment of the dial.

The tachometer drive cable is now threaded through the hole in the firewall. Connect it to the engine, carefully feeling to make sure that the male end of the cable fits into the drive slot in the back of the engine before doing up the nut.

The other end of the drive passes through a slot in the top decking, in front of, and in line with the back of the tachometer.

With this end of the drive connected to the instrument, support the slack drive and outer sheath under the decking with an aluminium clip. *Avoid sharp bends in the drive and sheath as these quickly lead to breakage.*

The installation of the pipelines, the wiring and other details are shown in Fig. 57.

Fitting the Carburetter

Unpack the carburetter and, having removed the wooden blanking plate on the induction manifold, bolt it on. There is little clearance for the nuts and they must all be started at the same time and tightened up gradually and evenly. The carburetter securing nuts are wire-locked with 22 s.w.g. soft iron locking wire. Connect up the magneto advance-and-retard linkage.

With the carburetter throttle closed and the pilot's throttle lever in the closed position (fully aft), take a length of $\frac{3}{16}$ in. dia. mild steel rod and cut and bend it to pass between the carburetter lever and the long lever on the bulkhead throttle torque-shaft. Thread the ends of the rod and screw on a 2 BA plain nut and a ball-joint housing. The plain nut is to lock the ball-joint in the correct position. Fit the rod in place and open the throttle fully with the cockpit lever. The throttle should now be fully open against the stop on the carburetter. If this is not so, adjust the length of the tie-rod to suit.

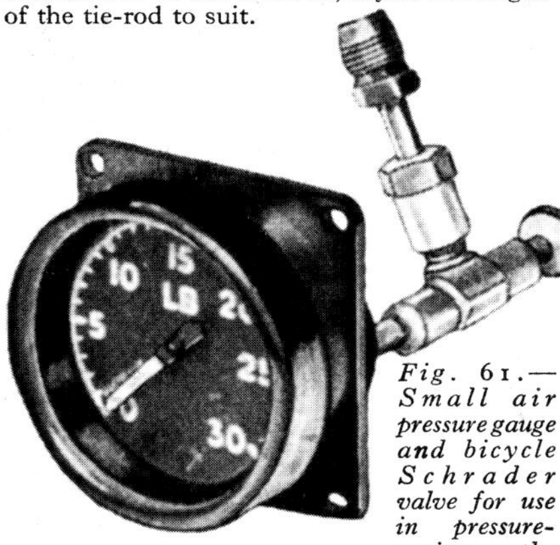

Take another piece of $\frac{3}{16}$ in. dia. rod about 4in. or 5in. in length and thread one end to take a plain nut and $\frac{3}{16}$ in. fork end and connect this to the choke control lever mounted by the throttle on the carburetter. This will project through the cowlings.

Connect the petrol feed pipe from the petrol filter to the carburetter. All pipeline nuts must be wire-locked against undoing, using soft iron wire. Check also that there are no loose or unlocked nuts on the engine

The Petrol Tank

The petrol tank is made from 22 s.w.g. tinned steel sheet and contains between 6 and $6\frac{1}{2}$ gallons. The joints are lap-seamed and soldered using tinman's solder. One of the several types of domestic gas-operated blow-torches which are available is ideal for this job. The steps in the forming of the tank flanges are shown in Fig. 59.

To make the float for the contents indicator, thread two large vacuum-flask corks on a piece of piano-wire and solder a washer above and below. Shape the completed float with sandpaper, then with three or four coats of shellac. Shellac is available in flake form from chemists and should be pounded into small pieces and dissolved in methylated spirit to form a running syrup. An alternative float can be made from a carburetter float of the right diameter to pass through the filler neck. This is soldered to the wire in place of the cork-retaining washers.

The actual filler-cap is of the ordinary motor-car type with a " half-turn " spring lock against two projections from the inside of the filler neck. It is usually possible to purchase the filler-cap complete with neck for riveting to the tank top. However, the plans illustrate how to make a filler neck if a ready-made one is not available.

Drill a hole in the cap and braze in a length of copper tube to act as a guide for the contents indicator wire to pass through. Now thread the indicator rod through this tube from underneath and, holding the wire at the top, lower the float into the tank and screw on the filler cap. Hold the rod immediately above the guide tube with pliers and bend at this point through 90 deg. The completed filler-cap and contents indicator are shown in Fig. 60.

The sump and water-trap is made and riveted and soldered to the tank bottom.

Support the tank on the top decking of the fuselage with packing under the sides. Make up the attachment brackets and see that they are the correct shape and angle before removing and soldering them to the tank.

Before fitting the tank to the fuselage, it must be tested for leaks. Remove the filler-cap and wire on a thick rubber seal cut from, say, a heavy inner-tube. Make an adaptor to fit one of the sump plugs to take a small air pressure gauge and a bicycle Schrader valve (Fig. 61). Use a bicycle pump and pressurise the tank until not more than 3 p.s.i. is shown on the pressure gauge. The tank should hold this pressure for fifteen minutes without dropping. If a rapid drop is observed, then

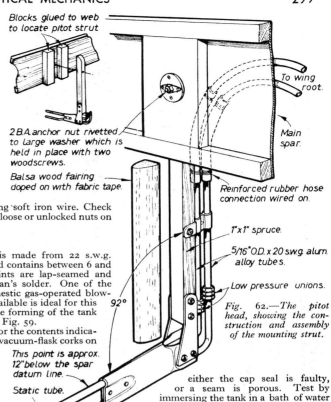

Blocks glued to web to locate pitot strut

To wing root.

Main spar.

2 B.A. anchor nut rivetted to large washer which is held in place with two woodscrews.

Balsa wood fairing doped on with fabric tape.

Reinforced rubber hose connection wired on.

1"x1" spruce.

5/16" O.D. x 20 s.w.g. alum. alloy tubes.

Low pressure unions.

92°

This point is approx. 12" below the spar datum line.

Static tube.

Pressure tube.

Fig. 62.—The pitot head, showing the construction and assembly of the mounting strut.

either the cap seal is faulty, or a seam is porous. Test by immersing the tank in a bath of water or, if impracticable, by painting strong soapy water along all the seams. The presence of bubbles will disclose the leak. After making good the defect, test again to prove the remedy and to check for other possible leaks.

Do not put water in the tank since it is very hard to dry out thoroughly. If the tank is not to be installed for a time, put about half a pint of thin oil into it and swill it around to prevent possible corrosion.

Paint the outside with primer in readiness for installing in the fuselage. Avoid straining the attachment brackets when fitting it and see that the tank is not touching any of the wires or pipes on the top decking. Wrap the top of the tank with $\frac{1}{8}$in. thick felt.

The copper fuel feed pipe from the tank to the filter should be made next. Since the fuel system is gravity-operated, avoid upward bends in this pipe which could cause air-locks. To absorb and damp out vibration in the pipe, a single coil should be provided between tank and bulkhead. The coil is arranged horizontally and in a *descending* line from the tank to the bulkhead. Make it of sufficient diameter to avoid crushing or flattening the tube.

A rubber grommet protects the pipe from chafing where it passes through the firewall.

The Pitot Head

This is an item which the constructor will have to buy or obtain from his nearest aerodrome engineer. It consists of two small pipes, one of which registers ram air pressure at the open end. The other pipe is closed at the forward end but has a number of perforations around it which are open to the ambient, static air pressure. The difference between the two pressures thus recorded is the pressure resulting from the forward motion of the aircraft and is a measure of airspeed.

Mounted below the leading edge of the starboard wing (Fig. 62), the pitot head is connected through special low-pressure unions or reinforced rubber tubing, to the airspeed indicator on the instrument panel.

(To be continued)

Fig. 61.—Small air pressure gauge and bicycle Schrader valve for use in pressure-testing the tank for leaks.

Building the 'Luton Minor'

Part 9 Deals Mainly with the Windscreen and Engine Cowlings

(Continued from April issue)

THE aluminium tubing is $\frac{5}{16}$ in. o.d. × 20 gauge and it is secured to the rear face of the starboard wing main spar with aluminium clips every three feet or so. The tubing is easily bent to shape by hand, but the radius of the bends must be not less than about 3in. to avoid kinking. Lead the two wing pipelines to the root end so that they protrude about $1\frac{1}{2}$in. below the undersurface (Fig. 63).

The ends are joined with 3in. lengths of reinforced rubber hose wired to their respective pipes which pass down the front wing-pylon side struts, one per strut. See Fig. 57.

Get an assistant to watch the airspeed indicator and *very gently* blow into the open-ended tube of the pitot head until the person watching the instrument signals that the needle is pointing to about 70 m.p.h. Place the tongue over the tube end, thus holding in the pressure. The instrument needle should remain steady for at least ten seconds. If the needle rapidly returns to zero, it is apparent that there is a leak somewhere in the pipeline. Try tightening the low pressure unions (if they are used) or checking the wiring-on of the rubber joints. Repeat the test until the line is satisfactory. An alternative method to test the pipeline is to use a manometer.

The Overtank Cowling

This is made of 18 gauge half-hard commercial aluminium sheet. The exact shape should first be found using stiff brown paper. The hole for the tank filler neck should be as small as possible and it is advisable to start by making this hole in the metal sheet, allowing a safe margin on all other dimensions. Position the metal with the filler neck protruding through the hole (do this with the cap *off* so the metal fits snugly round the actual neck), then strap the metal down to the longerons. The edges can thus be marked accurately, the metal removed and cut to size. Smooth the edges with wire-wool or emery cloth.

Having cut and trimmed it, paint the inside with primer and, when dry, fit the cowling, screwing it to the top longerons with $\frac{1}{2}$in. R.H. brass woodscrews. The attachment at the front is achieved with pop-rivets through the firewall flange. Use $\frac{1}{8}$in. dia. domed-head pop-rivets $\frac{3}{32}$in. overall length. The local motor-repair works will most likely loan a pair of pop-rivet " lazy tongs " or pop pliers to do the job. Alternatively, the cowling can be bolted using 6 B.A. mushroom-headed bolts and stiff-nuts at about 3in. pitch to the firewall flange.

Finally, the top instrument-panel attach-ment bracket is made and riveted to the cowling and the panel connected to it with the special rubber vibration mounting.

The Windscreen

This is made of $\frac{1}{8}$in. thick clear Perspex sheet and is shaped so as to stand at an angle of 60 deg. to the overtank cowling to which it is attached.

The exact shape of the screen is shown in 1in. squares in Fig. 64. Do not cut the Perspex to this shape until it has been curved.

Perspex sheet cannot be bent without heat as it is brittle. When softened by heat, it is easily spoiled by finger impressions and dirt and is readily distorted by uneven bending. It is therefore vital to do the job carefully and properly.

Make a paper pattern of the screen shape and obtain a rectangular piece of Perspex out of which the shape may be cut. Cut also two panels of clean thin aluminium or duralumin the same size and place the Perspex in the middle. Clamp up one end only between battens of wood.

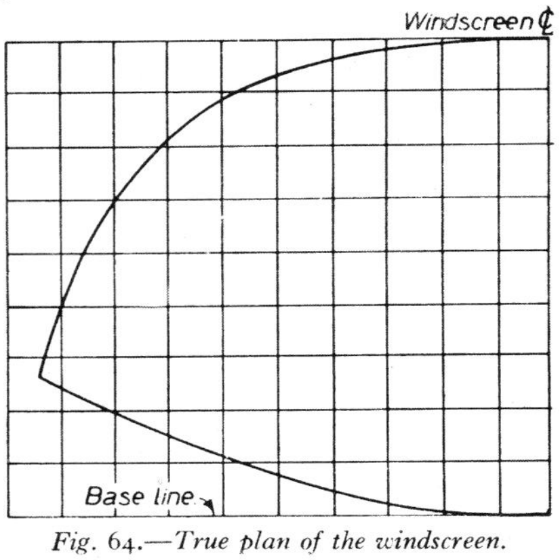

Now find an old tin tray large enough to take the sandwich and about 4in. in depth. Fill this with water and dissolve in it two or three pounds weight of ordinary cooking salt. The presence of salt raises the boiling point of the water.

Place the tray on a gas-jet and bring to the boil. Carefully put in the clamped-up sandwich. Use thick gloves or a kitchen oven-cloth to avoid a scald. After boiling for about ten minutes, quickly remove the sandwich and, holding it by the clamped end, bend it to the desired radius over a cylindrical can or drum by pressing down on the other end with a batten of wood. This procedure is illustrated in Fig. 65. Do not force the bend—it may be necessary to reheat the sandwich several times before the right bend is achieved.

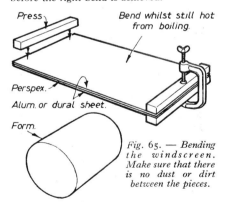

Fig. 65. — *Bending the windscreen. Make sure that there is no dust or dirt between the pieces.*

When cooled, remove the aluminium panels and mark out the plan of the screen using the paper pattern and a chinagraph pencil. Take particular care not to scratch the surface and work on a cloth-covered table. Fretsaw to shape using a coarse blade. The saw should be worked slowly using the full length of the blade as otherwise the heat generated will tend to melt the plastic locally and trap the blade. Polish the edges.

Try the screen on the overtank cowling to see that the shape is correct and then fit the aluminium clips which mount the screen in place. Drill oversize clearance holes in the Perspex for the 4 B.A. bolts. The screen brackets are fitted to the overtank cowling with 4 B.A. bolts or pop-rivets, but take care when drilling the holes—the fuel tank is close underneath. Temporarily fit the screen.

The wing pylon struts are now faired to a streamlined shape with plywood strips and doped fabric. Use red oxide cellulose tautening dope or clear " glider " dope and

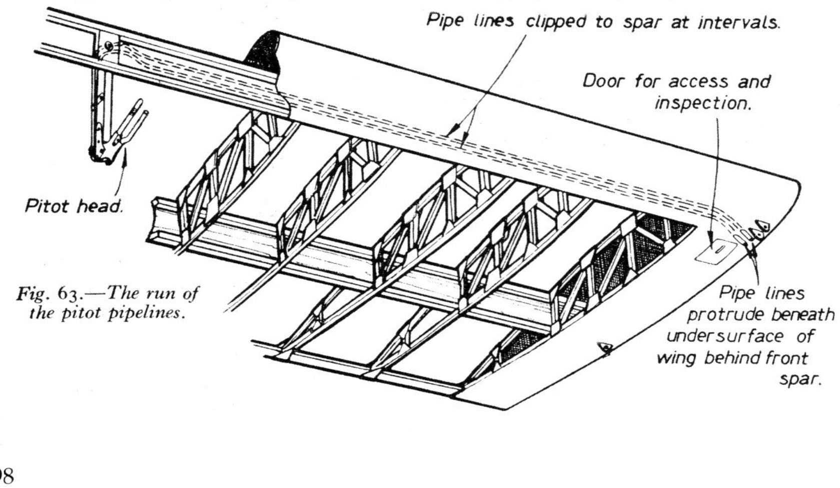

Fig. 64.—True plan of the windscreen.

Pipe lines clipped to spar at intervals.

Door for access and inspection.

Pitot head.

Fig. 63.—The run of the pitot pipelines.

Pipe lines protrude beneath undersurface of wing behind front spar.

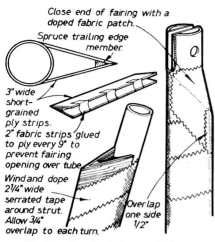

Close end of fairing with a doped fabric patch.

Spruce trailing edge member.

3" wide short-grained ply strips.

2" fabric strips glued to ply every 9" to prevent fairing opening over tube.

Wind and dope 2¼" wide serrated tape around strut. Allow ¾" overlap to each turn.

Overlap one side ½"

Fig. 66.—Details of the strut fairings.

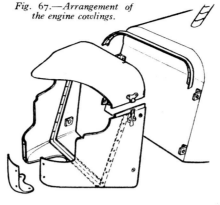

Fig. 67.—Arrangement of the engine cowlings.

2½in. wide serrated linen aircraft tape. Thoroughly dope the fairing and the tube before winding on the fabric. Use plenty of dope. The process is shown in Fig. 66.

Engine Cowlings

The exact shape of these must be found by careful use of brown-paper patterns and patient fitting. All the cowlings are of 20 gauge half-hard commercial aluminium and they are all single-curvature, thus dispensing with difficult three-dimensional shaping.

Start with the lower cowling which can be cut from a 6ft. × 3ft. sheet of metal. Begin at the centre underneath, cutting a trapezoidal piece of paper which overlaps the underside of the fuselage by about 4in. (this can be trimmed later and allows a margin in case the cowling has to be brought forward due to inaccurate cutting) and which reaches to the front of the carburetter in a straight line. Cut a "U" piece out of the paper to enable it to slot round the carburetter. Stick the paper with adhesive tape to the fuselage and the carburetter, keeping it as taut as possible. The sides are made in a similar manner, allowing a good margin of overlap at the fuselage and to the bottom paper pattern. Stick the paper to convenient parts of the engine, making cutouts for the magnetos, induction pipes and so on.

Do not try to save time and effort by marking out one half of the cowling and transferring this pattern to the other. Being a horizontally-opposed engine, the two cylinders are *not* in line and there is a variation between the two sides.

Stick the side patterns to the bottom pattern, then remove the paper as one piece and lay it flat on the metal. Cut round the pattern using hand metal shears (" tin-snips"), preferably of the angled head type, allowing a full inch extra on the upper limits of the sides and also around the engine cut-outs.

Bend the metal from the centre-line as shown in Fig. 68. The fuselage end—or rear end—of the cowling forms three sides of a square, the corners folded to near right-angles, but at the front the sharp lower corners have merged into a curve. This is done using a batten of wood as a bending block, pivoting it at the rear end as a " vanishing point," and making a series of closely-spaced gradual bends.

Offer the cowling into place and mark where it touches the engine, trim it to suit and

repeat again until, gradually, the cowling becomes a snug fit to the engine. Do not try to trim it to a perfect fit at one attempt—careful, patient fitting will be rewarded with a neat and pleasing finished cowl.

Allow ½in. clearance around the induction pipes. Bend in the sides at the front and strap them in place with transparent adhesive tape while the small curved " chin " cowling is made. Also strap this on and drill the holes straight through both thicknesses of metal for the securing screws.

Remove the cowling and rivet 2 B.A. anchor nuts behind the holes in the sides for the chin cowling at the front.

Fold up three 1in. × 1in. angles of the same material as the cowling and rivet them with countersunk rivets to the cowling sides and bottom. As the cowling metal is quite thin, it is advisable to " dimple " the rivet holes rather than countersink them in the normal fashion. Dimpling can be done very

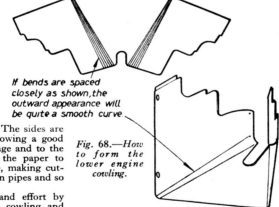

If bends are spaced closely as shown, the outward appearance will be quite a smooth curve.

Fig. 68.—How to form the lower engine cowling.

simply by driving each rivet before clinching as shown in Fig. 69. Note how the ends of the reinforcing angles are trimmed to avoid placing undue stresses on the first and last rivets in the row.

Make and fit the anchor-nut brackets which fit to the firewall and to the engine mounting to take the 2 B.A. cowling screws. Note that the cowlings are not positively attached to the engine, thus permitting the engine to move slightly in its rubber mountings without damage to the cowlings.

Stick strips of felt around the top edges of the cowl sides at the front where they bend around the engine crankcase. Use a petrol and oil-resistant adhesive.

Drill a hole through which passes the choke-control lever and fit a rubber grommet in it. The cowling can now be fitted, the choke control rod threaded through its hole and the entire fitted to its brackets with pan-head 2 B.A. screws. Do not use ordinary cheese-headed or round-headed screws as the small

heads will quickly tear through the aluminium in service.

The top cowling is very much simpler to make and again a paper pattern is employed and the cowling made from the centre-line.

The cowling fasteners are of the toggle type and must be a tight fit when locked. It is a good idea to fit a thin rubber sealing strip under the rear edge of the top cowling to rest on the support ledge *after* fitting the toggles so as to tension the cowlings in the locked position. The exhaust pipe and carburetter hot-air muff can now be fitted.

Inspection

The airframe of the Luton Minor is now complete save for covering and painting. This must not be attempted until after the aircraft has been examined by an approved inspector. Details of how to arrange this are available either from Phoenix Aircraft or the Popular Flying Association.

Prior to the visit of the inspector—who, incidentally, comes to advise and assist the constructor and not to obstruct—the amateur should carefully go over every part of the aircraft himself and look for insecure bolts, unlocked nuts or turnbuckles and so forth, paying particular attention to those parts of the airframe which will be covered and thus out of sight. See that the controls move freely and easily, that no cables chafe and that they are tight enough to be free from slack or sag without being so tight as to drum when plucked. A good test of this last mentioned item is to measure with the fingers as shown in Fig. 70. Do this on an unsupported length of cable at least 3ft. from a pulley or fairlead.

Fit the anti-vibration discs to the piano-wire bracing in the wings. These are of red fibre (*not* leather) and are laced with waxed thread.

(To be continued)

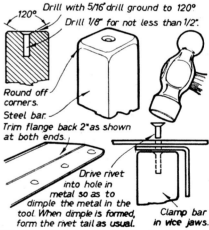

Drill with 5/16" drill ground to 120°

120°

Drill 1/8" for not less than 1/2".

Round off corners.

Steel bar.

Trim flange back 2" as shown at both ends.

Drive rivet into hole in metal so as to dimple the metal in the tool. When dimple is formed, form the rivet tail as usual.

Clamp bar in vice jaws.

Fig. 69.—Forming the dimples for the rivets in the cowling stiffeners.

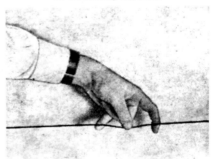

Fig. 70.—Checking the tension of a control cable. It should be possible to deflect the cable about ⅜in.

Building the 'Luton Minor'

Fitting the Propeller

IT is advisable to run the engine at this stage in the presence of the inspector in order to ascertain that no portion of the airframe vibrates excessively or in such a manner that, for example, a cable is made to chafe a rib.

Start by putting a gallon of oil in the engine. The grade of oil should be Aeroshell 100 or equivalent. Remove the sparking plug blanks.

The propeller normally fitted is a wooden, two-bladed one. Known as a Z.5931, it has a diameter of 5ft. and a pitch of 2·9ft. The direction of rotation, viewed from the front, is anti-clockwise.

By hand, turn the engine over until the impulse starter on the port magneto is heard to give a loud and distinctive click. This will be produced on every second revolution of the crankshaft. If there is no click, the starter may be jammed. It is easily freed by *lightly* tapping it with the haft of a hammer or a screwdriver handle.

Having found exactly which position of the hub produces the impulse, remove the nuts and washers from the six propeller attachment bolts on the engine hub and take off the circular bearing plate.

Set the propeller on the hub so that the impulse occurs with the propeller in approximately the horizontal position (Fig. 71).

It will be found that the propeller bolts tend to push back behind the hub back-plate. They can easily be worked forward with a thin spanner or screwdriver but the engine must not be turned until all the bolts are drawn forward, the bearing plate fitted and the washers and nuts in place. This is because the heads of the bolts, protruding too far behind the hub back-plate, will foul the bracing webs on the front of the crankcase. These are easily broken with the leverage which it is possible to exert inadvertently by turning the propeller.

Tighten the propeller nuts just sufficiently to prevent the bolts turning. Now tighten up half a turn on opposite bolts around the hub, thereby evenly clamping the propeller to its hub (Fig. 72).

Stand a trestle or a box in such a manner that the tip of the lowermost blade of the propeller just touches it. Turn the propeller through 180 deg. and repeat for the other blade. By adjusting the tension of the hub bolts, set the propeller so that there is not more than $\frac{1}{16}$in. difference between the blades measured against a fixed point (Fig. 73). The operation is called "tracking the propeller" and it is vital to do this whenever

Part 10 Deals with Propeller and Engine, Registration and Covering

the propeller nuts are tightened or the propeller refitted. Failure to check this could result in serious engine vibration and damage. Lock all the hub nuts with split-pins.

Turn the propeller about fifty revolutions to circulate the engine oil. It should be possible to register a low reading on the oil pressure gauge in this manner.

The sparking-plugs approved for the J.99 J.A.P. engine are Lodge N.14 type which are fitted with two solid copper ring washers and a shrinkage washer each. Set the plug gaps to 0·018in. before fitting them.

The plug leads are connected as shown in Fig. 74.

Running the Engine

Stand the aeroplane in an open space facing into the wind and preferably on grass or

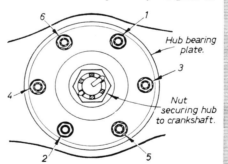

Fig. 72.—The correct sequence of tensioning the airscrew hub nuts.

concrete. See that there are no loose stones or pebbles which might be sucked up into the propeller. Get a competent assistant to sit in the cockpit and make sure that he understands which way the throttle works (fully back for closed) and the operation of the switches (*up* for on). As there is no fabric on the tail, enabling the elevators to be used to keep the tail down, a second assistant should stand by the leading edge of the tailplane to prevent the tail rising. Failure to observe these precautions could result in the aircraft tipping up on its nose when the engine is running, breaking the propeller, possibly damaging the cowlings and carburetter and probably seriously damaging the engine.

Place wooden blocks or bricks in front of the wheels as chocks and put about two gallons of petrol in the fuel tank. The correct

grade of fuel to use is 73 octane (unleaded). If motor spirit is used, use the ordinary cheap mixture as some of the better petrols contain lead which is injurious to the cylinder heads. It is not advisable to operate continually on neat motor petrol except in an emergency.

Check that the ignition switches are off. Turn on the petrol cock under the tank. Pull out the choke control. Turn the propeller over in an anti-clockwise direction (the direction of engine rotation) six times with the

Material Selection

SOME constructors have asked what they should do with lengths of prepared spruce containing small flaws. The presence of large knots, holes, splits of resin-pockets renders that part of the timber unsuitable for use. If, however, it is possible to cut so as to miss such flaws, this is in order. It is very difficult to obtain absolutely perfect timber although the constructor must naturally obtain the best he can. Planned cutting ensures that timber with slight blemishes need not be discarded although, when in doubt, ask or discard.

Rib stock should be examined for imperfections, the best lengths used for the capstrips and any slightly defective lengths cut, the useless portion discarded, and the remainder used for the short rib bracing members.

The more highly stressed parts of the aircraft demand the best possible timber. The spar flanges, for example, must be absolutely free from defect, the most important faces being the upper one of the top flange and the lower one of the bottom flange, these faces being the most highly stressed. The solid tailplane spars have their maximum bending stresses in the top and bottom edges. This means that the importance of perfect material is greatest near the top and bottom and least at the centre where the stresses decrease appreciably. From this explanation, it will also be apparent that scarf joints in spar flanges must be avoided if possible. Should any primary structural members require scarfing, the constructor should approach Phoenix Aircraft Ltd., for advice beforehand.

Plywood, likewise, often contains minor defects which can be cut out with careful marking-out. The spar webs must be of absolutely perfect material and scarf-joints made very carefully.

Complete kits of selected timber and plywood are available from Phoenix Aircraft Ltd., together with synthetic-resin glue, brass brads and all other materials and sundries.

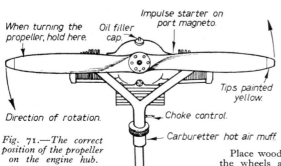

Fig. 71.—The correct position of the propeller on the engine hub.

When turning the propeller, hold here.

Oil filler cap.

Impulse starter on port magneto.

Tips painted yellow.

Direction of rotation.

Choke control.

Carburetter hot air muff.

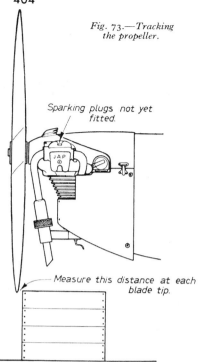

Fig. 73.—Tracking the propeller.

Sparking plugs not yet fitted.

Measure this distance at each blade tip.

throttle closed. Always treat the propeller with respect for, if the switches are incorrectly wired, or there should be a fault in the earthing, the engine might start suddenly.

Set the switches to "on" (contact) and open the throttle about ⅜in. on the pilot's lever (*throttle set.*) Turn the propeller briskly over the compression whereupon the engine should start. A small amount of "throttle-pumping" (moving the ever backwards and forwards an inch or so) may be needed to get the engine to run smoothly. Complete information on engine starting, failure to start, etc., is given in the Luton Minor Pilot's Handling Notes available from Phoenix Aircraft Ltd.

Caution! Stand clear of the propeller. When the engine is running, the propeller is almost invisible. Cultivate the habit of walking round the nose of the aircraft in a wide arc. If it is necessary to stand close behind the propeller during the running, keep one hand firmly on a strut, move slowly and think before each action. It pays!

Almost as soon as the engine starts, the oil pressure should rise rapidly. If this does not happen, stop the engine immediately and locate the source of the trouble, which might be a leaking union. Let the engine warm up for five minutes or so at 700 r.p.m. Carefully push in the choke control by hand and continue running for about ten minutes. Close the throttle and switch off. *After* switching off, open the throttle fully until the propeller stops, then return it to the closed position.

Remove the top cowling and look for oil leaks. The J.A.P. is normally a very clean engine and any oil seepage can be traced to weeping pressure line joints or, in extreme cases, a faulty gasket between the rear cover and the crankcase. A small quantity of oil may seep past the seals on the magneto drive gearbox after prolonged running, but this is unavoidable.

If all is correct, refit the cowling and re-start the engine. After four or five minutes at idling r.p.m., open the throttle smoothly to 1,600 r.p.m. There are certain inherent flat spots in the J.A.P. engine which only manifest themselves on the ground. Pass through these smoothly and quickly.

Switch off the port magneto switch and note the drop in r.p.m. on the tachometer. Switch on again and repeat on the other magneto switch. The drop should be not more than 50 r.p.m. Now gradually open the throttle fully. The tachometer should show a speed between 2,100 and 2,200 r.p.m. Do not run the motor at full throttle for longer than a few minutes. Ease back to about 1,800 r.p.m.

During the time the engine is running, the assistant must remain in the cockpit. Check over the airframe to see that all is well and then close the throttle, allow the engine to idle at 700 r.p.m. for a minute or so to cool off, and then stop the motor.

The inspecting engineer will now express his views on the aeroplane and may ask for certain small items to be attended to which are necessary.

Registration

At this point, the aeroplane must be registered with the Ministry of Aviation. This step may be taken earlier if required, but the actual registration mark must be known before painting the aircraft.

Write to the Secretary (A.R.G.1), Ministry of Aviation, Berkeley Square House, London, W.1, and request Form C.A.1. Complete this and return it to the Ministry together with the fee of thirty shillings. You will then be issued with a "G-A . . ." registration which will identify your aircraft so long as it is in existence.

Dismantling the Aircraft

Before fabric-covering and painting, remove the wings, the engine, the tail-unit and

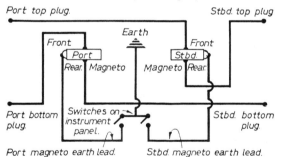

Port top plug.   Stbd. top plug.

Earth

Front   Front

Port   Stbd.

Rear. Magneto   Magneto Rear.

Switches on instrument panel.

Port bottom plug.   Stbd. bottom plug.

Port magneto earth lead.   Stbd. magneto earth lead.

Fig. 74.—Wiring diagram for plug leads and ignition switches.

the undercarriage. It will be necessary to drain out the engine oil before removing the motor. Never lift the engine by the exhaust pipe or the carburetter.

Materials for Finishing

The tools and materials needed for fabric-covering and finishing are a 10in. or 12in. double-ended sail needle, a pair of pinking shears, a soft-lead pencil (2B), a 12in. ruler and a sewing machine.

The fabric used is either DTD 343 madapolam or DTD 575 light aircraft mercedised cotton. The whole aircraft can be covered with madapolam but, for durability, it is recommended that the DTD 575 be used. If it is desired to cover the plywood fuselage, then madapolam only is suitable for this.

Fabric is available in nominal widths of 52in. and is bought by the yard. An approximate purchasing estimate is as follows: Each wing = 12yd.; tailplane elevators and rudder = 9yd.; fuselage (decking only) = 3yd.; fuselage (complete) = 12yd.

Serrated-edge tape, made of the same grade of fabric, is available in various widths and the constructor will need one 150yd. roll of 2¼in. wide and about 30yd. of 3in. wide tape. He will also need 100 yd. of 1in. wide cotton webbing tape.

A ball of W.30 linen thread and a block of beeswax complete the fabric requirements.

The materials for doping are as follows: 5 gal. of red oxide tautening dope (add about three more if the fuselage is to be covered with madapolam); 1 gal. aluminium sealer undercoat, 1 gal. cellulose filler (for use on fuselage whether fabric-covered or not); one tin cellulose stopper (used on fuselage); 1 gal. each of second finishing colour and primary finishing colour. These last two should be of the high-gloss type with nitro-varnish added. Additionally, about 3 to 5 gal. of cellulose anti-chill thinners will be needed.

For rubbing down, a dozen sheets of medium (120 or 180) grade wet-or-dry abrasive paper will be wanted together with half a dozen sheets of fine (220) and a few sheets of very fine (320) grade.

A word on equipment. If at all possible, use a proper spray gun with a compressor which will give—and maintain—about 60 p.s.i. pressure. Equipment which does not provide such pressure, demands the use of an excessive amount of thinners. On the finishing coats in particular, the thinners content should be as low as possible (with reservations described later), it being better to increase spray pressure to aid atomisation. If a vacuum cleaner spray kit has to be used, do not expect such a good finish unless you are prepared to take additional time and spend much longer rubbing down and polishing.

First coats of red dope must be brushed and the constructor should obtain some good new paint brushes. It is well worth the extra few shillings to get the best rather than spoil the finish with loose hairs. Two brushes 2in. or 3in. wide and two 1in. wide are ideal.

Covering the Rudder

Sandpaper the edges of the rib capstrips and spars to remove sharp edges. Run the hands over all edges and surfaces which will be in contact with the fabric to check for roughness, lumps or hard glue and protruding

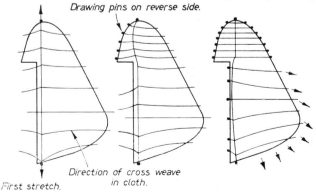

Drawing pins on reverse side.

Direction of cross weave in cloth.

First stretch.

Fig. 75.—Stages in fabric covering the rudder. Notice how the fabric weave is kept straight.

brads. See that there are no staples left in the structure unless they are of stainless steel.

Try to keep the weave of the fabric square, i.e. the threads should run vertically and horizontally, not diagonally. Also try to keep the threads straight by even tension in the cloth.

Cut a piece of fabric large enough to cover one side of the rudder. Lay the rudder on top of it and, using drawing-pins, fold the cloth over the edge member and pin it to the side which is uppermost. Start at the top of the rudder, then using drawing-pins, fold the cloth just sufficiently to produce light longitudinal ripples each side from the top to the bottom where the fabric is again folded over the edge and pinned. Now pin the fabric from the top down to the end of the leading-edge bow. With practice, the right degree of stretch can be achieved so that when the trailing-edge fabric is tautened for pinning, the vertical weave remains straight. The illustration shows the manner in which the top of the rudder is covered. This is possibly the hardest portion of the aircraft to cover, and the sequence should be followed closely. Avoid excessive tension in the cloth —it is only necessary to stretch it gently.

When the rudder top is covered, pin down the front of the spar to the bottom, then pin from the middle of the trailing-edge round to the bottom. The correct angle of tension can easily be found by experiment. It is likely that odd wrinkles may appear here and there, but the removal and repositioning of the pins will smooth them out.

Take a 1in. brush and a tin of red dope and carefully dope the fabric to the edge members. Do not allow the dope to trickle or drip on to the bare fabric now or at any time. Such drips will make almost immovable blemishes in the finish which will be most unsightly. It is very easy to allow dope to drip down to the inside of the fabric from the back edge whilst putting on the first side of fabric, so be cautious. If dope does get on to the fabric in this manner, rub it well in with the fingers, dispersing it as much as possible.

When the fabric has been doped to the edge members and allowed to dry, remove the drawing pins and, with a sharp knife, trim the cloth overlap to the full width of the edge member, this remaining flap being doped down thoroughly with about three coats of dope. Allow it to dry well before starting the other side.

The second side is covered in precisely the same manner except that this time the

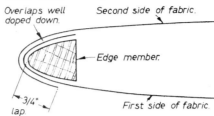

Fig. 76.—Section showing how the fabric is overlapped and fixed at the edge member.

drawing-pins pass through the first fabric flap into the member (Fig. 76). Once more dope the edge down and, when set, remove the pins. This time, however, the surplus fabric is cut back to about ¾in. from the edge all the way round and doped down. Well dope the edge and allow to dry.

The first two coats should be thickly applied by brush and worked well into the fabric. Work one rib bay at a time with a wide brush and use a stippling action, first from side to side and then up and down.

The fabric will go very soft and spongy and may well remain this way after the first coat has dried. There is no cause for alarm, however, as the second coat (applied after stitching) will immediately tighten up the cloth on drying. When later covering other parts of the aircraft, it will be found that in certain cases the fabric softens enough to allow it to come into contact with part of the underlying structure not normally touched by the fabric. There may be a tendency for the fabric to stick to such places during drying. Where there is a likelihood of this happening, gently hook the fabric up at intervals with a bent pin during drying. The pin holes will vanish with the second coat. Another point to watch is that when the fabric does touch the underlying structure, the dope brush will leave a streak of dope against the obstruction. This will set as a hard ridge in the finish even though the cloth no longer fouls the structure. Take care to avoid this if you want a good finish.

After the first coat has been applied, the cloth is ready to be stitched to the structure. There are two schools of thought here; one being that stitching should be done before doping is done, and the other that a coat of dope should be applied first. This latter principle is best adopted by the amateur since any faulty tensioning of the cloth, which might result in the sheet creeping, will not result in wrinkles round the stitching or, in extreme cases, actual bending of the ribs beneath.

A word of warning. Cellulose dopes and thinners are highly inflammable. Never try to accelerate drying with a naked light or red-element heater and never dope in a room with an open fire. Should heat acceleration be required, infra-red " black heaters " may be used or, on small areas, an ordinary electric light lamp and shade supported a foot or so from the surface to be dried will suffice.

In the next article, stitching, doping, final inspection and flying will be dealt with together with a materials list.

(To be continued)

Building the 'Luton Minor'

Part 11 Deals with Stitching, Doping, Final Inspection and Flying

STITCHING consists of looping a continuous thread through the fabric on one side, round the rib inside, through the cloth the other side and back to the first side via the other side of the rib, a knot then being tied before leading the uncut thread to the next stitch.

The materials used are rot-proofed thread (spec. W.9), 1in. wide cotton webbing and a block of beeswax through which each piece of thread will be drawn and prepared for use.

The tools required comprise a pair of sharp nail-scissors, a 10in. or 12in. double-ended sail needle and, possibly, a small curved needle.

The best position for stitching is with the surface upright, and whilst on the wings two people will be needed, the tail surfaces may be tackled single-handed.

Fig. 77 illustrates the type of stitch, how it is made and the correct pitch of the knots. For a professional finish, the knots should all be arranged to come at the edge of the cap-strip along each rib and they should be arranged to come at alternate sides of the rudder ribs, i.e. the first rib will have the stitches on the port side, the next on the starboard, the third on the port again and so on. On the tailplane

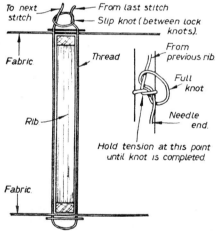

Fig. 77.—The rib stitch.

and wings, the stitches will all have their knots on the lower surfaces. Each knot must be tight and must not rely on the link to the next stitch for tension. If it is necessary to join the thread during stitching, arrange the join so that it can be pulled inside the surface to minimise irregularities on the external covering.

Doping

The first two coats of red dope at least *must* be brushed into the fabric by hand. This applies to fabric-covered plywood and to unsupported fabric (such as on the wings and tail unit). These first two coats should be as thick as possible without causing runs or blobs. Dope in a warm, draught-free atmosphere. Below about 50 deg. F. dope dries very slowly and develops a milky colour known as " blushing." Blushed dope will not serve its purpose.

Avoid doping in direct sunshine in hot weather as the dope will dry before it has had a chance to be brushed in, leaving a patchy covering. Similarly, do not overbrush—any

apparent brush-marks will vanish with drying.

Do not dope or spray in a confined space without adequate ventilation. Some people are affected by the fumes of dope and, if much work is to be done, drink plenty of cold milk before and after each spell of work.

It is supposed that the first coat of dope has been applied to the wings and tail before stitching. The next operation is the application of the serrated tapes which cover the lines of stitches and also protect the leading edge, tips and trailing edges of the surfaces. The illustration (Fig. 78) shows typical taping applications. Note how the edge tapes are always put on last to cover the ends of rib tapes. The rib tapes on the wings at the main spar are trimmed to a narrow " V " with the pinking shears to prevent peeling in the slipstream. The chordwise seams in the wing fabric are covered with a continuous tape passing from the trailing edge forward, over the leading edge and back to the rear again.

When all the tapes have been affixed in this manner and are dry, give the complete surface one good coat of red dope and leave to dry for an hour or so.

Applying Madapolam to the Fuselage

First apply three good thick coats of red dope, allowing thorough drying between each coat. Cut the madapolam into strips running from nose to tail and, with the fuselage upside down, apply the bottom strip first. Begin at one end and, working a few feet at a time, apply red dope to the wood and stretch the madapolam over and on to the tacky surface. Rub the dope through with a thinners-soaked cloth pad, carefully excluding all air bubbles. Avoid over-saturating the cloth with thinners. When the full strip is applied and is dry, trim flush with the sides and then apply the fuselage side strips. The edges of these are also trimmed flush and a 2in. wide serrated-edge fabric tape is then doped along the edge. Note that the fabric decking is covered separately and that the decking fabric

should overlap the fuselage sides by 2in. the edge being sealed with a 2in. tape as before.

If the fuselage is not required to be fabric-covered, still apply the three coats of red dope, rubbing down with abrasive paper between each coat.

On the wings and tail, *very lightly* scuff over the fabric with medium abrasive paper, used dry to remove any roughness. Do not exert any pressure and be ultra cautious on sharp corners, otherwise the fabric will be damaged.

" Pulling Over "

For a really professional, smooth finish on the wings and tail, take a cloth pad soaked in thinners and " pull " the fabric over to lay the fibres after the second coat of dope. Start at one side of the surface and work in one direction only. The pad should be wet enough to soften the dope surface, but must not be running. This preparation takes time, but later the very smooth surface which results will take a high-gloss finish really well.

The third coat of dope on the fabric-covered surfaces may be either brushed or sprayed, but at all events it should be thickly applied.

Allow this coat to dry and then examine the surface. The process of pulling over may be repeated, but it should not be necessary.

Spray on a fourth coat. Dilute this with about 30 per cent. thinners.

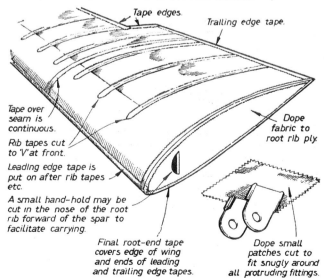

Fig. 78.—Taping operations.

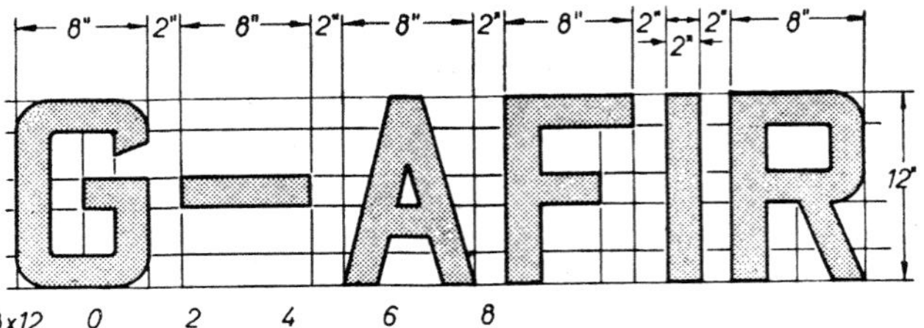

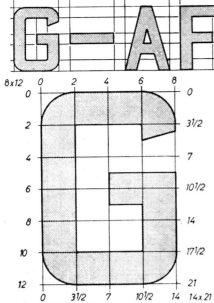

Fig. 79.—*The thickness of the strokes in the letters is equal to the width of the spaces between the letters. The dash is made the full width of one letter as shown.*

Although aluminium sealer is not vital, it is advisable to spray a general coat of this now as it will assist in the detection of any light spots or "holidays" in the finishing coats. Give this coat a good rub with medium-grade wet abrasive paper. The fuselage may be given one or more coats of filler, rubbing down between each, the final coat being rubbed with fine paper.

Colour Scheme

Scheme out the approximate paint scheme which will be used. Choose the first or main colour and the second colour which will be used for the registration letters and any flashes or trimming lines. It is this second colour which is applied first.

Assuming the colours to be silver (first) and blue (second), the blue areas are marked out first using white chalk (*not* pencil or wax crayon), allowing a good margin on all sides.

Spray these areas evenly in blue, but make no attempt to get a clearly defined edge to the areas, i.e. let the spray mist away at the sides. These finishing coats should contain nitro-varnish to provide a high gloss. These dopes take a little longer to dry, and about three to four hours should be allowed. Lightly scuff the misted areas with medium wet abrasive to remove the spray dust which has formed hard lumps on the surface of the undercoat. Avoid scuffing the areas of colour which will show. Spray a second coat on these areas and repeat the process.

When absolutely dry, mask in the registration letters, flashes and so forth, using 1in. wide paper masking tape. This tape is quite expensive at about 10s. per roll, but do not be tempted to use transparent or any other form of adhesive tape as these products strip off the underlying dope layers.

Edge round the letters with the tape, filling the centres with newspaper cut to shape. Make sure that the edges are well down and that there are no joins under which the spray may blow. Joins in the paper should be amply overlapped then sealed with an off-cut of masking tape. The illustration, Fig. 79, shows the correct sizes for registration letters, the larger size (14in. × 21in.) being used for

the wings and the smaller (8in. × 12in.) for the fuselage.

Mask out also parts which are not required to be sprayed. On the fuselage, completely paper across the cockpit and across the engine mounting, etc.

The first main coat is now sprayed. Do not attempt full coverage with the first coat—it is better to apply two medium coats than to risk runs and blemishes from one thick application.

A few points are worth noting on cellulose spraying. The higher the spray pressure, the less the amount of thinners required in the mixture. Too low a thinners content, however, will produce an "orange-peel" finish. The lower the thinners content, the brighter and higher the gloss of the finish will be. Fifteen to 20 per cent. is the lowest thinners content which should be used.

Too much thinners produces a "wet" spray which contains little dope and which runs readily.

Finishing coats should be sprayed at a pressure between 45 and 65 p.s.i. Mix thinners with the dope in a clean can or jar—never in the pot of the spray gun. Keep the gun clean, flushing through by spraying a little clean thinners after use. Spray evenly, maintaining about 12in. between nozzle and surface and hold the gun at right-angles to the surface

When absolutely dry, carefully peel off the masking tape and newspaper.

For final burnishing, special cellulose polishes are available. Wax polishes and car polishes may be used, but remember that if at any time it is necessary to touch up the paintwork all traces of the wax must first be removed with spirit or detergent.

Final Assembly

Refit the windscreen and then proceed with the erection of the complete aircraft as before. Connect all control cables and rig the controls as shown on the rigging diagram on Drawing No. 12.

Fit the engine and propeller, not forgetting to track it before locking the hub nuts with split pins.

With the aircraft in the rigging position, check the incidence of the wings and the dihedral, tighten the bracing wires and again check the incidence. Using a steel tape or a length of flexible wire, check the alignment of the aircraft by trammelling as detailed in Fig. 80.

Any necessary adjustments can be made on the bracing wires by slackening the forward one on one side and the rear one the other side. The opposite front one is then carefully tightened to the desired position.

When all is set, tension these wires equally until they produce a *low* drumming sound when twanged.

Wire lock the turnbuckles and wire-strainers on these and all the control cables. The correct method is shown in Fig. 81.

The gap between the two wings at the centre-section is covered with a strip of thin duralumin, tensioned underneath the wing by a wire-strainer.

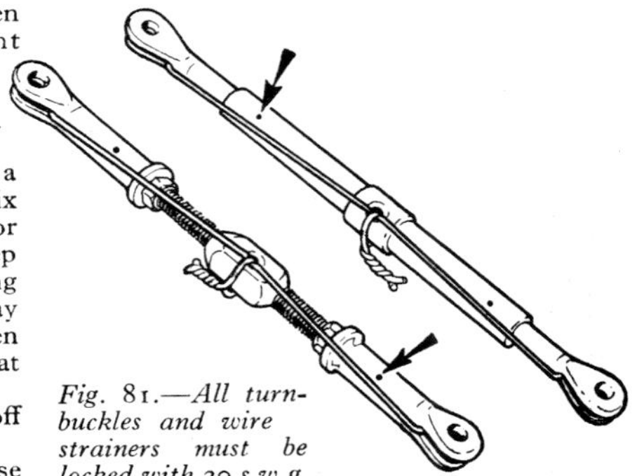

Fig. 81.—*All turnbuckles and wire strainers must be locked with 20 s.w.g. soft iron wire as shown. The arrows indicate the "safety" holes. It must not be possible to insert a pin through these, otherwise insufficient length of thread is being subjected to the tension load.*

Centre of Gravity

The centre of gravity of the aircraft must be within the limits shown in Fig. 82. If it is outside these limits, any attempt at flight might prove dangerous.

The exact position of the C.G. is computed by a simple calculation using three bathroom scales or two and a spring balance.

The aircraft must be in a complete state with all cowlings, seat cushions and fairings

(*Continued on page* 457)

RIGGING DATA

MAINPLANES	INCIDENCE	DIHEDRAL
(Port and Starboard)	3 deg. ± 0 deg. 10min. Measured across spars at root end and outboard of lift struts	0 deg. + 0 deg. 30min.—Zero Measured along front spar
TAILPLANE	0 deg. (NOMINAL)	ZERO

CONTROL SURFACE	RANGE OF MOVEMENT Measured at trailing edge of surface		RELATIVE TO
Aileron	6in. up (min.)	3½in. down (min.)	wing trailing edge
Elevator	7in. up (min.)	5in. down (min.)	tailplane chord
Rudder	10in. port (min.)	10in. stbd (min.)	Fin chord

Angle of fin centre-line to horizontal = 90 deg. ± 0 deg. 15min.
Rigging Datum: Top Longerons at cockpit level fore and aft and across.
Cross Trammel Engine mounting top bolt to front lift strut top bolt port and starboard variation = ⅛in.
   "   "   Rudder centre hinge pin to rear lift strut top bolt port and starboard variation = ⅛in.

Fig. 80.—*Table giving details of the rigging.*

in place. Seat a person of normal weight in the cockpit (or place a weight of about 160 lb. 12in. forward of the seat back) and half fill the petrol tank with petrol (approximately 3 gallons) or place a weight of 24 lb. centrally on top of the tank. The engine sump should be filled with the correct amount of oil.

Stand the aeroplane on two sets of scales, one under each wheel, and trestle the tail so that the top longerons are horizontally level. Either stand the tail-wheel on a third set of scales or suspend it on a spring balance. Tie a safety wire loosely to the tail-wheel and anchor it to a weight in case the aircraft should tip up.

Suspend a plumb-bob on a cord over the wing adjacent to one side of the fuselage so that it just clears the ground. This is shown in Fig. 82.

Add the two weights registered on the scales under the main wheels. Measure accurately the distance between the main wheels and the tail-wheel at their respective points of contact with the scales. Fig. 83 refers.

Example Calculation:

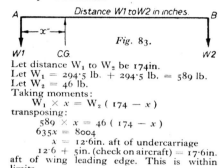

Fig. 83.

Let distance W_1 to W_2 be 174in.
Let $W_1 = 294.5$ lb. $+ 294.5$ lb. $= 589$ lb.
Let $W_2 = 46$ lb.
Taking moments:
$$W_1 \times x = W_2 \,(174 - x)$$
transposing:
$$589 \times x = 46\,(174 - x)$$
$$635x = 8004$$
$$x = 12.6 \text{ in. aft of undercarriage}$$
$12.6 + 5$in. (check on aircraft) $= 17.6$in. aft of wing leading edge. This is within limits.

If it is desired to move the C.G. forward, the pilot's seat may be shifted forward by 1in. To move the C.G. back, move the seat back by up to 2in.

In extreme cases where a motor heavier than the J.A.P. is used, it may be necessary to affix ballast to the stern-post as detailed in Fig. 84.

Fuel Flow Test

With the fuel tank half full, it must be proved that sufficient fuel is delivered to the carburetter, and this is checked by undoing the pipeline connection at the carburetter and draining fuel into a can or measure, timing delivery. This must be done at the carburetter end, this being the last link to the engine. The flow should be a minimum of three times the maximum consumption, giving a result of at least 8 gallons per hour.

Insurance

Before any aircraft flies, it must be covered by third-party insurance. Phoenix Aircraft Ltd. have been successful in obtaining a special coverage for their constructors with one of the most experienced Lloyd's aviation brokers. The third-party coverage for the Minor costs between £7 10s. and £10 per annum. Also available is full comprehensive cover at an annual premium of 7½ per cent. declared value should the Minor owner require. Only third-party insurance is mandatory.

Pilot's Licence

No person may act as pilot of an aircraft without holding a valid licence. Whilst under instruction, the pupil pilot must hold a student's pilot licence. This costs 10s. and is granted on the satisfactory passing of a simple medical examination which may be conducted by any private doctor in accordance with a Ministry of Aviation form.

Normal flying training comprises 40 hours' flying, of which at least 15 must be as pilot in charge or " solo." At the discretion of the instructor, the student pilot may complete some of these 15 hours' solo flying in his own single-seater aircraft under the supervision of his instructor. The Minor lends itself admirably to use as a single-seat trainer due to its docile handling characteristics.

At all times until the successful passing of a simple written and oral examination followed by a flight test for the issue of the full private pilot's licence, the student pilot must fly under supervision and all his solo flights shall be authorised by a qualified instructor.

Once the private pilot's licence has been obtained, the amateur pilot may fly as and where he wishes within the simple limitations of the regulations and safety rules laid down to avoid airways, danger to the general public and danger to himself and his machine.

Full information regarding flying instruction is available upon request from the Popular Flying Association, Londonderry House, 19 Park Lane, London, W.1, together with lists of addresses of flying clubs.

The Permit to Fly

The Permit to Fly carries no drastic restrictions for the amateur pilot, excepting that special permission is required to fly the machine out of the British Isles. Should the amateur wish to fly to France, for example, he should inform the Popular Flying Association beforehand in order that the necessary permit may be arranged.

With the aircraft fully assembled and ready for flight, the final inspection must be carried out. This is a thorough check of the complete aircraft to ensure that everything is perfect. As soon as any snags have been rectified, the inspector will sign the aircraft logbooks (one engine and one airframe which are obtainable through H.M. Stationery Office) and recommend that the aircraft be granted permission to cover test flights. The Minor will have to complete 5 hours' trouble-free flying during which time it shall not be flown outside a radius of 5 miles from the airfield nor shall it land away from the airfield. As soon as this 5-hour period is up, the Minor will receive its full Permit to Fly, which costs 10s. per year. This document must at all times be carried in the aircraft.

Preparations for Flight

The first flight trials should be conducted at a licensed aerodrome. This is desirable from many aspects, the main being that experienced engineers and ground staff, fuel and oil, etc., are readily to hand. Where possible, it is suggested that, to minimise disruption to normal aerodrome routine, test flights (certainly the early ones) should be carried out during the week-days. Most flying clubs operate mainly at week-ends and the air is rather crowded for this type of flying.

The weather should be clear with at least 5 miles visibility and a cloud base of not less than 1,500ft. Surface wind should not be more than 10 m.p.h. and should be in such a direction that take-off and landing may be directly into wind without being hazardous due to obstructions.

At all times before flight from an aerodrome, notify the aerodrome control. The reasons for this should readily be apparent. For initial tests, the controller will arrange that the airfield is solely at your disposal and that no other aircraft may baulk your take-off or landing.

First Flight

Since test-flying must be conducted by a competent pilot and to a schedule which may be obtained on application from Phoenix Aircraft Ltd., only specific information will be given on this stage.

For the first flight, it is not necessary to fill the fuel tank and thereby increase the weight unnecessarily. Three gallons in the tank is a

1/4" thick lead sheet. Cut and shape to correct weight.

2—1/4" B.S.F. bolts centrally fitted 4" apart on stern-post.

Fig. 84.—Fixing the lead ballast.

safe minimum for this test flight.

Warm up the engine for 5 minutes with the nose headed into wind.

The following cockpit check should be memorised—the easy way is to remember the initial letters and their order:

T—Throttle friction nut—TIGHT
M—Mixture—Choke control IN
F—ON and sufficient for flight. Check that indicator reads correctly.
G—Gauges—Altimeter set, oil pressure O.K.
H—Harness—TIGHT.

Slowly taxi the Minor into take-off position, having first run up the engine to maximum r.p.m. and also having checked the magnetos on the switches. Line up into wind and smoothly open the throttle.

The Minor displays little or no tendency to swing on take-off, although care should be exercised in cross winds to keep the nose straight. The tail will rise almost immediately as the aircraft rolls forward.

Do not attempt to haul the aircraft off the ground at too low an airspeed—this results in porpoising and can only serve to prolong the take-off distance. The true unstick speed is about 28 m.p.h. and it is good practice to hold the machine down to about 32 m.p.h. before breaking ground decisively with a slight backward pressure on the stick. Once clear of the ground, allow the speed to build up to about 40 m.p.h. before climbing away. Ease back on the throttle slightly to produce about 2,150 r.p.m. and climb steadily to 1,000ft.

The throttle is then set to cruising r.p.m. and the full effectiveness of the controls may be checked.

(To be continued.)

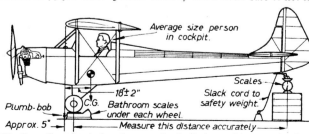

Average size person in cockpit.

18"±2"

Scales

Plumb-bob

C.G.

Bathroom scales under each wheel.

Approx. 5"

Slack cord to safety weight.

Measure this distance accurately

Fig. 82.—Completed aircraft set up in the rigging position on scales showing the position of the centre of gravity.

Building the 'Luton Minor'

Part 12 is the Concluding Article in This Series

Flying and Operation

IF the aircraft flies in a pronounced nose down—or tail down attitude—requiring firm pressure on the controls to maintain level flight, land immediately and adjust as follows:

Nose down. Check the centre of gravity location. If within limits, remove the tailplane and fit new front spar brackets to lower the leading edge of the tailplane by up to ⅛in. If the C.G. position is found to be too far forward, adjust the seat position and/or fit ballast to the stern post. (Fig. 84, last month's issue.) Expert advice should be sought before adding any ballast.

Nose up. Check the centre of gravity location. If within limits, remove the tailplane and fit new front spar brackets to raise the leading edge by up to ⅝₆in. Do not lower

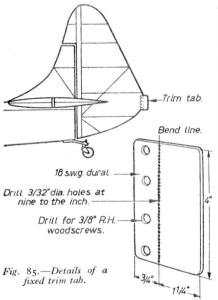

18 s.w.g. dural.

Drill 3/32" dia. holes at nine to the inch.

Drill for 3/8" R.H. woodscrews.

Trim tab.

Bend line.

Fig. 85.—Details of a fixed trim tab.

the rear brackets—these must remain the same. If the C.G. position is found to be too far aft, adjust the seat position and/or remove ballast (if fitted).

If the aircraft persists in tending to turn one way or the other, check first that the rudder bar is in the neutral position when the rudder is neutral—if one rudder cable is longer than the other then the effect of centralising the rudder bar will be the unintentional application of rudder.

If this is not the cause, the rudder must be induced to "fly" to one side, and this is achieved by screwing a small aluminium trim-tab to the rudder trailing edge. If the aircraft turns to port, fit the tab to the port side of the rudder; for a starboard correction, fit it to the starboard side. The tab and its fixing are detailed in Fig. 85. One or two trial flights may be necessary to determine the correct amount of bend required on the tab to maintain straight flight with the feet off the rudder bar.

Should the aircraft fly one wing low, check that the incidence of both wings is the same both at the root end and outboard of the lift struts. Adjust, if necessary, to the limits on the rigging diagram. If this fails to reveal the cause of the trouble, examine the positions of

the ailerons in the free position (hands off) in level flight relative to the control column. If the aileron flies high on the low wing (aileron trailing edge above the wing trailing edge), adjust the rigging of the control cables to lower it, remembering the correct cable tension must be maintained and also that there must be no more than ⅜in. droop on each aileron on the ground (Fig. 86).

Flight Characteristics

The Minor is extremely easy to fly and the stick forces are very light throughout the full range of normal manœuvres and airspeeds. Control at the stall is exceptionally good when the aircraft is correctly rigged and there is no tendency to spin. The aileron drag with this type of aircraft makes it possible to perform an incipient spin if the stick is held over at the stall. Recovery is immediate upon centralising the stick and lowering the nose.

There is no definite stall warning other than the general sloppiness of the controls as the speed lowers. The machine will settle in a nose-up attitude with the throttle closed and the stick held back.

The Minor sideslips very easily both to port and to starboard, although the slip to port is somewhat greater. Its extreme manœuvrability enables the owner-constructor to experience the true joys of flying.

The high rate of sink enables a very short landing run and it is normally advisable to approach with a small amount of power on. For a power-off approach, come in high as if to over-shoot and, once the threshold has been crossed, surplus height and speed may be quickly lost by a series of short sideslips to either side.

Complete information on flying is available

in the Pilot's Notes for the Minor which cost 7s. 6d. per copy post free from Phoenix Aircraft Ltd.

Landing Grounds

Many constructors will wish to use fields other than licensed aerodromes for their flying. Assuming that the field is suitable and is smooth with good approaches and ample room, the only requirement is that the pilot shall have the permission of the landowner to use the field. Additionally, the pilot must ensure that his flying may not create a hazard or nuisance to nearby homesteads or populous areas. Never indulge in unnecessary low flying or stunting and the regulations state that, except for the purposes of landing and taking off, no aircraft may be operated below 500ft. over open country or below 1,500ft. near any town or populous area. This is as much for the safety of the pilot and the preservation of his aircraft as for the safety of the general public.

If use is to be made of private land as a landing site, it is sound practice, wherever possible, to advise the local police beforehand. They cannot stop you flying so long as you have the consent of the landowner, but by warning them of your intentions you can avoid the embarrassment of a full-scale turnout of the emergency services brought about by a member of the public who, upon seeing an aeroplane descending in a field, may assume the worst! Additionally, the police

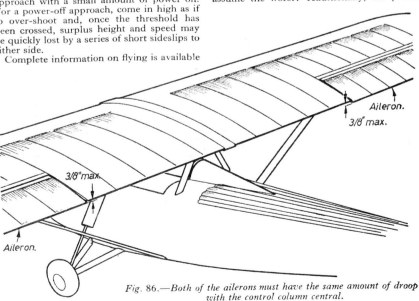

Aileron.

3/8" max.

3/8" max.

Aileron.

Aileron.

Fig. 86.—Both of the ailerons must have the same amount of droop with the control column central.

are very co-operative and in many instances can prove of invaluable assistance in deterring the endeavours of " souvenir-hunters."

Never leave your aeroplane unattended in an open field without picketing it down and never leave an aeroplane in a field with cattle—the smell of dope acts as an aperitive to cows and many cases are on record where cows have actually eaten tail-units and ailerons.

Licensed Aerodromes

There are many private aerodromes dotted around the countryside and any flying club will provide information as to airfield locations. Most airfields are free to light, private aircraft, although some (municipal airports in particular) charge a nominal landing fee of between 2s. 6d. and 5s. The extortion of exorbitant sums of money from the pilots of ultra-light aircraft for landing fees is one of the few banes of ultra-light flying. If the amateur is asked for more than half-a-crown, then he should ask the landing fee for an Auster and tender one-third of that sum since his aircraft weighs less than one-third the weight of an Auster. Fortunately, aerodromes where such practices exist are very few and far between—and they have a reputation.

A large number of operational Royal Air Force airfields are also available to the amateur pilot by prior permission—normally only a telephone call beforehand is necessary to secure landing clearance.

Maintenance

The Minor requires very little maintenance and a weekly general check and lubrication of the moving parts of the controls are normally all that is required for the airframe. The engine oil should be changed every 25 hours by draining and cleaning the filter in petrol. Every 10 hours or so check the tappet settings with the data shown in the engine log-book and also check the propeller for security together with the engine mounting bolts.

If the engine begins to run roughly, to vibrate more than usual or to develop a sporadic " knock," the fault can almost always be traced to loose mounting bolts or a loose propeller.

Always keep your aeroplane clean. A well-groomed aeroplane is a handsome tribute to its constructor and, furthermore, by thorough and regular cleaning any minor damage or defect is much more likely to be detected.

Full details as to maintenance and periodic

overhauls are contained in the Luton Minor Servicing Manual available from Phoenix Aircraft Ltd. at 7s. 6d. post free.

Never jeopardise the future prospects of the amateur flying movement by indulging in unimaginative or stupid flying and, when operating at a licensed aerodrome, observe meticulously the airfield discipline which applies to everybody in the common interests of safety.

Do not be tempted to take chances. If something " isn't quite right " do not trust to luck that it will " sort itself out." Such action could cost you your aeroplane—if not worse. If the weather looks doubtful it is better not to fly and fly another day than to risk your Minor. Listen to and consider advice given you by more experienced flyers.

The " Major "

For the amateur who wishes to construct a practical two-seat light aeroplane, the Luton Major is a thoroughly proven machine which features folding wings and full dual control in cabin comfort. Embodying many design features of the Minor, the Major is simple to construct and was originally designed to fulfil a stringent Air Ministry specification for a training aircraft.

Materials

Every part and all materials necessary for constructing the Minor are available from Phoenix Aircraft Ltd. The constructor must bear in mind, however, that should he decide to purchase his metal fittings ready made, his aeroplane will cost more than if he were to purchase the raw material and fabricate everything himself. In this manner, the Minor airframe may be built for between £150 and £175, depending on the wheels and instruments used and the finish desired.

For the convenience of constructors, materials have been grouped together into kits and the following are available:

A pilot entering a Minor.

	£	s.	d.
Kit A Spruce for the tail assembly	7	10	0
Kit B Spruce for the two wings	19	0	0
Kit C Spruce for the fuselage ..	19	10	0
Kit D Complete kit of plywood	30	6	6
Kit E Complete kit of spruce (contents of Kits A, B & C)	45	0	0
Kit F Complete kit of nuts, bolts, A.G.S. parts and etc. ..	12	0	0
Kit G Complete kit of sheet metal	4	0	0
Kit H Complete kit of steel tubing *Available shortly.*			
Kit I Complete kit of fabric, etc.	15	15	0

Sundries

	£	s.	d.
Synthetic resin glue	3	0	0
Mainwheels (depending on type) Pair £10 to £18		0	0
Phoenix tailwheel	1	17	6
Set of Phoenix undercarriage shock absorbers	2	0	0
Brass aircraft gimp pins (⅜in. & ½in. × 20 s.w.g.) per lb. ..		10	6
10 cwt. extra flexible control cable per 150ft. coil	3	12	0
Streamlined steel tubing for lift struts	10	14	0
Lift strut adjustable end fittings (4 pairs)	3	0	0
Shoulder harness, nylon, quick release type	5	0	0

Instruments

	£	s.	d.
Airspeed indicator (calibrated in knots)	2	15	0
Airspeed indicator (calibrated in m.p.h.)	3	0	0
Altimeter (sensitive)	1	12	6
Oil Pressure gauge	2	0	0
Oil Temperature gauge	2	17	6
Tachometer	5	10	0
Phoenix Key Ignition Switch set	2	0	0

If at any time the amateur constructor should experience any difficulty in the construction or operation of his Minor, the designers will be pleased to advise.

This series of articles has been specially prepared for *Practical Mechanics* by A. W. J. G. Ord-Hume of Phoenix Aircraft.

A view of the completed Minor.

Post-war revival of the pre-war Luton LA.4 Minor was G-AFIR originally built in 1938. At that time the colour scheme was dark green and white and the original engine was an Anzani inverted V twin. Here the engine is the 37 hp Aeronca JAP J.99. During several post-war rebuilds, this machine went through several stages of evolution in the development of the LA.4a including flying experimentally as a fully-enclosed cabin aircraft. Its 1948 colour scheme was bright red with silver registration letters outlined in black. G-ASAA, below, also began life as a LA.4 and was a development prototype. Pictured here at Sandown Airport in a recreation of 1930s Moth colour scheme – bright white with light blue outlined in yellow. This stunning colour scheme won plaudits at the PFA Rally Rochester in 1962.